Buildings Don't Lie

Better Buildings by Understanding Basic Building Science

(The Movement through Buildings of Heat, Air, Water, Light, Sound, Fire, and Pests)

Important information for anyone who designs, builds, owns, repairs, works, or lives in a building.

by Henry Gifford

Photos by Henry Gifford unless otherwise noted

Published By Energy Saving Press LLC, New York City

First Edition, Third Printing: February 2020

Printed in Turkey

Copyright 2017 by Henry Gifford

ISBN 978-0-9990110-0-3

Library of Congress Control Number: 2017919652

Introduction

This book is about what falls between the cracks in the building industry—the issues, such as occupant health, building durability, and year-round comfort and energy efficiency, that the industry has never paid enough attention to. These concepts are rarely taught in architecture or engineering schools. They are also hard to learn on the job since it can take years for mistakes to become apparent, and the people who made them are rarely around to learn from them.

The term for this frequently neglected but all-important subject matter is "building science," which I once heard someone (sorry, I forgot whom) define as "the study of the movement of heat, air, water, light, sound, fire, and pests through buildings." Though this may sound dull to the uninitiated, it is anything but. How these things move—or don't move—through a building is the difference between living or working in a building that is comfortable, safe, durable, and energy efficient and living or working in one that not only is too hot or too cold or both, but also needs constant maintenance and is potentially unsafe and certainly wasteful.

If you understand the underlying science, you'll have the tools to improve buildings from the start. Even the most basic understanding of building science gives a person the power to evaluate advice, make her own decisions, and create her own solutions to problems, even in unfamiliar, complex situations. Understanding building science is getting more important all the time because, as building materials and methods continue to evolve rapidly, learning by experience gets less and less practical.

Most of this science has been well understood for a long time. But some testing methods—like measuring a building's air leakiness with a blower door and checking insulation with an infrared camera—are so new that the people who built the first instruments for taking such measurements are still making important contributions to the field. Terry Brennan, who coined the term "unplanned airflow" back when the idea was unheard of, built his own blower door before they were commercially available, using spring-loaded shower curtain rods for the frame. In 1982, he used it to measure air leakage through wall sections using different insulation and airtightening methods. He insulated the underside of a roof with spray foam in 1973 and wrapped a house with exterior foam boards in 1982. Joe Lstiburek (the L is silent: STEE-brick) imported almost-lost knowledge from Europe and Canada to the United States, disseminates the knowledge generously, and, remarkably, makes progress in bringing sanity to building codes. Marc Rosenbaum built what was then the world's lightest bicycle for his thesis at the Massachusetts Institute of Technology (and rode it), built a very energy-efficient house in a cold climate back when doing so required building your own high-performance windows, and still designs buildings and teaches widely based on his experience. And back when blower doors were strictly a research tool used by research scientists, Gary Nelson had the vision to imagine them as a tool used by contractors to improve the airtightness of buildings, so he started making and selling them. If I boast that I have a friend who owns his own wind tunnel, that's who I am talking about.

In a field so bustling with activity, and so important to the world, it is high time to take stock of our knowledge about buildings and synthesize it in a way that is accessible to a wide audience. I've also introduced a few new ideas and terms of my own: using a laser pointer to determine if window glass has a low-e coating; understanding that a fire in a building "flashes over" when latent cooling stops; dividing the history of buildings into three stages; and calling the optimum sequence for the layers of an assembly the "perfect sequence." The concept of the "first freeze" location in a building and calling the sides of a wall the "dry side" and the "wet side" are also probably new.

Fortunately, a big shift is afoot in the building industry. Instead of just fixing problem buildings, our industry is starting to use building science to pro-actively design better buildings. The desire for truly energy-efficient buildings is one of the driving forces behind this trend. It is my hope that real progress in energy efficiency will reduce the incidence of military activities in the Middle East and elsewhere, and that this book will both inspire and enable more people to design and build comfortable, healthy, long-lasting, energy-efficient buildings. And for everyone connected with buildings in any way, even if simply by living in them, I hope this book serves to increase their enjoyment of buildings through a better understanding of how to make them beautiful, comfortable, safe, durable, and energy efficient.

Table of Contents:

Acknowledgements:

I would like to thank all the people who helped with this project, including my most excellent editor Hannah Wallace, my sharp-eyed copy editor Molly Wallace, my proofreader Stuart Tanenbaum, Isca Greenfield-Sanders for her cover design and page design and parchments for old quotes, Giorgio Guidi for most of the illustrations, Phebe Horschel for photoshopping many of the photos well enough to significantly clarify their messages and for all her other contributions to moving the project along, Gina Boehler for teaching me about page layout software, my writing tutor Grace Suh for her patience, Cynthia Hill for telling me "if you want to learn to take good photographs never leave home without a camera," my photography teacher Adam Eidelberg, the nice people in the United Nations Security Department, and the people who read rough copies and looked for factual errors or inconsistencies: Andy Cohen, Isabel Draves, Cynthia Hill, Karin Greenfield-Sanders, Timothy Greenfield-Sanders, Leah Kreger, Patrick McElhone, Kirstie Stramler, and my brother, Neal Gifford.

I would also like to thank Bill Gates and all the other people at Microsoft Corporation, Michael Dell and the other people at Dell, Inc., and all the people at Nikon Corporation, Canon, Inc., Adobe Systems, Hewlett-Packard, and DJI for their products, as well all the people at all the other companies that keep quality high and prices within reach of many people by producing high quality products that compete with these companies. Without these companies and their products a project like this would have been much more difficult, time consuming, and expensive to complete, and the quality would have suffered from the need to have a larger percentage of the work done by people who do not understand the book's subject matter.

Most of all I would like to thank Chris Benedict for pioneering much of the good work being done in building design today. Since she founded her architecture firm over twenty years ago, she has designed about eighty buildings, all in keeping with sound building science principles. All those buildings are beautiful, comfortable, durable, healthy for the occupants, and very energy efficient, while none of them has cost extra to build compared to code-minimum standard construction. Some things shown in this book will appear to be unusual, and maybe even impractical, to some people in our industry, but 100% of what is shown in this book is normal in at least one segment of the building industry*. Chris' work has helped make many of the good practices shown in this book the new normal in more parts of the industry. Chris designed the first energy efficient houses in New York City (the first anyone even claimed were energy efficient), the first two PassivHaus apartment buildings in the US, and was probably the first architect in the US to own a blower door (yes, she uses it on every building). She took the lead on revealing actual building energy use by printing out an energy use history from the utility company website and handing out copies to people on tours of buildings she designed. She started doing this many years ago, when energy measurements were kept even more secret than they are today. Her work has been the inspiration for much of this book, and much of what this book shows is her work. The huge gap between Chris Benedict's work and standard industry practice is what this book attempts to fill.

* The name of one industry segment where thermostats in every room have been normal for over 50 years is "Europe".

Chapter 1 **HEAT** Basic Science

WHAT IS HEAT?

Heat is the ultimate form of energy because all energy is either heat now or on its way to being transformed into heat. Understanding the basic science of heat is critical to understanding almost anything in the world because nothing happens without energy.

What this book calls "heat" is what a physics textbook might call "internal energy," which every substance possesses in the form of molecular motions, including vibration. Not too long ago, nobody knew what heat was. By 1857 our understanding had advanced to this stage:

> *Nature of our Knowledge concerning Heat. – When we place the hand upon a stove with a fire in it, a feeling of warmth is experienced, while if it be made to touch ice, there is a sensation of cold. The impressions are supposed to be caused in both cases by the same force or agent; in the first instance, the impulse passing from the heated iron to the hand; in the second, from the hand to the ice. What the nature or essence of this thing is, which produces such different feelings by moving in opposite directions, and which makes the difference between summer and winter, nobody has yet discovered. It is named heat. Some have conjectured it to be a kind of material fluid, exceeding subtle and ethereal, having no weight, existing diffused throughout all things, and capable of combining with every known species of matter; and this supposed fluid has received the name of caloric. Others think heat is not a material thing, but merely motion: either waves, or undulations produced in a universal ether, or a very rapid vibration, or trembling of the particles of common matter, which is in some way contagious, and passes from object to object. Of the essential nature of heat we understand nothing, and are acquainted only with its effects:-our information is limited to its behavior.[1]*

The last of these explanations turns out to be what we now understand to be correct: "A very rapid vibration, or

Photo of a dog taken with an infrared camera (also called a thermal camera), which "sees" infrared heat radiation only and does not see light that is visible to the human eye. An infrared camera can be built with the camera designer's choice of which colors are assigned to which temperatures. In this photo, and all other infrared photos in this book, white is hot and black is cold. The dog's nose is black, showing that it is cold, and her head looks hotter than other parts of her body because a thinner fur covering provides less insulation and a high blood flow rate (she is very smart) brings a lot of heat to her head. The white spots on the floor are where she stepped a moment ago, leaving behind heat signatures of her paws.
Model: Lucky.

trembling of the particles of common matter, which is in some way contagious, and passes from object to object." Modern experiments show that the hotter a substance gets, the more intensely its molecules vibrate.

Heat is a form of energy. All forms of energy can do work. Other forms of energy include chemical energy (a tank of fuel), potential energy (water at the top of a waterfall), and kinetic energy (a football flying toward the goal after someone kicks it). All types of energy can be measured in some way. A thermometer is used to measure the concentration of heat in something.

Quantity of Heat vs. Temperature

A thermometer does not measure how much heat is in something. It measures the concentration of heat in something. The difference can be understood by thinking of hot water bottles used for warming beds.

1   Edward L. Youmans, M.D., <u>The Handbook of Household Science</u> (New York: D Appleton & Co., 1864 [1857]), Page 17.

In the days before houses had central heating systems, a house might have had a stove in the kitchen that was used for cooking and for warming the kitchen and nearby rooms. The bedrooms, of course, had no heat. Before people went to bed, they put bottles of warm water into the beds to warm them.

If someone heated up a pot of water on the stove and used it to fill two water bottles, a large bottle and a small bottle, the water would be the same temperature in each bottle. But the large bottle would contain more heat, and could add more heat to the bed, because it contained more hot water. It would not contain water that was more hot—a thermometer would show that the water in both bottles was at the same temperature.

If there were two equal-sized pots of water on the stove, one might get heated to a higher temperature than the other (perhaps one is on the center of its burner and one is off-center). Described another way, there would be a higher concentration of heat in the hotter pot of water. If two equal-sized water bottles were filled, one from one pot of water and one from the other, the water bottle with the hotter water would hold more heat and would warm the bed to a higher temperature. In this case, a thermometer would show the water in one bottle as hotter than the water in the other bottle.

Heat Is Moving All the Time

Most objects are constantly exchanging heat with other objects, often gaining heat by one means while losing heat by another at the same time. This constant flow of heat takes place silently, all around us, all the time, and needs to be understood to understand any branch of science.[2]

How Heat Moves from One Object to Another

There are approximately three ways heat is moved from one molecule to another. The three that are usually listed are conduction, radiation, and convection. But this list of three ignores another important one: latent heat, the energy released or absorbed when substances change

phase between gas, liquid, and solid. And convection is really a movement of heat-carrying fluid[3] from one place to another, not heat movement from one molecule to another. Whatever the count, all are important to science. Each will be discussed below.

Heat Movement by Conduction

Conduction moves heat between substances that touch each other, always from the hotter thing to the less-hot, or colder, thing. Examples include heat conducted from a cup of hot tea to a person's hand, or from a person's hand to a glass of iced tea. The greater the temperature difference, the faster the heat moves.

If two water bottles touch each other, no heat will be conducted from one bottle to the other if they are both filled from the same pot of water at the same temperature. This is true even if one bottle is larger than the other: heat will not be conducted from one bottle to the other if they are at the same temperature. But if the bottles are filled from different pots of water at different temperatures, heat will be conducted from the hotter bottle to the less-hot bottle, regardless of the size of the bottles.

A hot water bottle in a bed will conduct heat to the bedsheets touching it, until the bottle and the surrounding bedsheets are at the same temperature, at which point no more heat will be conducted.

Heat Movement by Radiation

Radiation is how the sun heats the earth without air or anything else in between to conduct heat. The energy is moved by a combination of visible light and invisible infrared light, also called infrared radiation, or infrared heat radiation. "Infra" means below, which describes infrared's wave frequency: just lower than visible red light. (Frequency and wavelength are explained on Page 271.) Infrared light behaves much the same as visible light. It moves at the same speed as visible light, generally in a straight line, and depending on what gets in its way, it can fully or partially pass through, be absorbed by, or be reflected by objects.

2   The description of heat in this book is simple while being complete enough to yield a deep understanding of most branches of science, including building science and other terrestrial applications. More detail would be necessary for understanding heat movement in the subatomic size range or for more theoretical topics.

3   Fluids are substances that can flow. Gases, such as air, and liquids, such as water, are both fluids. Generally speaking, a gas takes the shape and the size of its container, a liquid takes the shape but not the size of its container, and a solid doesn't take either the shape or the size of its container.

Sunglasses, for example, transmit some visible light, which is why we can see through them. But at the same time, they absorb and reflect some visible light, which is how they protect our eyes. The visible light they reflect is how we find them when we misplace them. Sunglasses also transmit, reflect, and absorb infrared radiation.

In the 1700s, before scientists understood what infrared radiation was, they were experimenting with its absorption and reflection. Here is a description of what was probably the first science experiment that Benjamin Franklin, the famous American scientist, ever did:

> *My Experiment was this. I took a number of little square Pieces of Broad Cloth from a Taylor's Pattern-Card, of various Colours. There were Black, deep Blue, lighter Blue, Green, Purple, Red, Yellow, White, and other Colours, or Shades of Colours. I laid them all out upon the Snow in a bright Sunshiny Morning. In a few Hours (I cannot now be exact as to the Time), the Black, being warm'd most by the Sun, was sunk so low as to be below the Stroke of the Sun's Rays; the dark Blue almost as low, the lighter Blue not quite so much as the dark, the other Colours less as they were lighter; and the quite White remain'd on the Surface of the Snow, not having entred it at all.[4]*

Franklin's experiment measured the combined warming effects of both infrared radiation and visible light, which each make up approximately half the heat radiated by the sun to the earth. In astronomy, it is important to consider the warming effect of visible light, such as the light emitted by stars. But most objects on the earth's surface do not emit visible light unless they get hot enough to catch on fire. For this reason, when thinking about radiant heat movement in buildings, it is usually reasonable to ignore heat movement by visible light (except for sunlight) and think only about invisible infrared radiation.

After Benjamin Franklin's work in the early 1700s, physicists figured out how to measure the warming effect of infrared radiation itself, even though it is invisible to the human eye. In 1800, the famous astronomer and telescope builder William Herschel was studying the sun with colored filters on the eyepiece of a telescope when he noticed that red filters became warm when the magnified

TO FIND THE COLD, LOOK FOR THE MOLD. This photo shows the effect of heat movement by infrared radiation. The pipe in the photo supplies water to an apartment building from the city water supply pipe under the street. Cold water flows through the pipe any time anyone uses water, which keeps the pipe cold most of the time. Heat exchange by radiation has cooled the part of the wall to the right of the black pipe, causing a mild case of mold growth. (The relationship between cold and wet and mold will be explained in detail in later chapters, but for now, all that needs to be understood is that cold things tend to be wet, and mold only grows on things that are wet.) The iron pipe is painted black and therefore has a higher emissivity and absorption than the copper pipe below it, which enables the iron pipe to absorb more infrared radiation from the wall. As soon as the heat is absorbed, the moving water carries it away, preventing the pipe from warming up enough to emit much heat back to the wall. The difference between the amount of heat radiated from the wall to the pipe (more) and that radiated from the pipe to the wall (less) cools the wall near the pipe. This process is called radiant cooling. The wall below the moldy part, facing the copper pipe, is not moldy because the copper pipe does not cool the wall enough to grow mold, since it is not as large as the iron pipe and—despite its surface being oxidized—is slightly shiny, and therefore does not absorb as much infrared radiation.

sunlight passed through them. He investigated further by using a prism to split sunlight into the familiar rainbow of colors. He exposed a thermometer to one color at a time and compared its temperature reading to a reference thermometer nearby.[5] In 1800, he presented a paper to

5 Science History Quiz: How did some scientists compare how much heat was in each color of the spectrum in the early 1800s without using a thermometer? To find out how they did this, turn to Page 564.

4 **Letter from Benjamin Franklin to Miss Mary Stevenson, September 20, 1761, in <u>The Writings of Benjamin Franklin</u>, Albert Henry Smith, ed. (London: MacMillan & Co., Ltd., 1906), Page 115.**

Infrared photo taken at night shows clouds in the sky. Clouds absorb infrared radiation emitted by the earth's surface during the day and night, and emitted by the sun during the day. All day and night they emit infrared radiation, which is why they are visible in this photo.

the Royal Society of London in which he said:

> the Doctor [Herschel referring to himself] announced some observations which seemed to indicate that there are two sorts of rays proceeding from the sun; the one the calorific rays, which are luminous and refrangible[6] into a variegated spectrum; and the other the invisible rays, which produce no illumination, but create a sensible degree of heat, and appear to have a greater range of refrangibility than the calorific rays. To the latter he assigns the name of *radiant heat.*[7]

Herschel's thermometer measured the heating effect of infrared radiation coming from the sun. Not all the infrared radiation that strikes a thermometer or anything else is absorbed. Just as different thermometers can reflect visible light to varying degrees, thermometers (and anything else) can be more or less reflective on the infrared spectrum. Something painted flat black will absorb more infrared radiation (and more visible light) than something painted shiny silver. This is why some firefighting suits are shiny and silver colored: fire radiates infrared radiation, some of which reaches the firefighter's suit, but the shiny silver coating reflects most of the infrared radiation, reducing the amount of heat absorbed by the firefighter.

Infrared radiation is absorbed and re-emitted by some of the gas molecules making up our atmosphere, but not others. Gas molecules made of two atoms, including the oxygen and nitrogen that together make up about 99 percent of our planet's atmosphere in the form of O_2 and N_2, do not reflect or absorb infrared radiation in significant amounts—they are transparent to infrared radiation. Other gas molecules, usually molecules with three or more atoms, such as carbon dioxide (CO_2) and water vapor (H_2O), do absorb and re-emit infrared radiation. Clouds, which are made up of small particles of either liquid water or solid water (ice), absorb and emit infrared radiation, as seen in the photo at left. The cloudless part of the atmosphere looks transparent to the infrared camera because it is made up mostly of molecules with two atoms each, nitrogen (N_2) and oxygen (O_2), which do not absorb (and therefore do not re-emit) infrared radiation. Molecules that absorb infrared also give off, or emit heat in the form of infrared radiation. Hotter substances radiate much more heat than cooler objects, and objects painted flat black radiate more heat than objects painted silver or white.[8]

In the example of the hot water bottle used to warm the bed, at any point where the bedsheets and the bottle do not touch, infrared radiation is constantly emitted by the bottle and the sheets surrounding the bottle and radiated through the air between the bottle and the sheets. Because the bottle is hotter than the sheets, it emits more infrared radiation than the sheets. The sheets absorb infrared radiation emitted by the water bottle, and the water bottle absorbs infrared radiation emitted by the sheets. When the bottle eventually cools to the same temperature as the bed, it will emit and absorb infrared radiation at the same rate as the sheets because there will be no temperature difference between the bottle and the surrounding sheets.[9]

6   Refrangible means able to be refracted, or broken up into the different colors of the rainbow.

7   William Herschel, "Experiments on the Refrangibility of the Invisible Rays of the Sun," <u>Philosophical Transactions of the Royal Society of London</u> Vol. 1 (1800-1814): Pages 22-23.

8   To be more specific, substances radiate heat in proportion to the fourth power of their absolute temperature, multiplied by their emissivity. "Emissivity" is a characteristic of a surface that describes how well the surface emits infrared radiation compared to something painted flat black. Absorption is generally proportional to emissivity, but absorption and emissivity on different light wavelengths are strongly influenced by an object's color. Being proportional to the fourth power means a small increase in temperature causes an enormous increase in radiation.

But for most purposes it is sufficient to understand that hotter substances radiate much more heat; shiny substances reflect more heat, radiate less heat, and absorb less heat; and when shiny substances get dirty or are painted flat black, they reflect less heat and absorb and radiate more heat.

9   Assuming the emissivities of the water bottle and the bedsheets are the same.

Heat Movement by Convection

Convection is the movement of fluids caused by difference in weight: heavier moving down and lighter moving up. Fluids usually get larger as they get hotter. Described another way, a certain quantity of a substance usually takes up more space as it gets hotter. The reason for this is that the heat causes the molecules to vibrate more, which causes them to spread out away from each other. If air gets hotter in a container that prevents it from expanding, for example in a bicycle tire that gets hot from friction with the road, the air pressure rises. If air is not in a container when it gets heated, the increased vibration causes the molecules to spread out and occupy more space. This makes a hot fluid lighter per unit of volume, which causes it to flow upward in a mix of cold and hot fluids. This is why people say "heat rises"—not because heat actually rises but because hot fluids rise above cold fluids, just as oil, which is lighter than vinegar, rises through the vinegar when oil and vinegar in salad dressing separate.

A classic example of convection is smoke going up a chimney because the smoke is hotter, and therefore lighter, than the surrounding air. Convection is usually thought of as one of the three ways that heat is moved, but strictly speaking, convection is a movement of mass (molecules) from one place to another. The movement is driven by, or derives its energy from, a difference in temperature and carries mass with heat in it from the hotter area to the colder area. At the molecular level, individual molecules do not heat each other by convection, which is a larger-scale process involving movement of molecules (mass) from one place to another.

Heat Movement by Latent Heat

Latent heat is the energy bound up in the force of attraction between molecules. It is one of the main ways the earth's atmosphere is warmed, it is an important cooling mechanism for animals including people, and it is the energy that must be added to water to dry out buildings when they get wet.

The word latent comes from the Latin word "latere" (to lie hidden). Latent heat movement is not as obvious as radiation or conduction, and is hard to find with a thermometer, yet it has the potential to do work.

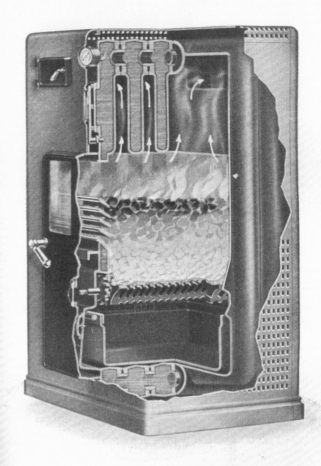

IDEAL ARCOLA PARLOR HEATER

Cutaway view showing water-surrounded ash pit, large combustion chamber and fire travel.

This cast iron boiler, from 1925, is moving heat by both radiation and conduction. The drawing illustrates how radiation, conduction, and convection are all important to heat movement. Heat is moving from the fire to the cast iron boiler by infrared radiation from the fire, by visible light radiation from the fire, and by conduction from the flames and the hot smoke. Then, the heat moves from the cast iron to the water in the boiler by conduction only. The boiler is connected to a chimney (not shown) filled with smoke that is hotter, and therefore lighter, than the air outside the chimney and furnace, causing the heavier air to push into the bottom of the boiler and push the smoke through the boiler and up the chimney by convection.
The Ideal Fitter, 21st ed. (New York: American Radiator Company, 1925), Page 69. (Yes, radiator companies gave out free hardcover, colored catalogues in the 1920s.)

Latent heat could be said to "hide between molecules," because it is the heat released or absorbed in the change of phase between solid, liquid, and gas for all substances. It is the energy that must be added to ice to separate ice crystals into liquid water, and it is the energy that must be added to liquid water to separate water drops into water vapor. Heat absorbed by a pot of boiling water on a stove is more obvious than heat absorbed by water slowly

Rubbing alcohol feels cold on skin because as it evaporates quickly it absorbs latent heat from skin.

evaporating, but in both cases, when the water changes phase from liquid to gas, it absorbs the same amount of heat. One way to make the latent heat absorbed by evaporation more obvious is to find an example of fast evaporation.

Rubbing alcohol at room temperature feels cold on the skin because it evaporates quickly. As it evaporates, the liquid alcohol separates into individual gas molecules. The energy to overcome the forces of attraction between the liquid molecules is in the form of heat that moves from the skin and nearby air to the alcohol. The same process takes place when water boils: the water changes from liquid to gas, absorbing latent heat in the process.

Latent heat also flows in the other direction. It is released when water vapor condenses into liquid water, or when liquid water freezes into ice. And the amount of heat is equal in each direction. Described another way, the amount of heat released when steam condenses into liquid water is equal to the amount of heat liquid water absorbs when it turns into steam. (Steam is a gas made of 100 percent water vapor.)

The amount of heat involved is not trivial. For example, when water vapor in the earth's atmosphere changes phase from a gas to a liquid, producing clouds, heat is released. This latent heating is a major source of warming for our planet's atmosphere.

When steam from an iron condenses to liquid water on clothing, it releases energy as latent heat in an amount equal to about seven times the heat released when the

resulting boiling-temperature water cools to room temperature. In the other direction, heating a pot of water on the stove from room temperature to boiling temperature takes about one-seventh of the amount of heat required to turn the boiling-temperature liquid water into water vapor. (The same is true in a steam boiler—see Page 524.)

No latent heating or cooling is involved in the example of the water bottle used to warm the bed because (assuming the water bottle does not leak) no water is evaporating and no water vapor is condensing into liquid.

Heat movement via latent heat is important to many branches of science, including building science, and should never be ignored.

Latent Cooling of the Fastest Animal on Earth (Over a Long Distance)

Picture an open savanna in Africa many thousands of years ago. An early human approaches a watering hole, and the deer, cattle, and other animals retreat past rock- or spear-throwing distance. The human takes a drink, chooses the most delicious-looking animals, and runs toward them. The animals sprint fast enough to easily get away, but the human doesn't give up and keeps jogging at a steady pace, while everyone, in a race to the death, starts getting hot—human and animals alike. Furry animals have limited or no ability to sweat (evaporation does cool a dog's nose, as shown on Page 1), so they pant in short breaths, increasing evaporation and therefore latent cooling from their mouths and the large wet surfaces of their lungs. Lungs have an enormous surface area and are always wet, which facilitates a lot of evaporation. (See the drawing on Page 7.) But the human can sweat and is being cooled by latent cooling from a larger area: mouth, lungs, and skin. If the human has timed the attack properly, the chase coincides with the afternoon peak temperature. The animals know they are running for their lives, but eventually their bodies simply get too hot for the necessary bodily chemical reactions to continue, and they will stop running to avoid overheating to death.

The animal stands there panting, staring glassy-eyed at the approaching human. Rock, club, or spear, it doesn't matter how the end comes. Superior cooling ability is one of the critical factors allowing humans to outrun any animal in a long race under the right conditions.[10] Latent cooling from sweat evaporating from the entire surface of a person's skin can cool him much faster than any furry animal can cool himself. Some anthropologists say this advantage—our ability to sweat—was critical to our early survival and development as a species.

Latent cooling doesn't simply mean removing water. Pouring some hot water out of a teacup does not cool the remaining water, and sweat dripping off a runner does not cool the runner. Latent cooling or heating always involves a change of phase between solid, liquid, and gas.

Evaporating water, as in the visible vapor leaving a teacup, does cool the water remaining in the cup. Sweat evaporating from a runner's skin does cool the runner.

Drinking cool water on a hot day feels better than drinking room-temperature water, and does remove slightly more heat from the body than room-temperature water, because more heat is conducted from the body to cool water than to room-temperature water. But the temperature of the water makes only a small difference because the main cooling power of drinking water is the latent heat the water absorbs when it evaporates from our skin or lungs.

If a person drinks water at body temperature, no heat will be conducted from the person's body to the water because the water is at the same temperature as the person's body. But the water will still cool the person by latent heat when water evaporates from his lungs and skin. If a person drinks room-temperature water, the water is cooler than his body, which will cause heat to be conducted from his body to the water, making him ever so slightly cooler. Drinking water from a water fountain will cause about twice as much heat to be conducted from his body to the water (assuming the water from the fountain is cooled by a refrigerator built into the fountain, or by running through underground pipes).

10   An argument in a Welsh pub about who could run faster—humans or horses—resulted in the 22-mile Man Versus Horse Marathon, held annually since 1980. Some years the humans win. Humans would presumably win every year if the race was held in a warmer climate. A longer race would also help the humans.

In 1990, anthropologist Louis Liebenberg, studying "persistence hunting," as reportedly practiced by native people around the world, witnessed hunters !Nam!kabe, !Nate, Kayate, and Boro//xao run down antelope in the heat of the day in the Kalahari desert in Botswana.

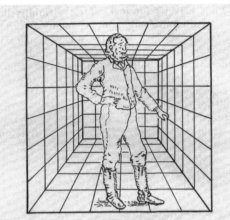

Fig. 2. -The area of this room, walls, floor and ceiling, 6 by 6 by 6 feet, represents the amount of surface in the lungs of an ordinary man through which all the blood of the body passes about twice every minute, to be brought close to the air which is changed by the act of breathing 15 to 20 times per minute.

This 1908 illustration shows that the surface area of a person's lungs is surprisingly large: 216 square feet, or 20 square meters. Modern estimates say our lungs are four times that size.
Franklin H. King, <u>Ventilation for Dwellings, Rural Schools and Stables</u> (Madison, Wisconsin: published by author, 1908), Page 4.

Yet as mentioned earlier, the temperature of the water hardly matters. The latent heat absorbed by the water as it evaporates will be about 40 times as much heat as gets conducted to the room-temperature water and about 20 times as much heat as gets conducted to the cooler water from the fountain. That means drinking cool fountain water cools the body only 1/40th more than drinking room-temperature water, which proves the temperature of drinking water hardly matters.

Understanding latent heat is critical to understanding building durability. Buildings mostly get wet with liquid water (rain, leaky pipes, etc.) but dry almost exclusively by evaporation. Drying by evaporation requires adding heat equal to the latent heat of evaporation of the water.

Latent heat also has a profound effect on people's comfort. People's bodies are almost always exchanging heat with their environment, usually by conduction, radiation, and latent cooling simultaneously. Latent heating of a person's body is possible under unusual circumstances, such as in a steam room, where water vapor condenses out of the air onto a person's body, releasing latent heat in the process.

Understanding how heat movement affects people's comfort is critical to understanding how to make buildings comfortable for people. To fully understand how heat affects people, and moves through buildings, it is necessary to first understand the laws governing heat.

THREE FUNDAMENTAL LAWS

All heat movement in the universe is governed by the three laws of thermodynamics. (Another law is sometimes called the fourth law of thermodynamics, which can be ignored for building science.) It might make more sense to call them the three laws of energy because these laws govern the movement of all forms of energy, not just heat. These three laws are unbreakable and apply to everything that happens in the whole universe, all the time.

Third Law

The third law of thermodynamics is mentioned here first because it is the easiest to understand. The third law says that it is impossible to cool something to absolute zero.

The concept of absolute zero implies a system with no energy or heat, which would occur if something were cooled to a temperature of -273 °C (-459 °F), at which point all molecular vibration would stop. But nothing can ever be cooled to absolute zero because doing so would require something colder to absorb the heat, which is impossible: nothing can be colder than absolute zero. Therefore, nothing can be cooled to absolute zero. This is an interesting concept but has no practical application in building science.

First Law

The first law of thermodynamics is also easy to understand. It says that energy in a system is conserved. "Conserved" means that the amount stays constant. Described another way, energy can neither be created nor destroyed.

Another way of stating the first law is that the amount of energy in an isolated system remains constant. An "isolated" system is anything anyone chooses to draw an imaginary line around, where nothing, including energy, crosses the line. Picture a building as an isolated system. What the first law says about this system is that the amount of energy in the system—the building—stays constant.

A real house is an "open" system, which means energy can enter and leave the house. For example, energy can enter the building as electricity coming in through the wire from the utility company, and it can leave by light shining out a window. But the first law means that over a long period of time, the amount of energy entering the house equals the amount of energy leaving the house. Or, energy in = energy out because a house cannot create or destroy energy. The only difference between the amount of energy entering the house and the amount leaving would be the amount of energy the house could store; for example, if someone turned the thermostat up, heat would accumulate in the house until the thermostat was satisfied and sent a signal to the heating system to turn off.

An imaginary line drawn around a real-world house would have a lot of energy crossing it, but the amount crossing in one direction (fuel or solar energy to heat the house during the winter) would be equal to the amount crossing in the other direction (heat escaping the house, no matter how well insulated it is) over a long time. A well-insulated house would not allow much heat to leave, therefore much less fuel is required to keep a well-insulated house warm during the winter.

If the house has a large number of efficient and optimally oriented, unshaded solar electric panels, and does not use much electricity, it can export more electricity to the power company than it takes from the power company. But the energy exported from the "system" (in this case, the building and the solar panels) entered the "system" from the sun, so the total amount of energy entering the building is equal to the amount of energy leaving the house. The solar energy "used" to operate lights and other electric-powered devices in the building is, of course, not really used up because the first law says energy cannot be destroyed (or created). Most of the electricity turns into heat, which goes back across the imaginary line as heat escaping from the house. A little probably also leaves the house as light shining out a window.

If the house had solar thermal panels (the type that heats water, not the type that makes electricity), the system would gain heat from the sun during the day, which could be stored in a tank of water in the house. At night, when someone might take a shower or wash some clothing, most of that heat would go down the drain with the hot water. Over a long period of time, the system gains the same amount of energy, or heat, that it loses. If the panels themselves were seen as a system, they too would gain and lose the same amount of energy over time.

Likewise, the electric utility company's power plant is a building that exports electricity continuously, but to do this it needs a constant supply of either coal, uranium, gas, oil, running water under pressure, wind, or solar energy.

Energy enters a power plant as chemical bonds in fuel and becomes heat as the fuel burns. The power plant turns some of the heat[11] into electricity, which makes it obvious that heat is a form of energy. But this idea was not clearly understood by scientists until surprisingly recently—the mid-1800s. The broader public did not understand this until even later, as evidenced by the "caloric theory" still being given serious consideration in 1857. (See Page 1.)

One of the people who did important work in this area was the English physicist James Joule, for whom the joule, the standard unit of energy, is named. In 1845, theorizing that heat was another form of the energy that could be used to lift a weight, he experimented with a falling weight tied to a string that turned a paddle wheel in a container of water. His family owned a brewery, so he knew how to insulate containers of liquid and make accurate temperature measurements. He measured the increase in the temperature of water resulting from the friction of mixing the water and published his theory of the "mechanical equivalent of heat." This and other experiments of his led to widespread acceptance of the idea that mechanical energy, electric energy, and heat were all different forms of energy, which could be converted from one form to another but could neither be created nor destroyed.[12]

11   About a third of the energy input to a nuclear or fossil-fuel-burning power plant of the dominant types in use today (2017) gets to the customer as electricity. Newer gas turbine power plants are more efficient. (Depending on distance between the power plant and the customer, about 10 percent of the heat "lost" is transmission loss: heat created from electricity flowing through the wires and other equipment that transmits the electricity from the power plant to the end user—the rest of the two-thirds "loss" comes out of the power plant as heat.)

12   When Amelia Grimes married James Joule in 1847, he was still curious about heat and energy, so on their honeymoon in Switzerland he measured the temperature of water at the tops and bottoms of waterfalls. What his measurements showed is not known, but the two of them remained married until Amelia's death in 1854.

It would take a massive waterfall to measure a difference in temperature from the top to the bottom because water has such a high thermal mass (see Page 13). Ignoring latent cooling from evaporation and other factors, the temperature in a river at the bottom of a 1,000-meter-high waterfall will be one degree Celsius higher than the river's temperature at the top of the waterfall.

Understanding the first law can help clarify decisions about saving energy. One thing to consider when figuring out what will work is the question of how energy will be "lost" if a proposed energy-saving measure is not implemented.[13] The energy has to go to a specific place and take a specific path to get there. Energy cannot simply disappear. For example, when considering whether insulating a house will save energy, one question to ask is what will happen if the insulation is not installed: during the winter, more heat will move from indoors to outdoors, requiring the heating system to supply more heat. Similarly, during the summer, more heat will move from outdoors to indoors, and the air conditioner will run more and use more electricity to move more heat from inside the house to the outdoor part of the air conditioning system (explained on Page 511). Because the amount of energy entering a house equals the amount of energy leaving either with or without insulation, the explanation of how insulation saves energy conforms with the first law.

If someone offers a product he claims will save energy but cannot explain where the energy wasted without buying the product goes, or how it gets to that place, the proposed energy-saving measure should be viewed with skepticism. "Less efficient" is not a place that wasted energy can go and does not explain how energy will leave a building or other system. The first law would have to be violated for energy to simply disappear, which is impossible.

Second Law

The second law of thermodynamics is simple but has a wide range of implications. It says that heat flows from hot things to things that are less hot. Described another way, the second law implies that heat will never flow spontaneously from a cold object to a hot object. The second law also implies that work is necessary to move heat from a cold object to a hot object, which is why a refrigerator needs electricity to cool food. The second law

13   The first law says that energy is never lost or destroyed, it just goes someplace else. Usually it turns into a form that is less useful, such as a large amount of heat spread out to a low temperature—for example, the heat conducted through the walls of a building during the winter. An energy-efficient building does not "use" less energy, nor does it actually "save" energy, despite the commonly used language. All the heat that keeps any building warm during the winter ends up back outdoors, but the amount that flows into and then out of an energy-efficient building is much less than the amount that flows through a poorly insulated, or less energy-efficient, building.

also implies that each time energy is changed from one form to another, some energy is changed into a less useful form. For example, as a car engine changes the chemical energy in fuel into mechanical energy to move the car, some of the energy in the fuel becomes heat in the air around the car, which is not useful.

The second law also says that energy is required to create non-randomness, or order. Entropy is a measure of disorder, or randomness in a system. A house that is warm on a cold day is an example of non-randomness, as is a box of marbles sorted into neat rows of black and white marbles. Examples of randomness include a house at the same temperature as outdoors, or black and white marbles mixed randomly. The second law also says that the amount of entropy (disorder) in an isolated system never decreases but always increases until it reaches the maximum possible value. For example, if a house at room temperature and the cold winter air surrounding it are seen as an isolated system, heat will move from the house to the outdoor air until the heat is evenly distributed (same temperature) throughout the system: the house and the outdoor air. Heat will never spontaneously become unevenly distributed within the system. Adding insulation to the house will slow down the rate of heat movement between indoors and outdoors, but no amount of insulation can stop it completely. Entropy will continue to increase in the system until the house and the surrounding air are at the same temperature. (Remember: the house and air in this example form an isolated system, therefore no energy is being added to the house.)

Another implication of the second law is that if a ditch is dug connecting two lakes, water will flow from the higher lake to the lower lake and stop flowing when the surfaces of the two lakes are at the same level. The sizes of the lakes do not matter: the levels of the lakes will become equal.

The second law also explains why, if a piece of glass makes a hole in a bicycle tire, air will flow out of the tire (increasing entropy, or randomness) until the air pressure is equal on both sides of the hole. The second law also demands that after the hole is patched, energy is required to pump air back into the tire.

The second law also applies to concepts not directly related to heat, such as accumulating water on top of a mountain, or removing water vapor from indoor air.

Entropy can also describe a lack of information, such as black and white marbles mixed randomly.

In accordance with the second law, not all of the energy entering an electricity-generating power plant comes out as electricity. At least half of the energy leaves as heat. In China, Russia, and Europe, much of this heat heats water which is piped around cities to heat buildings and faucet water. A few cities in North America use "waste" heat from electricity-generating plants, as do many hospitals and college campuses (see "cogen system" on Page 544). Still, much of the heat is at too low a temperature to be useful (like the heat in the large glass of mixed hot and cold water on Page 11), so it ends up as "waste" heat going up a chimney or into a river with cooling water.

The implications of the second law are profound. If the sun were to stop shining tomorrow, all the heat on the earth would flow from hot to cold, leaving everything at the same temperature,[14] and eventually all the water on the earth's surface would reach the same level.[15]

Understanding the second law makes it easy to tell if a movie is being played forward or backward; reversing the movie would show many events that would be breaking the second law. For example, a movie of a box of black and white marbles arranged in neat rows spilling onto the floor played backwards would show the marbles spontaneously arranging themselves in rows, which is impossible without the input of energy (and a decrease in entropy).

The first and third laws can be understood fairly quickly, but a complete understanding of all the implications of the second law might take longer because the second law covers many subjects and can get very abstract.

14   Basic physics explains that as fast-moving hot molecules collide with slower-moving cold molecules, they usually give some of their momentum to the cold molecules. "Usually" averaged over countless collisions means heat is always conducted from hot to cold. Basic physics also explains that hot objects radiate more infrared radiation to cold objects than cold objects radiate back, explaining why infrared radiation moves heat from hot things to cold things. As there is apparently no thermodynamics explanation for the direction that convection and latent heating or cooling move heat (both of which depend on conduction and radiation to move heat anyhow), perhaps it is fair to say that there are only two true forms of heat movement—conduction and radiation—because these are the only two whose direction can be explained by the second law.

15   Ocean levels are also influenced by the earth's rotation, and by the moon, both of which can be ignored for this example.

APPLICATIONS OF THE THREE LAWS

The First Law and Airplanes

An airplane flying through the air and the air near the plane can be thought of as an isolated system. The engines burn fuel, which contains energy in the form of chemical bonds. The energy is released as heat, some of which the engines turn into mechanical energy (as hot gases expand, they turn turbine blades, which are like large propellers inside the engine). Most of the mechanical energy pushes the plane forward, while a little is used to generate electricity or pressurize the air in the passenger cabin.

The plane's movement causes friction against the air passing over the plane's surfaces, which generates heat. The plane also mixes the air it passes through, leaving a turbulent wake behind it. The turbulent air continues swirling around for a time after the plane passes, until friction in the air converts the kinetic energy of air movement into heat. The noise generated by the engines vibrates air and other objects. Vibration is movement, which involves friction, which also creates a little heat. The electricity generated by the engines and used to operate lights and video screens mostly ends up as heat in the cabin and then in the air outside the plane. The exception is some light that is given off by the plane's lights, which goes into outer space or downward, heating up something on the earth's surface. Eventually, all the energy in the fuel is converted to heat. In conformance with the first law, none of the energy is destroyed.

Winglets on the ends of plane wings save as much as five percent of the fuel required to fly the plane. Without them, higher-pressure air under the wings slides off the ends of the wings, rushing toward the low-pressure air on top of the wings, creating spiral-shaped swirls of air extending a long distance behind each wingtip. The winglets separate the high- and low-pressure airstreams, reducing the swirling of the air behind the plane. Reducing the amount of turbulence following the plane reduces the amount of heat that will be added to the air through friction as the air swirls. Reducing the amount of heat the plane adds to the air behind it saves fuel. Described another way, the winglets allow the engines to move the plane forward at the same speed with less thrust, therefore using less fuel. It may seem strange to think that fuel use is impacted by what happens in the air minutes after the plane passes through it, but the first law says it must be: all the energy added to the air behind the plane comes from the fuel.

The First and Second Laws and Two Glasses of Water

Question: If two glasses are filled with water, one hot enough to take a shower with or heat a house with, and a second one cool enough to use for cooling a house, and the two glasses of water are mixed together into one large glass, is energy lost?

No. According to the first law, energy cannot be created or destroyed. What was lost, or destroyed, was the potential for the temperature difference between the water in the two glasses to do useful work, or for the temperature difference between the water in any one glass and the ambient air to do useful work. Because energy did not leave the system of water and glasses, energy was not lost when they were mixed. The glass of mixed water contains the same amount of energy that the two separate glasses contained together, which leads to the next question:

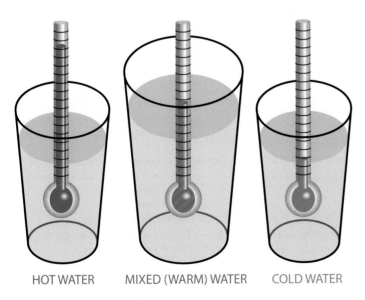

HOT WATER   MIXED (WARM) WATER   COLD WATER

Is energy required to separate the mixed water back into two glasses of water, one hot and one cold?

The answer is yes.

The second law says energy is required to separate the warm water back into hot and cold water, and it also says that no process or piece of equipment can ever be 100 percent efficient—some energy will always become inaccessible, or "lost," in processes that transform energy from one form to another. Of course, the "lost" energy is never really lost but degrades to heat in a form that is not useful, such as heat in the air around the equipment. In the case of separating the mixed water back into a glass of hot water and a glass of cold water, cooling equipment and energy will be required to remove some heat from half of the system (one of the glasses of water) and put it in the other half of the system (the other glass of water).

The Second Law and Solar Thermal Systems

Solar thermal systems typically heat water with solar panels on the roof and store the heated water in a tank. The second law has a lot to say about the optimal size of a solar storage tank.

It can be useful to do a thought experiment called "theorizing the extremes." Imagine a house with a reasonable number of solar thermal panels on the roof and an extremely large hot water storage tank in the basement—for example, the size of a large swimming pool. The water in the tank starts out cold, and stays relatively cold for a long time, because the house does not have enough solar panels to heat the water up to a very high temperature. The panels, however, work very well. The second law says heat moves from hot things to cold things, therefore the cold water circulating between the tank and the panels absorbs more heat from the solar panels than warm or hot water would, maximizing the amount of heat the panels are able to absorb from the sun. The second law also says that the hotter the panels get, the more heat they will move to surrounding air; therefore, sending cold water from the tank to the panels will cool the panels as much as possible, reducing heat movement from the panels to outdoor air. This means the larger the tank, the better the panels will perform because a larger tank will store more cold water for the panels to heat.

But the second law also has something else to say. The second law says that the heat in a large tank of water that is only slightly warmer than when it was cold is not very useful heat. It is called "low grade" heat because there is only a small temperature difference between the water in the tank and the ambient air. A person living in the house would experience this as the water not being warm enough to heat the house or take a shower with because the heat is spread out throughout too much water, like the heat in the mixed glass of water.

So, theorize the other extreme: a small tank the size of a bottle of soda. Because the tank is so small, the panels will easily heat the water in the tank to a temperature hot enough to take a shower with or to heat the house. But when the panels are filled with hot water they don't absorb as much heat from the sun as they would when they are filled with cold water from the large tank, therefore they move more heat to the surrounding air, reducing the amount of heat the solar panels capture and move to the tank. And because the tank is so small, it can only supply hot water to the shower for a few seconds, which is not very useful, even for the fastest shower-taker.

This thought experiment shows that the ideal size of the tank should be somewhere in between the two extremes and illustrates how understanding the second law helps explain the advantages and disadvantages of both extremely large and extremely small hot water storage tanks.

The Three Laws and Bicycle Riding

A bicycle, the person riding the bicycle, and an imaginary closed sphere of air can be thought of as an isolated system. The rider's body turns the chemical energy in the rider's food into mechanical energy and heat. If the rider is pedaling hard on a level road, about 98 percent of the mechanical energy is used to overcome the friction of moving through the air. The other two percent of the mechanical energy overcomes friction in the tires, pedals, chain, and so on. Almost all of this friction heats the air, and a little heats the road, leaving all the mechanical energy behind as heat.

The rider also leaves behind some water vapor. Water evaporates from the rider's lungs, and usually some sweat evaporates. Strange as it may sound, in the fields of air conditioning and building science, adding water vapor to air can be considered a form of heating the air. While this is certainly what some people sweating on a hot day would conclude, the science requires a little more explanation.

In the air conditioning industry, the amount of heat a piece of equipment can remove from air is called the "sensible cooling capacity" of the equipment. The amount of water the equipment can condense out of the air is called the "latent cooling capacity," or simply the "latent capacity." Removing water vapor from hot, humid air makes people feel cooler, increases entropy, and requires electricity to operate the equipment, just as energy is required to separate the large glass of water on Page 11 into one glass of cold water and one glass of hot water. Adding water vapor to indoor air generally increases the load on the air conditioner, which illustrates how it is reasonable for someone in the air conditioning industry to consider adding water vapor to air a form of heating air.

The heat added to the air around a bicycle rider that can be measured with a thermometer is called "sensible heat," because it is: heat that can be sensed with a thermometer. Adding water vapor to air (for example, by sweating) is sometimes called adding "latent heat" to the air, and removing water vapor from air (for example, with a dehumidifier) can be considered a form of cooling the air.

There are charts that show the "total enthalpy" of air according to its combined heat and water vapor content (enthalpy is the total energy in a system compared to absolute zero, or some other agreed-upon reference). The more heat and water vapor in the air, the higher the enthalpy of the air, and the larger the combined (sensible and latent) load on a cooling (air conditioning) system.

Of course, all the processes in the bicycle rider's body also obey the laws of thermodynamics. In compliance with the first law, all the heat given off by the rider came from chemical energy in the rider's food, with no energy being created or destroyed. The rider's body gains or loses heat in accordance with the second law. The third law generally has no relevance to a bicycle rider.

THERMAL MASS

One more property of materials important in building science is "thermal mass," or the amount of heat an object or a substance can hold. Some branches of science call this a material's "heat capacity." This concept is important for understanding how buildings heat up and cool down and which side of walls insulation works best on, which will be explained in Chapter 16: Building Enclosures.

Physics textbooks usually list the heat capacity of different materials: how much heat is required to raise the temperature of a certain weight of a material one degree. Imagine a physicist hires a plumber to install a radiant heated floor on top of an existing floor. The plumber explains that adding another layer of flooring is a bad idea because a floor with a higher thermal mass takes a longer time to heat up or cool down. The physicist might argue that adding another layer of material won't change the heat capacity of the original material. The physicist is correct—adding material does not change the characteristic of a material. But all layers of flooring will heat up when the thermostat calls for heat, and the plumber is thinking of the thermal mass of the entire floor, not per weight of material. The plumber is also right: adding material does add thermal mass, which takes more heat (and time) to heat up and cool down.

Building assemblies with a high thermal mass take a long time to heat up or cool down, thereby reducing the peak amount of heat a building's heating system has to add on a cold night and reducing the peak amount of heat a building's cooling system has to remove on a hot day. Depending on how the term is used, "high thermal mass" can accurately describe a large quantity of material or a material with a high heat capacity, or both. Water has a high heat capacity, and porous materials absorb water vapor when exposed to air, which further confuses things.

The roofs of the famous adobe buildings built hundreds of years ago in the desert of southwestern North America were made of a material with a high heat capacity: wood. But the roofs had a low thermal mass because the wood was dried out from the sun and because there was not much of the material: the roofs were not very thick. But the dried mud walls were thick enough to have enough thermal mass to even out the day and night temperatures in these buildings. The walls were able to absorb enough heat during the day to keep the building significantly warmer than outdoor air at night. Of course, thermal mass works the other way, too. The walls cool down at night, and it takes so much heat to heat the high thermal mass walls during the day that the buildings remain cool enough to be comfortable during the hot desert days.

HEAT AND PEOPLE'S COMFORT

When people complain that a room is hot or cold, it is often assumed that air temperature is the only thing that needs to be corrected. But this is an oversimplification that can frustrate attempts at providing comfort. Other factors that contribute to a feeling that a room is too hot or too cold include:

- Infrared heat exchange. (How much heat is being gained by a person's body by absorbing infrared radiation versus how much heat is being lost by the person's body by emitting infrared radiation?)

- Air movement. (Is the air relatively still? Is there a fan? Is air being moved around the room by convection? Is air moving through leaks in the building?)

- Evenness of air temperature, air movement, and infrared heat exchange within a room or a building, and on different parts of a person's body, at one point in time.

- Steadiness of air temperature, air movement, and infrared heat exchange over time.

- Humidity. (How much water vapor is mixed with the air? During the summer high humidity makes a room feel hot.)

- Feeling of control. (Psychological effect of people knowing they can control the temperature.)

Combined, these less obvious factors can and frequently do outweigh actual air temperature as a determinant of people's comfort. If these factors are favorable, it is more likely that the room will be comfortable for everybody, or at least that it will please a much higher percentage of people than could be pleased by trying to find a thermostat setting everyone will agree on. These factors are therefore very important to making a building comfortable for the people in it.

People's Comfort and Infrared Radiation

A person's body is constantly emitting and absorbing infrared radiation. Comfort is influenced by the difference between how much is emitted and how much is absorbed. Because body temperature does not vary much, the amount of infrared radiation a person emits is fairly constant, varying mostly because of differences in clothing. How much infrared radiation a person absorbs from his environment does change significantly, and this strongly influences comfort.

Picture a person getting into a car on a cold winter night, starting the engine, and turning on the heat. As the engine warms up, the heater starts blowing air heated by "waste" heat from the engine, which quickly warms up the air inside the car to a comfortable temperature.

But the person in the car is not satisfied so quickly because the car's seats, floor, ceiling, and doors are still cold and therefore not radiating much heat to the person; there is also no sun sending infrared radiation through the car windows. Both of these things combine to make the person still feel cold.

It is easy to mistakenly think that, because the car surrounding the person

During a cold night, the car's heating system is keeping the air inside this car at a comfortable temperature, as indicated by the purple thermometer inside the car. But because it is a cold night, and the car was just turned on, the materials the car is made of are still cold and are not radiating much heat toward the driver. There are no clouds in the sky, therefore there is no infrared radiation from the earth's surface being absorbed by clouds and re-emitted back toward the driver. The small amount of infrared radiation reaching the driver leaves him feeling cold, despite the warm air temperature in the car.

is cold, it absorbs more infrared radiation from the person than a warm car absorbs. This is not true. The surface of an object absorbs infrared radiation in proportion to the surface's emissivity (see Footnote 8 on Page 4). The object's temperature does not affect how much infrared radiation the object absorbs. The person emits about the same amount of radiation in a cold car as in a hot car (because his body temperature doesn't vary much), and the car absorbs the same amount of radiation regardless of the car's temperature. If the car is hot, it will still absorb the same amount of infrared radiation as a cold car absorbs.

What does change is how much heat the car radiates toward the person. A hot car emits much more heat than a cold car. And on a sunny day, a lot of infrared heat radiates in through the glass as well. The person absorbs more infrared radiation from the hot car, even with the air conditioning cooling the air to a comfortable temperature, while the person continues to emit about the same amount of heat as in any car. The car continues to absorb the same amount of infrared radiation, regardless of its temperature. The difference between emitted and absorbed, which is known as the "net" radiant heat exchanged, is what influences the person's comfort.

The same problem occurs in a room with a lot of glass. On a sunny day, people receive so much radiant heat that they feel overheated at the same indoor air temperature and humidity at which they would feel perfectly comfortable in a building with opaque walls. In some cases, a cloud passing in front of the sun changes people's comfort levels enough to cause complaints in the other direction: too cold. At night, radiant cooling can cause complaints that the same building that felt hot earlier in the day feels cold at the same indoor air temperature and humidity.

When a person absorbs more infrared radiation then he emits, that is called infrared heating or radiant heating. When a person absorbs less infrared heat than he emits, that is called radiant cooling. An example of radiant cooling of part of a wall is shown in the photo on Page 3. Parts of buildings can be used as radiant heating or cooling systems, as will be described in Chapter 18: Heating and Cooling.

People's Comfort and Air Movement

Fans make people comfortable during the summer because air blowing across a person's body can increase conduction of heat away from a person's body (as long as the air is cooler than the person's body), while also increasing latent cooling.

When a person's skin conducts heat to the air touching it, that air becomes warmer. A fan moves that air away from the person's body and replaces it with air that hasn't yet been heated by the person's body, allowing more heat to be conducted out of the person's body (as long as the air temperature continues to be cooler than the person's body).

When a person's skin evaporates water vapor to the air touching it, that air becomes more humid. If the fan moves the humid air away from the skin and replaces it with drier air, the sweat will evaporate more readily, cooling the person more and leaving the person feeling less sweaty. This is true even if the air is hotter than the person's skin but dry enough to cool the person by latent cooling.

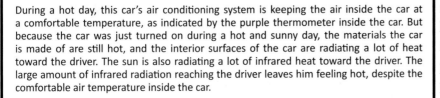

During a hot day, this car's air conditioning system is keeping the air inside the car at a comfortable temperature, as indicated by the purple thermometer inside the car. But because the car was just turned on during a hot and sunny day, the materials the car is made of are still hot, and the interior surfaces of the car are radiating a lot of heat toward the driver. The sun is also radiating a lot of infrared heat toward the driver. The large amount of infrared radiation reaching the driver leaves him feeling hot, despite the comfortable air temperature inside the car.

People's Comfort and Evenness of Air Temperature, Air Movement, and Infrared Exchange at One Time

People can perceive a room as being uncomfortable if the air temperature varies from one part of a room to another. This can be the source of complaints that are especially hard to answer because they can sound vague. Often, the person complaining sounds like he doesn't know what he is talking about, which is sort of true.

He may not know why he feels uncomfortable, he just knows he is uncomfortable. People usually dislike it if air is moving around in one part of a room because of an air conditioner or a leaky window or door, while the air is still in another part of the room. If one part of a room has a lot of glass, which can cause intense infrared heating or cooling, while the rest of the room has opaque walls, people can feel both hot and cold at the same time, too.

Achieving evenness within a space is one reason why radiators have traditionally been installed under windows. During the winter, the infrared radiation from the radiator cancels out the lack of infrared radiation from the window and the surrounding wall. Another reason is that the upward convection of air near the radiator counters the downward convection of air from the cold (and sometimes leaky) window, resulting in less air movement in the room. If the radiator were on the opposite wall, it would generate a convective current upwards, which would then cross the ceiling, fall down on the window side of the room, and finally sweep a current of cold air across the floor, as shown on the top of Page 513.

Perhaps the least comfortable environment is a warm ceiling combined with cold walls, which is common in rooms with poorly insulated walls or many windows and a heated room or hot roof above. The opposite—a cool ceiling and warm walls—generally feels more comfortable.

People's Comfort and Steadiness of Air Temperature, Air Movement, and Infrared Exchange over Time

If a room's unevenness is consistent, people may get used to it, but if it fluctuates they will be even more uncomfortable. For example, a building with a large heating or cooling load, and a correspondingly large heating or cooling system cycling on and off, causes a person to feel like they are too hot, then too cold, then too hot, in a never-ending cycle.

A building that is properly insulated and airtightened does not need the heating or cooling delivered as carefully as a less well-insulated and airtightened building. There are many reasons for this. One is that the amount of heat delivered to a well-insulated building is small and therefore easier to control. Another reason is that the amount of infrared radiation emitted by the indoor side of a well-insulated wall does not change much with changes in outdoor conditions. Another reason is that a well-insulated building will tend to have even temperatures between rooms because heat moves more easily through uninsulated interior walls than through well-insulated exterior walls, which helps even out temperature differences between rooms.

People's Comfort and Humidity

Providing comfort to occupants is one of the most fundamental jobs a building is expected to perform. But, in fact, many buildings do a poor job of controlling indoor humidity.

If indoor air is relatively humid, sweat does not evaporate readily, causing people to feel sticky and sweaty. In dry air, sweat evaporates quickly, providing abundant and immediate cooling.

Keeping a building's air dry during the summer is therefore important. An important side benefit of doing so is that sweat spends less time as a liquid on the surface of a person's body, or as a liquid absorbed in clothing, giving bacteria less opportunity to grow. This reduces body odor, which leads to a different type of comfort for people nearby.

During the summer, if indoor air is relatively humid, as it often is in poorly designed and built buildings, some people may complain and demand the air conditioner be turned up, which actually means adjusting it to a lower temperature. This well-meaning attempt at controlling humidity usually results in overcooling, often without achieving the desired reduction in humidity.

One non-obvious advantage of keeping the humidity in a building low during the summer is that different people with different metabolic rates or different amounts of clothing will sweat at different rates to control their individual comfort levels. This will allow a larger number of people to feel cool at one temperature than any temperature at a higher humidity level. The secret to finding the "perfect temperature" at which everyone in an air conditioned room will be comfortable, therefore, is to lower the humidity without overcooling. Controlling humidity will be explained in later chapters.

The opposite situation can also cause comfort problems. During the winter, indoor humidity can get too low, even lower than the best mechanical systems can achieve during the summer. This can cause a person to feel cold because dry air increases the latent cooling from a person's body. People automatically stop sweating when they are cold but can't stop latent cooling from their large and constantly wet mouth and lung surfaces. No number of blankets wrapped around a person will stop latent cooling from the lungs. Indoor air inside a modern-day building during the winter can be much drier than the air normally found in the natural environments our ancestors lived in for thousands of years. This leaves our bodies uncomfortable. The solution is to keep indoor humidity from dropping too low during the winter, which will be explained in later chapters.

The Psychological Side of Comfort

A large body of research shows that if people perceive they have control over the temperature in their environment, they tend to be more satisfied with the temperature. This is true even if a thermostat is installed on the wall but is not connected to anything. Some engineers, contractors, and facility managers boast about responding to chronic temperature complaints by mounting a thermostat on the wall, not connecting it to anything, and having the occupants thank them profusely.

However, it is far better to have a thermostat in each room that actually is connected to mechanical equipment that accurately controls each room's temperature. If the mechanical systems and the building enclosing them are designed with a working knowledge of building science, occupants will be comfortable, eliminating the temptation to resort to dishonest tactics.

A ceiling fan does not actually cool a room, but it can make people feel cooler.

The increased comfort that results will allow people to be comfortable at significantly lower temperatures during the winter and higher temperatures during the summer, yielding significant energy savings.

These combined factors—air temperature, infrared exchange, air movement, evenness of these factors within the space and steadiness over time, humidity levels, and a feeling of control—determine how warm or cold a person feels.

APPLICATIONS OF THE BASIC SCIENCE OF HEAT
How a Ceiling Fan Helps a Person Feel Cool

A ceiling fan can make a person feel cooler but cannot reduce the actual temperature of the room. If a fan is installed in a window, however, it can move outdoor air through a room, which can actually cool the room (if the outdoor air is cool) while also making a person in the room feel cool. Because a ceiling fan only moves air around within a room, it cannot actually cool a room.

All the electricity required to operate a fan motor becomes heat, which makes the room slightly warmer. But, despite making the room slightly warmer, a ceiling fan can still make a person in the room feel cooler.

A ceiling fan makes a person feel cooler because a person inside a building is surrounded by a layer of air that is warmer than room air (assuming room air is cooler than a person's body temperature, which it usually is). When a ceiling fan moves air around a room, it disturbs the thin layer of air near a person's skin, replacing it with cooler air from elsewhere within the room. This increases the heat movement from a person's skin, making the person feel cooler. (It also makes the person actually be cooler.)

A ceiling fan also makes a person feel cooler by moving humid air away from the person's skin. If a person is sweating, evaporating sweat makes the layer of air near a person's skin become more humid than the air in the rest of the room. When a fan circulates air within a room, it replaces the layer of humid air with drier air from elsewhere in the room. Sweat evaporates more readily in dry air than in humid air, which makes a person both feel cooler and actually be cooler.

If a ceiling fan is turned off, the layer of warm and humid air surrounding a person will be moved only by convection and therefore will stay closer to his skin for longer, making him warmer and more humid, which will make him feel hotter.

Why Deserts are Cold at Night

Several mechanisms related to water keep night temperatures warmer in wet climates than in deserts.

In wet climates, water's high thermal mass evens out the temperature by absorbing or giving off heat as the temperature changes. Heat from sunlight is absorbed by water in plants and soil, which limits the increase in air temperature during the day. At night, water in a wet climate gives off heat stored during the day. In a desert climate, there is little or no water to absorb heat during the day and give off heat at night, which allows extreme temperature swings between day and night.

Clouds also limit the difference between day and night temperatures in a wet climate. They absorb and re-emit some of the infrared radiation radiated from the earth's surface back to the surface, limiting nighttime infrared cooling. In a dry climate with no clouds in the sky, most of the infrared heat radiated from the earth's surface goes to outer space and keeps going.

In a wet climate, outdoor air is heated by latent heating at night. If the air temperature at night drops to the dewpoint temperature of the air (the temperature to which air needs to be cooled to start condensing water out of the air), latent heat is released when water condenses out of the air, preventing a further drop in temperature. Described another way, the process of condensing water warms the air. One example of nighttime condensation is "morning dew" formed on grass in a wet climate. In a desert, the dewpoint temperature of the air is too low (the air is too dry) to condense water out of the air; therefore, the air can get cold at night and still not produce dew or be a source of latent heating.

These mechanisms limit the temperature swings in a wet climate: water's high thermal mass, infrared radiation absorbed by clouds and re-emitted back to earth, and latent heating when water condenses out of the air.

SUMMARY

Heat is a form of energy, and all energy is either heat now or on its way to being transformed into heat. Heat is constantly moving between objects by conduction and infrared radiation, aided by convection and latent heating or cooling. The three laws of thermodynamics rule all movement of heat and, indirectly, everything having to do with energy.

People's thermal comfort is determined by much more than air temperature. It is also determined by infrared radiant exchange, air movement, evenness of these factors within a room, steadiness of these factors over time, humidity, and a feeling of control over the temperature.

Chapter 2 **HEAT** Applied Science

WHY IS IT IMPORTANT TO UNDERSTAND MOVEMENT OF HEAT THROUGH BUILDINGS?

Buildings are expected to keep people comfortable, which means keeping heat indoors during cold weather and keeping heat outdoors during hot weather. Thermal comfort for a person is more complicated, however, than simply maintaining the right air temperature. As described in Chapter 1: Heat - Basic Science, people's thermal comfort also depends on, among other factors, controlling net radiant heat exchange and keeping temperatures within a building even at one point in time and steady over time.

Uncomfortable buildings can use a lot of energy because people do whatever they can to achieve comfort, such as adding extra air conditioners or space heaters. When a building superintendant gets a complaint about a building's temperature, the priority is to stop the complaints, even if that means doing something that increases the energy bills or compromises the durability of the building. Comfort complaints take precedence; there is no excuse for leaving occupants uncomfortable in the modern world. And the more expensive the building, the worse the problem is because comfort expectations are usually higher in expensive buildings.

Well-designed, well-built buildings stay comfortable while using minimal heating and cooling energy. Unfortunately, many buildings, including some expensive ones, perform so badly that it is hard to keep people comfortable in them, regardless of how much energy is used. Most energy-inefficient buildings are uncomfortable.

Looked at another way, it is nearly impossible to design a building that is comfortable for people but is not energy efficient. Making a building comfortable, healthy, durable, and energy efficient requires limiting the amount of heat that passes through a building's enclosure. The "enclosure" of a building is the combination of the walls, windows,

This visible light photo shows part of a house built in a cold climate, in a relatively expensive area.

An infrared photo of the same house taken during the winter shows heat conducted through the framing (the studs that support the wall). (White is hot and black is cold in this and all other infrared photos in this book.) The wall is insulated, but the insulation is between the studs, allowing the studs to conduct heat straight from indoors to outdoors.

doors, roof, and basement or floor slab. A poorly insulated enclosure needs a heating system that can add a lot of heat all winter and a source of energy to supply all the heat. But that leaves occupants caught between cold walls and huge blasts of heat, which is not ideal for people's comfort. And an enclosure that allows a lot of heat to enter the building during the summer will also be uncomfortable, regardless of how much cold air the cooling (air conditioning) system blasts people with.

Heat Movement through a Building's Enclosure

About five mechanisms move heat through a building's enclosure: conduction, infrared radiation, convection, change of phase (latent heat movement), and leaking air.

Conduction and radiation can be reduced by insulating. Really well-insulated enclosures conduct and radiate only a small amount of heat. Insulation reduces conduction by trapping small pockets of air, just like clothing does. Air is a poor conductor of heat, and insulation holds the air still to stop convective air currents from moving heat from the hot side of the wall to the cold side of the wall. The more air contained by insulation, and the less the air moves around within the insulation, the better the insulation works, and the more comfortable occupants are.

Insulation also works by blocking infrared heat movement (heat movement by infrared radiation) between materials. Some insulation is shiny to reflect infrared radiation, and radiant barriers without insulation are also available. But any insulation reduces radiant heat movement by keeping the outdoor side of an enclosure colder during the winter, which reduces heat radiation from the outdoor side of the wall to outdoors (see the infrared photo on Page 19), and by keeping the indoor side of an enclosure cooler during the summer, which reduces radiant heat movement from the indoor side of the wall to indoors.

Water changing phase from liquid to gas removes a significant amount of heat from buildings. For example, as a building dries after a rainstorm, it cools a building. (Keeping a building dry will be covered in Chapter 6: Water - Applied Science.) People have successfully cooled buildings by spraying water on the roof. Unfortunately, this works best in dry climates, where water is scarce.

Warm air leaking out of a building and being replaced by cold air entering through other leaks (or through the same leak when the air moves in the other direction) increases the amount of heat required to keep any building warm during the winter, even a well-insulated building. For many buildings, both energy-efficient and not, air leaking through the building is responsible for about half the peak (maximum) and annual heating load. (Preventing air leaks will be covered in Chapter 4: Air - Applied Science.)

Unfortunately, insulation and air barriers are often installed improperly, which reduces performance. The photos on this and the following pages show badly installed wall insulation and its effects. Later pages in this and other chapters show properly insulated walls.

The photo above shows a badly insulated wall: it is built with steel studs on the indoor side of a concrete block wall, with fiberglass batt insulation between the studs. Similar walls with wood studs (which conduct less heat than metal studs) or a different type of structural wall material have similar problems.

The problems include the following:
1. The insulation is on the indoor side of the wall, which means that if water vapor condenses into liquid water on the cold side of the insulation, the liquid water will be close to the indoor side of the wall, regardless of which side of the wall is the cold side that day (depending on whether it is winter or summer), which can cause water damage. This problem and how to solve it are explained in detail in Chapter 16: Building Enclosures.
2. The metal studs act as thermal bridges, or heat superhighways, through the insulation, greatly reducing the insulating value of the wall. Described another way, heat bypasses the insulation and goes through the studs.
3. The insulation is wrinkled in places and missing in other places. Because insulation is hidden behind walls and ceilings, where nobody sees it, this type of sloppy installation is all too common.
4. Pipes in the wall make it impossible to install insulation without significant gaps. The solution is shown later in this chapter.

The photo at top left shows the indoor side of a wall. The photo at top right is the same view of the same wall, taken with an infrared camera during the winter. The black lines are where heat conducted through the studs (from warm indoor air to cold outdoor air) has cooled the wall. The black dots on the black lines are where screws are conducting additional heat. The electric boxes are cold because of cold outdoor air leaking through a gap in the outdoor side of the wall, then through the insulation between the outdoor and indoor sides of the wall, through holes in the electric box, and through the box to indoors. The **wall under the electric boxes** is probably cooled by outdoor air passing through the wall on its way to the electric box or by a gap in the insulation around a wire. Chapter 4: Air - Applied Science explains how to reduce air leaks.

The photo at right shows a wood stud wall in a one-story building. Six studs are grouped between the windows. A careful reading of the building code would reveal that some of those studs are not necessary. More skillful framing saves material and labor and makes a structure stronger. Also because both metal and wood studs conduct much more heat than insulation, reducing the number of studs in a wall reduces heat conduction through a wall during both winter and summer.

Ghosting on Outdoor Sides of Walls

Discoloration patterns on walls are indications of heat flow that can be seen without an infrared camera. The lighter-colored areas on the walls in the photos on these two pages show where the outdoor side of the wall was warmed by heat conducted from indoors to outdoors. The heat escaped through studs and through places where the insulation either is missing or was installed so badly it doesn't have any noticeable effect on the temperature of the outdoor side of the wall.

There are various mechanisms that cause "ghosting." One mechanism is different levels of biological activity (growth of bacteria and mold) caused by different temperature levels. Cooler parts of buildings tend to be wetter, as will be explained in Chapter 5: Water - Basic Science. Wetter parts of the walls encourage increased biological activity, making the wall darker. Another mechanism is dust adhesion, which is increased by tiny dust particles vibrating less and bouncing off air molecules less when the dust and the air are cooled by getting close to cooler parts of the wall. Different moisture levels also influence dust adhesion. Another mechanism is differences in levels of oxidization caused by differences in temperature, moisture levels, and biological activity. Finally, there are interactions between these and other mechanisms.

The photo at left and the inset photo below it show **light-colored lines** where studs conduct heat from indoors to the outdoor side of the wall. Ghosting generally forms during cold weather but is visible all year.

The photo below shows light-colored dots where fasteners holding insulating foam to the outside of the building are conducting heat from the indoor side of the wall to the outdoor side of the wall.

The photo at bottom shows **light-colored lines** where the interior walls and floor/ceiling slabs intersect with the exterior wall, conducting heat from indoors to outdoors.

GAPS IN INSULATION

The floors in a wood-frame house are typically supported by **floor joists** which are connected at their ends to a **rim joist**, sometimes called a band joist. The floor joists conduct heat to the rim joist, which has one side facing outdoors. The infrared photo at bottom left shows warm (white) vertical lines where the studs in the walls of the wood-frame house at left conduct heat and a much warmer white horizontal area at the (apparently uninsulated) rim joist. Part of the rim joist in the photo above (different house) is covered by **insulation**, which reduces heat movement. Even if the whole rim joist had been insulated, the insulation would still be interrupted by the floor joists, leaving a thermal bridge between indoors and outdoors. Insulation on the indoor side of the rim joist also makes the rim joist colder during the winter, which can cause water damage to the rim joist by reducing heat available for drying. The rim joist in the photo below was also insulated on the indoor side (removed before the photo was taken), which contributed to the **minor damage** from cold and the resulting higher humidity where the floor joists rest on the foundation. These problems can be avoided by insulating on the outdoor side of the building.

The photo at right shows the exterior of a house during the winter. The same house in the infrared photo (below right) shows a warm (white) horizontal band at the second floor rim joist. The band is not perfectly straight, which may indicate a partly successful attempt at insulating. The room in the lower left of the photo is much lighter colored than the rest of the house, which means either it is not insulated as well as the rest of the house or its temperature is much higher.

A more careful look reveals that the room is not insulated. The space between the studs in that part of the photo is lighter than the studs and therefore warmer. This indicates that the studs, despite being very good conductors, are not conducting as much heat as the wall; therefore, the wall between the studs must be uninsulated. In the other rooms, the wall between the studs is darker (cooler) than at the studs and is therefore apparently insulated.

The stone foundation is bright white in the infrared photo and is therefore uninsulated. The warm area of the wall just under the roof could be warm because of lack of insulation, but the gradual transition from cold (dark) to warm (white) indicates the warmth is probably due to cold outdoor air warmed by conduction from the exterior of the house rising by convection up along the outdoor side of the wall. The warm air collects under the eaves, where it warms the exterior of the wall in that area. The tops of the windows, like the tops of the windows in the infrared photo on Page 19, are warmer for the same reason.

The rim joist below is insulated on the indoor side with spray foam insulation, which greatly reduces heat movement, except where joists penetrate the insulation. A better approach will be described later in this chapter.

The balconies on the building in the photo at right are supported by steel joists that run continuously between indoors and outdoors. Steel is an excellent conductor of heat, therefore the balconies will cool the building during the winter by conducting heat from indoors to the balconies and then to outdoor air the same way cooling fins cool a motorcycle engine. This problem can be solved by using special brackets that support balconies without creating significant thermal bridges.

The indoor side of the roof deck (the plywood sheathing the shingles are nailed to) in the photo below is being insulated with spray foam insulation. When properly installed, spray foam can fill in behind pipes and wires. Blown-in fiberglass or cellulose insulation can also fill in around pipes and wires. With enough care, fiberglass batts or mineral wool batts can be cut to fit around pipes and wires.

Though the spray foam insulation in the photo below is filling the cavities nicely, it is being installed between wall studs and roof joists. The joists will still conduct heat between indoors and outdoors. Insulation between studs is better than no insulation, and insulation that neatly fills stud cavities is better than sloppy insulation. But to eliminate most heat movement, continuous insulation that is not interrupted by studs is best of all. This will be covered later in this chapter.

It is especially challenging to install continuous insulation where assemblies connect. An "assembly" is a series of building materials that make up a wall, roof, or floor.

For example, a roof or wall assembly is built out of a supporting structure such as wood or metal studs, barriers to heat, air; and water; usually a nice-looking layer on the indoor side; and a nice-looking yet water-resistant layer on the outdoor side.

The basement in the photo at right and the attic in the photo below are both insulated with spray foam insulation. In both cases, the spray foam insulation is installed continuously, with no gaps or interruptions. Described another way, both the basement wall assembly and the attic roof assembly have a continuous thermal barrier.

But in both cases, the insulation is interrupted where one assembly meets another assembly, allowing significant heat movement.

In the photo at right, there is an interruption at the **rim joist** where the basement wall assembly meets the first floor assembly. Even if the rim joist itself is insulated (hard to tell in the photo), the floor joists in the ceiling must penetrate through that insulation.

In the photo below, the insulation ends at the attic floor. Even if it continues again in the wall below, it is still interrupted by the attic floor.

The rooms on this page are insulated much better than most, yet the interruptions will allow heat to pass through the building enclosure.

Another problem here is that leaving insulation exposed as shown in both of the photos on this page creates a potential fire hazard. When a source of heat gets close to insulation, the insulation, which does not conduct much heat, gets hotter and hotter. This type of insulation would get so hot it might catch on fire. Fire codes and their interpretations vary, but most require covering some types of insulation with a fireproof barrier. Applicable codes should always be followed.

Unusually Neatly Installed Insulation that Still Has Gaps

The photo at right shows fiberglass insulation batts installed neatly. They are cut to the correct width to fit between studs that are not a standard distance apart. They are also carefully cut to fit around the electric boxes, and they are not wrinkled around the wires leading to the electric boxes.

The photo below shows foam insulation carefully cut to width and cut around electric boxes.

But in both of these photos, the insulation is interrupted by metal studs and by the floor/ceiling assembly. Though this problem might seem impossible to avoid, there is a solution.

THE SOLUTION: EXTERIOR INSULATION

The most practical place to install insulation with no interruptions is on the outdoor side of the structure of a wall (or roof or basement). This is true for both new construction and existing buildings that get retrofitted.

The photo at right shows blue foam insulation being added to the exterior of an existing house, and the photo below shows the house after wood siding was installed on top of the insulation. The roof was also insulated on the exterior at the same time, which is shown in the photo on the top of Page 401.

Photo: Timothy Greenfield-Sanders.

Photo: Timothy Greenfield-Sanders.

Exterior insulation not only avoids interruptions in the insulation, but it also avoids problems with condensation on the cold side of the insulation and keeps the structure of the building from expanding and contracting with changes in outdoor temperature. It also uses the thermal mass of the structure to slow down temperature changes inside the building, which reduces the amount of heating and cooling the building needs. Exterior insulation will be covered in detail in Chapter 16: Building Enclosures.

The building in the photo at right has a continuous layer of **mineral wool insulation** behind the bricks, which will cover everything but the doors and windows. The layer of green mesh prevents mortar that falls from the brick joints during construction from clogging the weep holes (water drain holes) in the wall. The yellow sheet material is flashing, which directs liquid water out of the wall. Water drainage will be described in more detail in Chapter 6: Water - Applied Science.

Mineral wool is made of fluffy fibers oriented in a way that discourages water retention. When water leaks through the bricks it will mostly drain down through the insulation, with minimal effect on the insulation's insulating value.

The building at right is being retrofitted with insulation. First, a **barrier material** is brushed or sprayed onto the concrete block wall, then a continuous layer of foam insulation is installed on top of the barrier material, and finally the bricks are installed as the outer layer. The barrier material should be a barrier to air and to liquid water. (See Barriers Glossary on Page 70.)

The building in both photos on this page has a continuous layer of foam insulation on the exterior wall. The photo below shows a **concrete block structural wall** with a barrier to air and to liquid water brushed or rolled onto the concrete blocks, then a layer of foam insulation attached to the wall, then a fiber mesh attached to the foam, then stucco[1] troweled onto the fiber mesh, and finally a **flexible acrylic finish layer** brushed on. The foam insulation also covers part of the window frames. Depending on the size and type of window, about half of the heat conducted through a window can be through the frame. Covering up part of the exterior of the frame is a clever way of reducing heat flow through a window.

The window is flush with the interior wall, as shown in the photo at left. The advantages of locating a window here include reducing summertime sunlight into the window (see the bottom right of Page 53), reducing the velocity of wind on the window (which reduces heat movement through the window), and reducing the amount of rain that wets the connection between the window and the wall (which prevents or reduces water leaks and extends the life of the connection). One disadvantage, however, is that the inset window leaves the window "returns" (top, bottom, and sides of the window opening) exposed to outdoors, which increases the building's exposed surface area, thereby increasing heat conduction through the wall.

1   Stucco is a mixture of Portland Cement, lime, sand, and water, plus other materials added to make it strong and flexible.

The exposed surface of a building is the sum of all the surfaces that touch outdoor air. A perfect square would have a small surface area (and therefore would be energy efficient) but would be boring. A good shape looks interesting, allows a good interior layout, and is designed with consideration for occupant comfort, as well as for durability and the energy costs associated with increasing exposed surface area.

The photo at right shows a wall system called insulating concrete forms. Hollow foam blocks with **plastic braces** in the middle get stacked on top of each other like Lego® bricks. The bumps on the tops and bottoms of the foam blocks hold the blocks in place during construction. **Steel reinforcing bars** get placed vertically and horizontally in the gaps between the pieces of foam, and then concrete is poured into the gap. The plastic brackets extend within the foam to almost the surface of the foam, where they are used to attach the next layers of building material to the walls.

The result is a steel-reinforced concrete wall with continuous layers of foam insulation firmly attached by the plastic braces to both the outdoor and indoor sides of the wall. A wall like this can support a building at least ten stories tall. Because the insulation is continuous (except at the small joints between pieces), the wall's thermal performance will be much better than that of a wall with interruptions in the insulation.

Both pieces of foam add to the insulating value of the wall, but the foam on the outdoor side of the wall is more important; therefore, products are available with thicker foam on the outdoor side of the wall.

The photo below right shows a window opening in a wall made with insulating concrete forms. The photo below shows the finished building.

The photos above show two views of a mock-up section of a wall for a house being built with ordinary **wood studs**, with two continuous layers of **foam insulation** on the outdoor side of the wall, held on by **long screws** through a **strip of wood** to which the siding gets attached. The strip of wood also provides space for an **air gap** behind the siding, which helps keep the wall dry, as explained on Page 393. The view from the other side of the wall shows

that the wall cavities between the studs are filled with **cellulose insulation** for additional insulation. Cellulose insulation is shredded newspaper with boric acid added for fireproofing, insect-proofing, and mold resistance.

The wisdom of insulating on both the indoor and outdoor sides of an assembly is covered on Page 399.

The photo at left shows a continuous layer of foam insulation being added to the outdoor side of the wall of a hotel. As indicated by the sign, the hotel is still open for business while the insulation is being added.

ROOFS

Roofs are similar to walls but are more complicated. First, they are sometimes separated from the rest of the building by an attic. Second, snow on a roof can melt and then refreeze, creating an "ice dam," which can cause water leaks. Ice dams are covered in Chapter 16: Building Enclosures. And, third, roofs usually include a material that is a barrier to water vapor, which can inhibit drying of a roof assembly.

Snow Patterns

Snow patterns can reveal a lot about how heat is flowing through a roof. The snow on the roofs of the houses above has melted in a pattern that shows that the **area below the skylights** is colder than the rest of the roof. Probably the skylights are filling a whole space between roof joists, blocking air from moving through insulation in that area, while warm air from inside the house is allowed to move through the insulation in other areas of the roof. (The photos on Pages 90 and 91 show how easily air can move through fiber-type insulation.)

The photo below shows a classic snowmelt pattern caused because the roof above the wood joists is colder than the areas between the joists. This is because the joists are thick enough to offer significantly more resistance to heat conduction than the uninsulated roof between the joists. Described another way, warm air from inside the house touches the underside of the uninsulated roof between the joists, warming the roof in those areas and melting the snow. The snow does not melt as quickly directly above the joists because the joists are more insulating than the roof deck. The snow on the eaves (roof overhangs) has not melted because the bottom side of the eaves is exposed to cold outdoor air.

In the photo at left the snow has melted off the roof above the living space (this cabin probably has no attic) but has not melted at the eaves. The eaves are not warmed by heat from indoors passing through the roof and are kept cold by their undersides being exposed to cold outdoor air.

The unheated barn in the photo below shows the opposite pattern. Sunlight on the siding or warm outdoor air—or both—melted the snow on the eaves before melting the snow on the roof above the interior of the barn. Radiant heat movement from the underside of the roof to the barn floor is probably contributing to cooling the roof (similar to the way radiant heat movement cooled the wall in the photo on Page 3).

The house on the right might have one room left unheated while a child is away at school. Or, more likely, the roof above that room got insulated when the skylight got installed, and the insulation is preventing heat from moving through the roof assembly and melting the snow, as it has done above other rooms.

The house below (shown from two angles) appears to have one room upstairs either unheated or insulated.

In the photo at right, the places where the snow has melted are the same distance apart as the dimensions of a piece of plywood. This hints that the places where the snow has melted are gaps between pieces of plywood, where warm air is leaking through.

Snow melted on the roof above the living spaces but not above the attics in the houses at left, showing that the attics are significantly colder than the living spaces.

Presumably the attic floors are insulated, which reduces the amount of heat passing from the living spaces into the attics. (Otherwise, there would be less snow near the roof peaks.)

The photos on this page show similar ways to judge insulation effectiveness without an infrared camera. **Frost** (water vapor condensed as ice), as seen in the photo at right, can be revealing. It is visible during mornings when the outdoor air temperature is just above freezing. Frost forms because infrared radiation from the roof cools only the insulated or unheated parts of roofs to a temperature below freezing, causing frost to form only on those colder parts of the roof. Frost does not form on the uninsulated parts of the roof because heat from the building keeps those parts of the roof too warm.

Frost has not formed on the **eaves** (overhangs) on the sides of the roof of the house at left. This is probably because they are warmed by infrared radiation from the ground and from nearby houses. Ice has formed on the **lower eave**, probably because the first-floor roof under that eave is insulated and therefore does not radiate much heat up under that eave.

The photo at left shows that rain dried much faster on one **part of a roof** than on the rest of the roof. The photo was taken during cold weather. Heat passing from indoors to outdoors through a poorly insulated part of the roof caused the rain to evaporate from that section before the rest of the roof.

**Snowy Roofs
Quiz #1**
Why do the roofs above the three stores in the photo at right show different amounts of melting? Turn to Page 560 for the answer.

**Snowy Roofs
Quiz #2**
Why is the snow on the roof of this unheated garden shed (see photo below) melted more on the right side of the photo than on the left side? Turn to Page 563 for the answer.

Ceiling-Side View of Thermal Bridges through Roof Insulation

The photo at right shows a ceiling in a house with some recessed light fixtures. The infrared photo of the same ceiling, below right, shows black lines, which are cold stripes below the wood ceiling joists. The photo was taken during the winter, when the joists are cold, because the attic above the ceiling is vented to outdoors, and the insulation is between the joists, allowing heat to bypass the insulation and be conducted by the joists directly from the ceiling to the attic. The thicker sections of the joists are where two pieces of wood overlap.

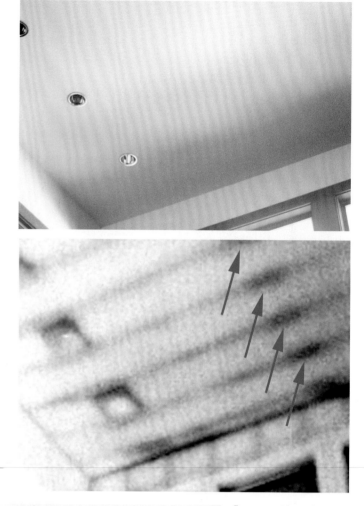

The photo below, of a different ceiling, shows "ghosting" where dust has collected on the colder parts of the ceiling. Dust ghosting on walls and ceilings usually occurs in houses that have large sources of dust, such as fireplaces or many candles. Some of the mechanisms that cause dust to adhere to colder surfaces are explained on Page 22.

The loft apartment in the photo below had a wood-burning fireplace. The ceiling is on the top floor of a building, the roof is directly above, and the insulation is between the steel joists, allowing the joists to serve as thermal bridges through the insulation. One of the steel joists and some of the fiberglass insulation can be seen where the ceiling is cut open.

Interruptions in roof insulation can be avoided by using the same strategy that avoids interruptions in wall insulation: insulate on the outdoor side of the assembly.

Insulating a roof on the outdoor side will be covered in more detail in Chapter 16: Building Enclosures.

BASEMENT WALLS

Basement walls are similar to above-ground walls, with two main differences: First, the outdoor side of a basement wall is constantly exposed to the soil. The temperature of soil fluctuates near the surface, but starting about two meters below the surface it is constant year round. And, second, because soil is almost always wet, the outdoor side of a basement wall is constantly exposed to water, too. This will be covered in more detail in Chapter 6: Water - Applied Science.

Just as with roofs and above-ground walls, the easiest way to avoid interruptions in basement insulation is to put it on the outdoor side of the assembly. This can be difficult to do on existing buildings but is still worthwhile because, as will be seen in Chapter 16: Building Enclosures, it is one of the only ways to keep a basement dry.

The basement walls on this page are made of standard reinforced concrete. They are both coated on the outdoor side with a black barrier material that is a barrier to both liquid water and water vapor, and then they have a layer of foam insulation, which will remain in direct contact with the soil.

Insulation installed in contact with soil will always be wet and might also be damaged by water or by freeze-thaw cycles. Termites and other insects might find it a cozy place to tunnel through, either to live in or to use as a route to other parts of a building. But the benefits of installing insulation here outweigh the costs. Before installing insulation in contact with soil, ask the manufacturer if the insulation is rated for contact with soil, and check local codes.

Wall Quiz #1
Why are parts of this house's wall light colored and other parts dark colored?
Clue: It is the same reason the wall is light colored between the bottoms of the two windows on the second floor.

Turn to Page 560 for the answer.

Wall Quiz #2
In the photo at left, why has water condensed on part of the wall in that striped pattern?
Clue: Water has not condensed on the lower left part of the wall where it can be warmed by infrared radiation from the part of the building at the bottom left of the photo.

Turn to Page 561 for the answer.

HEAT MOVING THE OTHER DIRECTION

Summer Heat Movement from Outdoors to Indoors

Throughout history, anyone with enough money could keep any building warm. Kings commanded servants or slaves to cut firewood or dig coal, which kept fires burning all winter. People rich enough kept a fire burning in every occupied room. And by the late 1800s, this ability to stay warm trickled down to the masses with the arrival of central heating systems with radiators in each room, heated by either hot water or steam. But cooling was another story: until relatively recently, cooling systems were not available to anyone for any amount of money.

Look how many chimneys this building has. Throughout the history of buildings, with enough money, anybody could keep any building warm by buying enough fuel and keeping enough fires burning. Not true for cooling because, before air conditioning, only good design and construction could keep a building comfortable during hot weather.

Before air conditioning systems became practical in the 1950s, buildings were designed and built to be as comfortable as possible during the summer in whatever climate they were located in. This is one of the reasons why buildings used to look different in different climates. Summer heat movement into buildings is dominated by sunlight, which made strategically designed shading features such as window awnings and porch roofs important. Walls with high thermal mass (like the adobe walls of houses in the North American Southwest) also played a role.

WHAT KEPT BUILDINGS COOL BEFORE AIR CONDITIONING?

There are several reasons why many old buildings were more comfortable without air conditioning than new buildings are without—or sometimes even with—air conditioning. Understanding why can make it easier to keep modern buildings more comfortable.

Lower Plug Loads

Find a pre-1950s house that is comfortable during the summer. Plug in a few computers that are never fully turned off, some cable boxes, digital clocks, a few large-screen TVs, a pile of electric kitchen and bathroom appliances, many lights, a dozen of those black transformer boxes that come at the end of electric appliance cords, cellphone chargers, and whatever else might make a modern person's life fulfilling. Don't forget to add another bathroom or two, fill them with appliances, and set up the hot water pipes to stay hot all the time so nobody has to wait for hot water.[1] All these sources of heat will warm the house. One watt of electricity going to an appliance is one watt of heat added to the house (except for any energy that leaves as light shining out the window). All that electricity adds up to more heat for the air conditioner to remove from the house.

Trees and Bushes

People used to deliberately plant trees and bushes where they would provide shade for the house, which reduced how much heat got into the house from sunlight warming the house. Deciduous trees are best because their leaves fall off in the autumn, just in time to get as much free heat from the sun as possible. Heat that comes from solar radiation warming a building is called "solar heat gain."

---

1   **This does save water by reducing the time people leave the hot water faucet open while they wait for hot water to arrive, but the energy implications are not straightforward. The question of energy required is complicated by overlapping effects of heat from the hot water pipes replacing heat required to heat the house during the winter, energy required to heat water, energy required to cool the house during the summer, energy required to pump water, the difficulty of accurately controlling hot water temperature if the water is not moving, and the use of different sources of energy for pumping water, heating water, heating the house, and cooling the house. What is clear is that using the smallest hot water pipes allowed by code, and insulating them, saves both water and energy. Shortening pipes by strategically locating bathrooms and kitchens close to the water heater is not easy but also helps.**

Higher Thermal Mass

Many old buildings were built with thick masonry walls, like the one in the photo at the bottom of this page. Because heating up all that mass took so much energy, it leveled out the temperature swings inside the building from day to night. This is how the old adobe buildings of the North American Southwest worked: the heat from the day didn't warm the thick walls enough to make it too hot but made them just warm enough to keep the building comfortable during the cool desert night.

In some regions, summer days are dry and warm, but not very hot, and nights get cool. In that type of climate, adding thermal mass by putting two layers of ordinary gypsum board[2] on the internal walls of a house can keep a house cool enough to make air conditioning unnecessary, especially when other strategies are also used. The money saved by not installing an air conditioning system can pay for the double gypsum board and other improvements, making the building not only more comfortable but also less expensive to build and keep cool.

2   Boards made of gypsum, a mineral dug out of the ground, and faced with paper or other material.

Thick masonry walls in old buildings are slow to warm up, which keeps these buildings cool during the summer. Newer buildings are built with less thermal mass to save money, resources, and space, but without air conditioning they get uncomfortably hot during the summer.

Shading Windows

Years ago, many windows had shading or awnings, which protected them from direct sunlight. Some still do.

Shutters folded out from the woodwork around the window on this old house. Because they are on the indoor side of the glass, they will not be as effective at protecting the house from summer overheating as shutters on the outdoor side of the glass would be.

The importance of protecting windows from summer sunlight cannot be overemphasized. Air conditioning equipment needs to remove all the heat coming from many sources, including heat from sunlight into windows, heat from lights and appliances, heat (and water vapor) from people, heat (and water vapor) brought in with air that leaks into a building or that comes in as ventilation air, and heat that is conducted through walls and roofs that are warmed by sunlight or conducted from hot outdoor air. Effective insulation is important during the summer but not nearly as important as it is during the winter because the temperature difference between indoors and outdoors is usually smaller during the summer in most climates. For most buildings in most climates, the dominant source of summer heat gain is from sunlight coming in through windows.

PEAK COOLING LOAD

The "cooling load" is the total amount of heat that an air conditioning system needs to remove from a building. The "peak cooling load" is the largest amount of heat that needs to be removed at any one time. In all but the driest climates, a cooling system also removes the latent heat released when the system condenses water vapor out of the air (the water sometimes seen dripping from an air conditioner).

New York - Flat-Iron Building and Fifth Avenue.

Buildings in New York City often had awnings on the windows, as shown in this old postcard. Old photos and postcards can be helpful in gaining permission to install awnings on historic buildings.

The largest portion of a building's peak cooling load is usually sunlight entering windows, which is a combination of direct sunlight and diffuse sunlight. Diffuse sunlight is the sunlight that lights a shady area: it is reflected off nearby objects and scattered by air.

Diffuse sunlight warms the shady side of a building. For an individual room, sunlight entering windows almost always dominates that room's peak cooling load.

Not only does solar heat gain through windows dominate the cooling load, but it also usually determines when the peak cooling load will occur because it is usually concentrated in a few hours each day. (Heat from other sources is usually spread out over many hours.)

Rooms with windows facing east usually peak in the morning, when the sun is low enough in the eastern sky to shine directly against (perpendicular to) the windows. Most buildings in their entirety peak in the afternoon, when the sun is low in the western sky; the outdoor air is warm; heat from lights, people, appliances, and sunlight has built up inside the building all day; and people have been adding water vapor to the building all day (both by breathing and maybe by sweating). Because solar gain into windows is usually such a large portion of the peak cooling load, reducing it is the easiest way to downsize a building's cooling system. The old methods of protecting windows from sunlight with shades still work today. However, there are two new technologies that can also be used to cut cooling loads while greatly improving summer comfort: improved window glass technologies and computerized shade calculations.

Both of these technologies can go a long way to fulfilling many people's dream of having a house or other building that feels comfortable with no air conditioning system.

Shutters mounted outdoors, where they will work much better than indoors because they will stop the sunlight before it gets through the windows (but only if somebody bothers to close them).

Improved Glass Technology

Not long ago, a standard window had a single pane of glass, and some windows are still being made that way. But now it is common for windows to have two or more panes, with special gases such as argon between panes and a special invisible "low-emissivity" coating on the glass. The beauty of a low-emissivity, or "low-e," coating is that it reflects infrared radiation, and absorbs and re-emits infrared radiation, but is invisible to the naked eye. It saves both heating and cooling energy, while making people more comfortable during both winter and summer. During the winter, the coating reduces free solar heat gain, but it also reflects infrared radiation from indoors back indoors all day and night, yielding an overall winter energy saving. The coating also yields an overall summer energy saving by reflecting solar radiation back outdoors.

A window with these features is one of the lowest maintenance and least expensive forms of heating and cooling available today, second only to an airtight connection between the window and wall.

Some low-e coatings are manufactured to be more reflective to solar heat than to heat emitted by the contents of a building. This is possible because the sun emits infrared radiation on a different wavelength than the infrared radiation emitted by objects inside a building. A coating optimized to reflect solar heat is a good choice in a hot climate. A coating optimized for reflecting infrared radiation emitted inside a building is a good choice for a cold climate. Different window coatings on different sides of a building may also be advantageous.

The cost of low-e coatings is small. If someone calculates the correct heating and cooling equipment sizes, the reduction in equipment size resulting from low-e glass can save more money than the coatings cost, while of course also making the building more comfortable and more energy efficient. Regardless of climate, there is no reason to ever buy windows without low-e coatings.

It can be difficult to determine if an existing window has a low-e coating. The drawing below shows a new way to detect one or more low-e coatings.

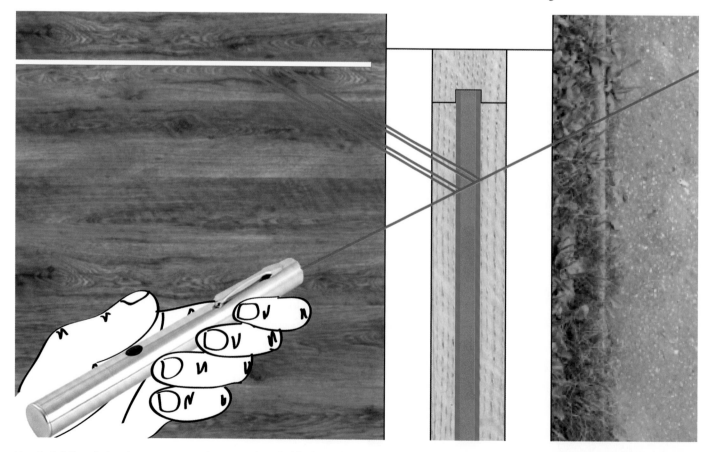

How to tell if a window has one or more low-e coatings: hold a laser pointer where its beam will reflect off the glass and onto a piece of paper or another nearby surface. Four reflections, one from each surface of each of two panes of glass, show that this is double-pane glass. Reflections from closer glass surfaces are slightly brighter, while reflections from surfaces further from the laser pointer are less bright because each pane absorbs and reflects some light. Surfaces with low-e coatings will return a noticeably brighter or larger reflection than surfaces without them.

The close-up of the photo at right reveals four reflections on the piece of paper, one from each surface of each pane of glass, indicating the presence of double-pane glass. **One of the reflections** is extra bright and extra large, indicating that the surface returning that reflection has a low-e coating on it.

The beam from some laser pointers is not round, therefore when the laser pointer is rotated, the four returns can blur together into two overlapping reflections, shown in the photo at left of the same window as in the photo above. Careful rotation of the laser pointer around its beam will produce more useful reflections, as shown in the photo above.

In the photo at right (see close-up below), four reflections, none especially bright, indicate that this is a double-pane window with no low-e coatings.

In the photo at the bottom of this page, **six reflections onto the wall**, one from each surface of each pane of glass, show that this is triple-pane glass. **Two brighter reflections** indicate that two surfaces have low-e coatings.

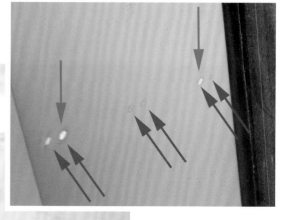

The more panes of glass a window has, the more insulating it is. Therefore, two panes insulate better than one, three better than two, and four better than three. Likewise, two low-e coatings are better than one. More panes and more low-e coatings are beneficial all year in any climate.

Computerized Shade Calculations

The two images below, and the four on the next two pages, were all generated by software. The software is told the location of the building, orientation with respect to north and south, time of day, and date. This building is in the northern hemisphere, and the corner shown faces south.

Simulation helps design shading that maximizes the view from a window, while avoiding direct sunlight, except perhaps for free winter heating. (Direct sunlight is usually not considered optimal for lighting purposes. This will be covered in Chapter 8: Light - Applied Science.)

Top: 9 AM on a typical January day. Bottom: 9 AM on a typical July day.

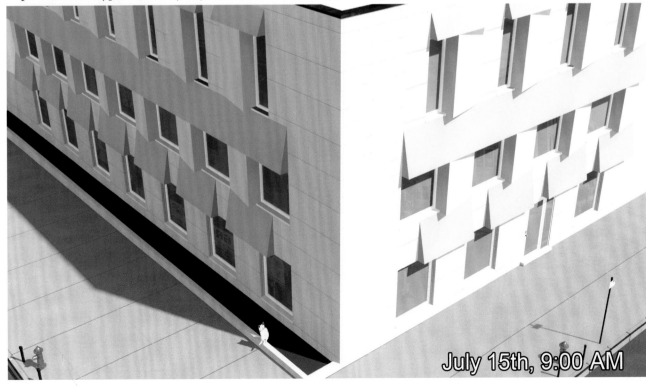

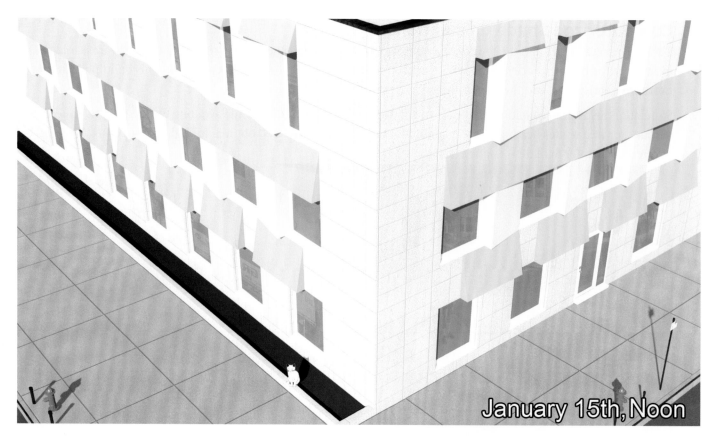

January 15th, Noon

Top: Noon in January. Bottom: Noon in July. Note how this design lets in more sunlight during the winter, when the sun is low enough in the sky to get below the shades above the windows. This provides some free heat. During the summer, less sunlight reaches the glass, which reduces the cooling load (the heat the air conditioning system has to remove).

Look at the shadows from the building, the signposts, the fire hydrants, and the cat to better understand the sun angles.

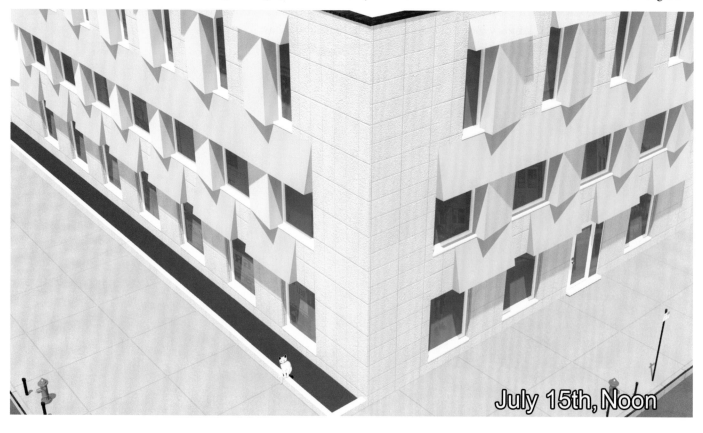

July 15th, Noon

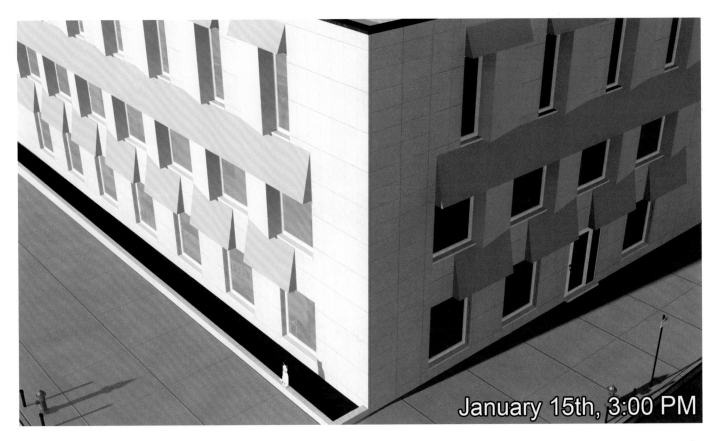

Top: 3 PM January. Bottom: 3 PM July. See how different sample shapes of windows and shading perform. In January, all the windows on the left side are almost completely exposed to the sun. In July, the first floor windows with no shading to the side are mostly exposed to the sun, the second floor windows with shading to the side are partly shaded, while the top floor windows, which have the same glass area as the others but are taller and narrower, are even more shaded.

Cutting Foam for Insulating and Shading

The photo at right shows a hot wire saw being used to cut foam that will be used as insulation, sunlight control, and decoration on the outside of the building shown on Pages 49-51.

The saw uses an electrically heated wire which quickly melts through the foam. It also has guides to help make accurate square cuts.

Model: Gabe Williams.

MODERN WINDOW SHADING

The same strategies that have always been used to shade windows still work, but now they can be improved upon with modern computer technology. Now as then, windows can be shaded on either the indoor or the outdoor side. Indoor shades are easier to adjust, clean, repair, and replace than outdoor shades. Unfortunately, indoor shades do not prevent summer overheating nearly as well as exterior shades because they stop the sunlight after it has already passed through the window glass. The sunlight will heat the glass and the shades, which will heat the indoors. Shades that stop sunlight before it gets through the glass work better because they keep the heat outdoors.

Traditional window shutters, as shown on the bottom of Page 45, are effective at protecting windows from sunlight at all times of day. But they block much of the light and most of the view.

Traditional awnings mounted on the wall above a window are still effective, especially for protection from the sun when it is high in the sky, at midday. They are less effective for protection in the morning or afternoon, when the sun is low in the sky.

Windows mounted close to the indoor side of the wall, as shown in the photos below, can be shaded by the wall at midday during the summer. Depending on the wall's orientation, the wall can also shade them in the morning and the afternoon, when the sun is low in the sky.

Newer types of shading, some of which are shown on the following pages, are also available. Some do a better job than others of protecting windows from the sun when it is low in the sky.

The windows in the top of this photo are inset into the wall, which will reduce the amount of direct sunlight that reaches the glass. Hopefully the lower floor has a larger cooling system because the windows there are mounted closer to the outdoor side of the wall, where they are exposed to direct sunlight. This will cause the inside of the building on that floor to gain a lot more heat from the sun during the summer.

These windows are set deep into the wall, where they will get lots of scattered and reflected light but very little direct sunlight, which will reduce the summer cooling load.

Staying Cool, European Style

The building above is a supermarket in Europe, with an external Venetian blind made of metal. The blind keeps the side of the building cool during the summer. Perhaps the shade reduces summer heat gain enough to help make the building comfortable without air conditioning.

The mechanism at right is a manual device used to adjust the shades seasonally, allowing the sun to warm the building during the winter. Scratches on the metal indicate that someone probably changes the position of the blinds as the season changes.

External Sun Shades

The window shades in the photo at right are on an office building in Europe. They can be rolled up, and the blades can be rotated, just as with any Venetian blinds, except they are manufactured to withstand wind and rain. Like all outdoor shades, they will protect the building from sunlight much better than if they were mounted on the indoor side.

They can be installed when a building is built, or retrofitted to an existing building.

The only rules preventing widespread use of external sun shades on buildings in other parts of the world are cultural, based on local habit.

The photo below shows a yellow building with external roll-up shades on the windows. The sides of the balcony facing the equator (left in the photo) have additional sun shades to give further sunlight protection.

The historic building in the background also has external sun shades on the windows.

Windows Heat Movement Quiz
Is it possible for significant amounts of heat to pass through a window in opposite directions at the same time (from indoors to outdoors, and from outdoors to indoors)? Turn to Page 561 for the answer.

The external sun shades in the photo at right are on the windows of a hospital office. They make it much more comfortable for the people in the office by cutting glare, reducing summer heating, and providing some privacy. At the same time, the shades still allow some light in.

The house below has a reflective metal roof and deciduous trees, which provide shade. The windows have more shading than most people would like, but perhaps the owner wants to stay comfortable without air conditioning regardless of what other people think.

The external sun shades on the building at left and below are fairly well designed. They are made of open slats, which allow some light in and allow people to see out, while blocking direct sunlight from overhead. They are not wider than the windows, so some sunlight will sneak by them on the sides. They also look nice and will improve comfort while saving energy.

The wide roof overhang also helps shade the windows.

Attractive and Effective Sun Protection

Both of the houses on this page have been enhanced by the addition of attractive sun shades.

Attractive sun shades that match the style of the house tend to stay in service much longer than ugly shades, which soon get removed.

The roofs of the house at right, built before air conditioning was invented, will protect the windows from direct midday sunlight, while still allowing plenty of sunlight into the house. The deeper overhang on the ground floor provides even more protection, and therefore more comfort, to the ground floor, where people spend more time during the day.

The roof of the house at left will protect the windows from all but an early morning or late afternoon sun. The lack of vegetation on the hills in the background makes it clear this is in a dry climate, where the roof overhang and some low-e, multi-pane windows could keep the house fairly comfortable without air conditioning. Some larger trees or bushes would also help.

Fun Designs that Work Well

The buildings on these two pages all have sunlight protection features that are shown off, instead of subtly blended into the facade.

All the sunlight protection details on these pages look like they will be effective, except of course the awnings on the top of Page 61, which are mounted too high to protect the windows from sunlight.

The features that protect the windows from the sun improve the comfort and energy efficiency of the buildings by reducing their cooling load. At the same time, they improve the quality of light inside the buildings by letting some sunlight in while protecting the occupants from glare and discomfort caused by direct sunlight.

The building on the bottom left of Page 61 was designed with the help of the computer renderings on Pages 49-51.

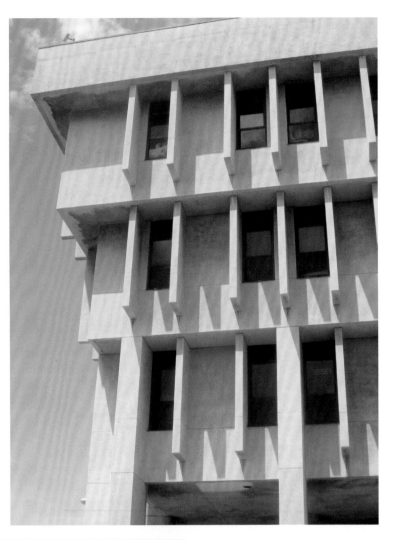

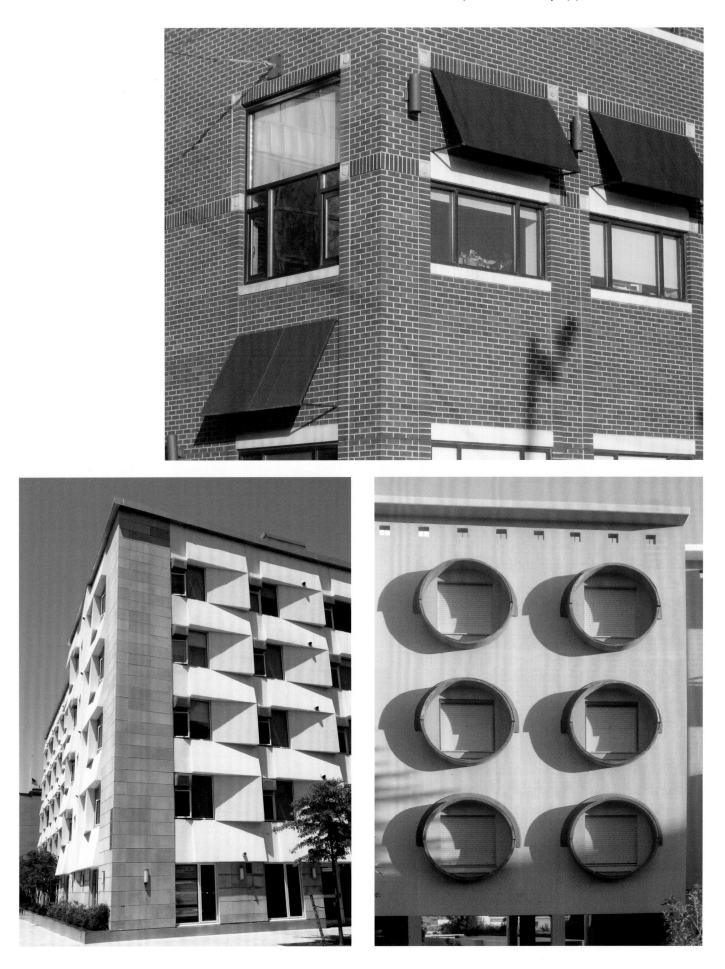

Comparing Designs

These two office buildings are located a few blocks away from each other in a hot, humid climate.

Which building keeps people more comfortable?

Which building cost less to build?

Which building costs less to maintain?

Which building costs less to buy energy for?

The building on the left has decent sun shading on the windows. The building on the right has none. The sun shading makes the building on the left much more comfortable for the people inside it because the shades protect people's eyes from some direct sunlight, while also reducing solar heat gain. The interior of the building on the right gets a lot more direct sunlight, so it needs a massive cooling system. The people in it are caught between large heat gain through the windows and blasts of cold air from the cooling system.

The building on the left presumably cost less to build because, assuming the cooling system is accurately sized, the sun protection allows a smaller and therefore less expensive cooling system, which offset any increased cost to build the wall. And with less space occupied by mechanical equipment, the building on the left has more usable space, too.

The building on the right will need regular work on that larger cooling system. The connections between the windows and the wall are boldly exposed to the elements, where they will fail much sooner than the ones on the building on the left. Therefore the building on the right will also cost more to maintain.

The overhangs on the building on the left will reduce energy use during the summer, while allowing some free heating during the winter. During the winter, the building on the right might need cooling on its sunny side at the same time the other sides need heating—a difficult and energy-intensive task for the mechanical system.

The building on the left will use much less energy overall and will also have a lower peak energy use.

Comparing Orientations

The designers of these buildings had enough land available to orient them in any way they chose. They are both narrow, rectangular buildings, with no windows on the short ends. The windows on the building at left face north and south, while the windows on the building at right face east and west. They are both located in climates with hot, humid summers. Which building is oriented to maximize comfort and minimize energy use?

The orientation of the building at the left, with its windows facing north and south, is optimal. This is because in the middle of the day the sun is too high to shine flat against the windows on the side of the building facing the equator and therefore does not create nearly as large a cooling load as it does when it is low in the eastern or western sky. (The overhangs above the windows also help protect the windows from overhead sun.) The orientation of the building at right is not optimal because it exposes its windows to direct sunlight from both the east and the west (east during the morning and west during the afternoon).

When the building at right was being designed, one of the architects on the design committee proposed rotating it 90 degrees on the site, which was expected to reduce the size and cost of the cooling system enough to save almost two percent of the cost of the building. The proposal was rejected on the grounds that the building would look better with a long side facing the river. This left the windows on one side facing west, where the low afternoon sun creates an enormous peak cooling load.

Afternoon peak cooling loads explain why the load on the electric grid in many areas peaks in the afternoon, and why blackouts tend to occur on summer afternoons on weekdays (when offices are occupied). Utility companies face the enormous expense of buying enough power plants and wires to meet peak loads, which leaves a lot of expensive equipment underutilized for all but a few hours of the year. Some of this cost is paid for by all customers, and some is passed on as fees paid by customers who use a lot of electricity when demand is high. Buildings designed to reduce peak cooling loads not only reduce owners' electricity bills but also save them the high cost of buying electricity at a time when demand is high.

Shading Windows from Midday Sunlight

All the sun shades on this page and Page 65 provide good protection from midday sun, but none of them provide good protection from a morning or afternoon sun.

The facade of the building at right comes straight out above the windows but is angled back on the sides (and bottom), which allows more sunlight to reach the windows from the sides than from the top. Whatever protection the facade offers from the side is reduced by the windows being so wide.

The building below has a full-width roof above the ground-floor windows, which will still provide shade when the sun is off to the side. The awnings on the top-floor windows are not significantly wider than the windows, thus some sunlight will reach the windows when the sun is off to one side.

The designs of both buildings on Page 65 leave their windows with virtually no shade when the sun is low in the sky. If the side of the building on the top of Page 65 faces the equator, then the shading is appropriate. The building on the bottom of Page 65 cannot, of course, have two sides facing the equator— the windows on one side will get direct sunlight from either the east or the west.

It is much more difficult to protect a window facing morning or afternoon sunlight than it is to protect a window from midday sunlight because it is hard to stop the sunlight at a low angle while still keeping the window open enough to provide a good view. A well-designed window opening looks attractive, maximizes the view from indoors, and minimizes direct sunlight into a window, especially during the summer.

Shading Windows from East and West Sunlight

All the buildings on this page and Page 67 have external sun protection that is designed to shade windows from the sun when the sun is low in the eastern or western sky. None of these shades, except the ones on the bottom of Page 67, are symmetrical because they are designed to shade the sun from one side more than from the other side. The shades in the photo at right protect the windows from sunlight shining from the left side of the photo but would not adequately protect the windows from sunlight shining from the right side of the photo. The shades in the photo below protect the windows from sunlight shining from the right side of the photo but not from sunlight shining from the left side of the photo.

The shades on this page do not provide good protection from the sun when it is high in the sky (except for the roof overhang on the top floor at right). This is not a problem if these walls face due east or west but could be a problem if they face more towards to the equator.

Page 67 shows successful approaches for shading from both low and high sunlight. The image at the top of Page 67 was taken with the photographer's back to the noon sun. The shades protect windows from one side when the sun is low in the east or the west, while also providing overhead protection from the midday sun, all while preserving a nice view from the windows.

The building on the bottom of Page 67 has different types of shading on different orientations. The shades on the right side of the building protect the windows when the sun is high in the sky, while the shades on the left protect the windows when the sun is low in the sky. The glass on both sides of the first floor is at least partly protected by an overhang.

Note that shades that protect windows from sunlight from the east and west generally have a relatively vertical orientation, which is in contrast to shades that protect from midday sun, which generally have a more horizontal orientation.

Window shape also plays an important role. Windows that are tall and narrow are easier to protect from east and west sunlight, while shorter, wider windows are easier to protect from midday sunlight.

Vines for Shading

The windows at right are shaded by vines growing in front of them. In this case, the vines are clinging to steel security bars.

The planter boxes in the photo below are part of the facade design, which solves what would otherwise be a challenge: growing vines high above the ground floor. Pieces of fishing line tied in front of the windows would give the vines something to cling to.

Vines protect windows from the sun at any angle, while still allowing high-quality, diffused light through.

Though vines provide some privacy, people in the building can still get a good view of outside by looking between the leaves the same way a child hiding in a bush can see someone looking for them while playing hide-and-seek.

WINDOWS GLOSSARY

A **double-hung** window, like the one at right, has two moving sashes, which slide up and down to open and close the window. Both sashes are closed in the photo. The stationary part of the window is called the frame.

The open window in the photo below right is a casement window. A **casement window** hinges open like a door. Some casement windows tilt open using hinges at the top or bottom of the window, others have hinges on the side. The pane of glass above the casement window and the pane on the right side of the photo are fixed in place.

Fixed windows are much less expensive than windows that open because they lack hinges and latches. Fixed windows are also the most airtight type. Described another way, much less air (and noise) leaks through fixed windows than through any other type. Casement windows are more leaky than fixed windows but not as leaky as double-hung or other sliding windows. This is because casement windows are manufactured with a flexible strip between the part that opens and the frame that gets tightly compressed when the window closes. Sliding windows, on the other hand, depend on seals that must be loose enough to allow the sashes to slide open and closed.

A **single-hung window** is like a double-hung window, except that only one sash slides open, while the other sash is fixed in place at the factory. This is a good compromise between a fixed window and a window that opens: it can open for ventilation, but it leaks less air and noise and also costs less than a double-hung window.

Multi-Pane Windows

Once upon a time, all windows had only one pane of glass, but now most windows are manufactured with more than one pane. Less heat passes through windows with more panes because the air (or other gas) between each set of panes acts as insulation. This improves comfort and reduces the energy required during both winter and summer. Better windows have argon or krypton (special gases) between the panes. Argon conducts less heat than air and is more viscous (reduces convective currents) than air, and krypton is even less conductive and more viscous. Good windows also have one or more low-e coatings, as described on Pages 46-48. Low-e coatings improve comfort and save energy by reflecting infrared radiation.

BARRIERS GLOSSARY

Air Barrier

An air barrier is a series of materials that air cannot leak through, joined to each other by airtight connections. An air barrier should also not leak air where it is penetrated (by pipes and wires, for example).

The rubber a car tire is made of and the metal a car wheel is made of are both materials air cannot leak through. An example of an air barrier is the wheel, the tire, and the airtight connection between the wheel and the tire. The hole where the air valve penetrates through the wheel is an example of a penetration. Air cannot leak through the valve penetration hole (between the metal and the valve) or the tire will go flat.

A material that is an air barrier might or might not be a barrier to water vapor passing through it by diffusion. Water vapor diffusion is explained in Chapter 5: Water - Basic Science.

Not all air barriers are also barriers to heat. For example, air cannot pass through a pane of glass, but heat can easily be conducted and radiated through the glass. Sheet metal, Tyvek®, and concrete are other examples of materials that can be good air barriers (assuming the concrete is not cracked) but are not good barriers to heat.

Barrier to Water Vapor (Vapor Barrier)

A vapor barrier is a series of materials that water vapor cannot pass through by diffusion, joined to each other by connections that water vapor cannot diffuse through. A vapor barrier should also not leak air at the connections between materials or where things (pipes or wires, for example) penetrate it, or the leaking air will move a lot of water vapor through the vapor barrier.

A piece of glass is a barrier to water vapor diffusion, whereas a piece of unpainted wood is not. If the wood gets painted, depending on how many coats and what type of paint, the paint could either slow diffusion or stop it completely.

Clear polyethylene is a vapor barrier material. If sheets of polyethylene stapled to wood studs in a wall cover 99 percent of the area of the wall, the polyethylene will be 99 percent effective at stopping water vapor diffusion through the wall. But, a 99 percent effective vapor barrier is not necessarily an air barrier. If there is no other air barrier in the wall, gaps where the sheets of polyethylene are stapled to the studs can allow leaking air to move large amounts of water vapor through the wall.

Barrier to Liquid Water (Water Barrier)

A liquid water barrier (as opposed to a water vapor barrier) is a series of materials that liquid water cannot pass through, joined together by connections that liquid water also cannot pass through. Connections should not leak air either, or an air pressure difference can push liquid water through the leak, as shown on Page 169.

Insulation, or Barrier to Heat (Thermal Barrier)

A thermal barrier (insulation) is a material or series of materials that slow down the passage of heat. Insulation works best in conjunction with an air barrier: if air passes through a thermal barrier, it will work as well as a sweater without a windbreaker on someone riding a bicycle on a cold day. No material is a complete barrier to heat. The best types of insulation only slow heat down. Some types of insulation, such as foam, are also an air barrier material that can be part of an air barrier (if joined to other air barrier materials with connections that do not leak air). Other types of insulation, such as fiberglass or mineral wool, are not air barrier materials.

SUMMARY

Walls, roofs, and basement walls are best insulated on the outdoor side, with continuous insulation that has no gaps. This is true for both existing buildings that are being renovated and new buildings.

Summer heat gain is dominated by solar radiation into windows. Indoor window shades help, but shades are more effective on the outdoor side, where they stop solar radiation from getting through the glass in the first place.

Heat movement through a window is reduced by adding panes of glass and adding special gases such as argon or krypton between panes. Low-emissivity coatings on windows reduce infrared heat movement through windows during both winter and summer.

Chapter 3 **AIR** Basic Science

WHAT IS AIR?

Air is the mixture of gases that we breathe, which is all around us and in our lungs at all times. Air at habitable altitudes contains between about one and five percent water vapor, depending on weather and altitude. Completely dry air is found only in a laboratory, although some badly designed and built buildings contain air that is too dry to be healthy for people. This will be covered in Chapter 5: Water - Basic Science. If all the water vapor is removed from air, the remaining air is about 78 percent nitrogen, in the form of N_2, and 21 percent oxygen, in the form of O_2. Described another way, dry air is mostly a mixture of two molecules of nitrogen chemically bonded to each other and two molecules of oxygen chemically bonded to each other. The remaining one percent of dry air is a mixture of other gases.

Most of the one percent is argon, the gas window manufacturers put between panes of glass in certain energy-efficient windows, as explained on the bottom of Page 69.

In addition, this one percent includes (as of 2017) about 0.04 percent carbon dioxide (CO_2), which we produce in our bodies and which plants use for photosynthesis and people use for making soda. It also includes smaller amounts of other gases including ozone (O_3), which is one part of the atmosphere that helps protect people from skin cancer by absorbing much of the sun's ultraviolet light when it stays very high above the earth's surface but harms our lungs when we breathe it as part of smog, and carbon monoxide (CO), which is harmful and potentially deadly to people and animals.

Many people are aware that breathing air containing high concentrations of carbon monoxide can kill a person. What is not as well known is that long-term exposure to low levels is also very unhealthy, causing a variety of neurological symptoms including depression, memory loss, and confusion. Physiological symptoms include nausea, lightheadedness, and headache, which are easily mistaken for the flu.

Air and People's Health

Air can be contaminated with other poisonous substances including radioactive gases and vaporized gasoline. Moving contaminated air away from people is wise, but ventilation must be done properly because air can also move contaminants towards people.

Air also contains dust particles. Gravity pulls heavy dust particles down to the surface of the earth in minutes or hours, but lightweight dust particles can stay mixed with air for weeks or months. Dust particles too small to get filtered out by our respiratory systems are small enough to lodge deep into our lungs and can be the most dangerous to people's health. Organic dust is also food for mold.

Air and Mold

Because air normally contains mold spores and dust, any surface exposed to air can grow mold if it is cooled enough to keep the relative humidity at the surface high enough (about 85 percent or higher) for long enough. (See Page 3 for an example.) Mold will grow on any surface, including glass, if the surface gets wet enough because mold spores and dust will stick to the wet surface, and the mold will eat the dust. Mold produces an assortment of nasty chemicals that can harm people's health.

Removing all the air from a building would stop mold but would make the building uninhabitable for people. Filtering out all or even most of the dust and mold spores from the air is not realistic either, without using large and expensive filters and fans, such as those found in laboratories, which require a lot of energy. The best approach is to accept that mold and mold food (dust) are always in the air around us and to prevent mold growth by using the strategies in Chapter 6: Water - Applied Science.

Air and Sound

Many substances including air transmit sound. Effective soundproofing between parts of a building or between indoors and outdoors requires stopping air leaks, as described in Chapter 10: Sound - Applied Science.

What Moves Air

Because air is a gas, it takes the size and shape of its container. There is no container for the earth's atmosphere, though one could think of gravity as a sort of container. Gravity pulls air against the earth's surface in a layer, like a second ocean. And just as water is constantly moving around in the ocean, air is constantly moving around in the atmosphere.

Wind in the atmosphere is driven by the sun heating the earth's surface in some places more than in other places, which heats the air more in some places than others. These differences in temperature cause differences in the density of the air, which cause it to move around the planet. Described another way, wind is mostly a giant form of solar-driven convection.

Air has low thermal mass. This is why increasing the temperature of air requires adding only a small quantity of heat to the air. Compared to water, the difference is drastic. Water requires over four times as much heat as the same weight of air to raise its temperature by the same number of degrees. And, because water weighs 784 times more than the same volume of air, raising the temperature of water requires adding 3,245 times as much heat as would have to be added to the same volume of air.

One effect of this is that adding a little heat to air raises its temperature enough to cause it to expand significantly. Most materials get larger when their temperature increases because, as described on Page 5, the increase in molecular motion pushes the molecules farther away from each other. If air in a closed container gets hot, it cannot expand, therefore its pressure will increase. For example, the air pressure in a tire increases when friction from driving heats the tire. This is why some trucks have a label showing the pressure the tire should be filled to when it is cold (to avoid confusion from different temperatures causing different pressures). Outside of a

Fig. 8.

This drawing illustrates air coming in the window at the right side of the room and falling to the floor because the outdoor air is cold and therefore heavier than the air in the room. The people's breath and the exhaust from the gas-burning lights are both rising because they are warmer than the air in the room. The people's breath is also spreading out some, while the exhaust from the gas lights is mostly rising toward the ventilation outlet in the upper left corner of the room and not spreading much because it is hotter than and therefore more buoyant than their breath.
Lewis W. Leeds, A Treatise on Ventilation (New York: Wiley, 1871), Page 45.

closed container, increasing the temperature of air will cause it to expand, making it lighter and causing it to flow upward by convection (the mechanism by which hot fluids rise). Each molecule still has the same weight, but because the molecules are more spread out, the air is lighter. This leads some people to say "heat rises."

Because of this, and because heat is usually flowing between all objects all the time, air is rarely standing still. For air to stand still, it would have to be in a room where all parts of the room are at exactly the same temperature and are not heating up or cooling down. A room like this does not exist outside of a laboratory. Air inside any normal room or building is moving all the time.

Air movement outdoors is also caused by temperature differences, as well as by water vapor being lighter than dry air. Together, these pressure differences create storms, including tornadoes and hurricanes.

Air pressure differences indoors are not as large as those outdoors because temperature differences indoors are smaller than outdoors, and because the difference in weight between dry air and humid air has only a minor effect indoors. But convection still causes significant amounts of air movement through buildings. This will be discussed in Chapter 4: Air - Applied Science.

AIR MOVEMENT THROUGH A CONTAINER

The rest of this chapter will explain air movement through a container, using a cardboard box as an example. Imagine that the cardboard box in the photo below is perfectly airtight. Imagine the tape is perfect. No air can leak in, and no air can leak out. (Or, imagine that the box is a building that was built as airtight as possible, all the doors and windows are closed, the ventilation system is off, and the ventilation openings are closed with dampers.)

Box with One Hole

One **hole** has been made in the box. Can a significant amount of air flow through the hole, or through the box?

No.

Because there is only one hole, air will have to flow into and out of the same hole at the same time. Air cannot flow in for a while and then flow out later because a lot of energy would be required to compress the air in the box while more was flowing in. Therefore, not much air will flow through the box.

Fan Blowing on the Box

What happens if a fan blows air on the hole? Will more air flow through the hole and through the box?

No. The fan makes energy available to move air, but it will make little difference to the air flow because, like in a room with only one window open, there is still only one hole, and the fan will not compress the air. Air cannot flow through the box because it needs both an entrance and an exit.

Box with Two Holes, One High, One Low, and a Fan Blowing on the Box

How much difference does adding a second hole make?

More air will flow through the box now because air can flow into the box through one hole and out of the box through the other hole. But because the fan is pushing air toward both holes, and air can't simultaneously enter through both holes (without a lot of energy to compress the air and something to hold the pressurized air in the box), the second hole doesn't make a very big difference.

Box with Two Holes at Opposite Ends of the Box and a Fan Blowing on the Box

Does it make a difference to close up one of the holes near the fan and add a hole at the other end of the box?

Yes, this makes a very big difference. The fan creates a difference in air pressure from one end of the box to the other, which moves a lot of air through the box. Despite the box now having the same number of holes, their location allows the fan to blow air into one hole, through the box, and out the other hole. A lot more air will flow through the box.

Box with Two Holes, Low, at Opposite Ends of the Box, and a Hole Covered by Cellophane Tape with a Flashlight Shining in the Hole

Energy from the flashlight will heat the air in the box to a temperature higher than the air outside the box the same way sunlight heats indoor air via a window. This makes the air in the box lighter than the air outside the box.

Will the heat cause much air to flow through the box by convection? No, because both holes are at the same height.

Box with Two Holes, One High, One Low, at the Same End of the Box, and a Hole Covered by Cellophane Tape with a Flashlight Shining in the Hole

Will the heat from the flashlight cause much air to flow through the box by convection? Yes. The light will heat the air

inside the box, which will make the air inside the box lighter, creating a pressure difference, which will move room-temperature air into the bottom hole and warm air out the top hole. The box has the same number and size of holes as before, but the positioning of the holes makes all the difference.

If one of the holes were located at the other end of the box, it would make little or no difference, as long as the holes were located with one high and one low. It is the vertical distance between the holes that is important to convection-driven airflow.

Two Boxes with a Hole between Them

Two boxes stacked on top of each other with holes between the boxes (shown at left with a gap between the boxes to make one hole visible) can act as one large box. When the boxes are stacked on top of each other, as shown below left, air can flow into one box, through the other box, and then out. If the flashlight shines on the hole covered by cellophane tape, the heat will move much more air through the two boxes than it would through one because heating a taller container of air creates a greater pressure difference.

What effect does closing up the middle hole, as shown below right, have? Strange as it sounds, closing up one hole will increase the convective-driven airflow through the boxes. This is like closing a hole halfway up a chimney that was allowing cold air to leak into the chimney: it will increase the draft[1] (convective force) and therefore increase the airflow in the chimney by increasing the vertical distance between holes.

1 Draft at the bottom of a chimney is equal to chimney height multiplied by temperature difference between inside and outside the chimney at the top, minus friction.

Two Boxes with One Hole High and Five Holes Low

Will more air flow through the boxes now than with only one hole high and one low?

Yes. But not much more. When the flashlight heats the air, it still has only one hole to escape from. Likewise, if the fan blows on the boxes, there is still only one hole up high for air to flow through.

The photo below illustrates that the amount of air that can flow through the boxes, or through a building, depends not only on the number of holes but also on their location. If three of the holes in the bottom of the box were moved up high, much more air would flow through the boxes, despite the number of holes being exactly the same.

If the box were to have three holes low on one end and three holes high on the other end, both the fan and the flashlight could move a lot of air through the boxes. Having holes at opposite ends of the boxes has another effect: air will flow through the whole boxes, instead of just up along one end.

Two Boxes with All the Holes Closed

As soon as the hole between the boxes is closed up, each box acts as an independent box, without any influence (except heat conduction) from the other box. Closing up all the other holes in each box prevents any air from flowing through either box.

The flashlight shining into the bottom box can only create a convective current of air inside that box. The air in that box will rise on one side of the box, and fall on the other, but remain inside the box the whole time.

The fan can blow and blow, but it will have no effect on a box with no holes, except perhaps to cool the warm side of the box with the flashlight shining on it and slow down the convective current inside. But no air will be blown into or out of the boxes because there are no holes.

BUILDINGS ARE LIKE BOXES

Air moves through buildings in the same way it moves through cardboard boxes. Just as no significant amount of air will move through a cardboard box with only one hole, no significant amount of air will move through a building with only one hole.

How much air will be moved through a building by wind, fans, or convection depends on the number of holes, their size, their shapes, their positions, and how well holes within the building are connected to each other. Accurately predicting how much air will leak through a building requires modeling many things, including airflow around the outside of a building, which requires modeling weather, a capability beyond the reach of today's computers. What can be said for sure is that fewer holes and smaller holes allow less air to leak.

SUMMARY

Air moves heat and water vapor, both of which are important to people's health and comfort, to building durability, and to energy efficiency.

Air movement through any container, including a building, requires an opening for air to enter, an opening for air to leave, and energy to create a pressure difference to move the air. The size and location of the openings and the amount of pressure difference all determine how much air will move through the container.

Chapter 4 **AIR** Applied Science

AIR MOVEMENT THROUGH BUILDINGS

Fresh air movement through buildings is necessary to keep them pleasant-smelling and healthy for occupants. The need for ventilation in buildings has been known for some time. During the 1700s, Benjamin Franklin wrote to Dr. Ingenhaus, physician to the emperor at Vienna:

You physicians have of late happily discovered, after a contrary opinion had prevailed some ages, that fresh and cool air does good to persons in the small-pox and other fevers. It is to be hoped, that in another century or two we may all find out that it is not bad even for people in health.[1]

Mr. Franklin may have been too optimistic about how soon people would accept the need for ventilation. Many buildings are still built today without ventilation systems (except for windows). But windows are a poor form of ventilation because they also admit pollen, dust, rain, snow, noise, and criminals. And the air they admit is usually too cold, too hot, too dry, or too humid. Furthermore, they rarely admit the right quantity of air, as has been understood for many years. In 1908, the author F. H. King wrote:

Is it urged that the wind will force air enough through the house and stable even with the closest possible construction? But how about the days and the nights when there is little or no wind? Then the windows may be opened? But who thinks to do this at the right time? Perhaps the one in the family who suffers most from insufficient change of air is too unselfish or too sensitive lest some one else would be disturbed by opening the windows, or perhaps the herdsman has too little thought for the animals in the stable to take the necessary trouble at the proper time. Clearly, if an abundant change of air is needful, a flow should be continuous and sufficient at all times, whether we are awake or asleep, and whether

attention is given to it or not. That an abundant change of air in the house or in the stable is needful there can be no doubt, and that this cannot take place unless proper arrangements are provided for it is likewise evident.[2]

Sometimes, such as when two windows on opposite sides of a house are open just the right amount on a day with a gentle spring breeze blowing in the right direction, the holes are sized and positioned to move the right amount of air through the parts of the building that need it, while removing stale air without moving it through the whole house. But most of the time, windows or other holes will not move the right amount of air in the right direction.

Buildings have holes in them—some intentional, some not. Air moves through those holes. Unplanned air leaks, otherwise known as construction defects, are not a good strategy for protecting people's health because they have the problems windows have, plus they remain open forever. There is no need for any intentional air leaks through a building. Zero air leakage is a suitable target, but, unfortunately, human error makes this impractical. However, air leaks should be avoided as much as possible.

Eliminating air leaks between indoors and outdoors, or within a building, is generally safe. The exception is when old-style combustion appliances, which depend on indoor air for combustion, don't get enough air. If this happens, they can release carbon monoxide into the building, which is dangerous. (Supplying air directly to combustion appliances is discussed in Chapter 18: Heating and Cooling.) Otherwise, eliminating air leaks makes a building more comfortable, safe, and healthy for occupants, more durable, and more energy efficient.

The only way to move the right amount of air through the right parts of a building at the right time is to prevent unplanned airflow by closing holes, then using a mechanical ventilation system. (Mechanical ventilation systems are described in Chapter 17: Indoor Air Quality.)

---

1   Lewis W. Leeds, <u>A Treatise on Ventilation</u> (New York: Wiley, 1871), Page 18.

2   F. H. King, <u>Ventilation for Dwellings, Rural Schools and Stables</u> (Madison, Wisconsin: Published by Author, 1908), Pages 2-3.

WHAT CAUSES AIR TO MOVE THROUGH BUILDINGS?

There are three important mechanisms that move air through openings within a building, or through openings between indoors and outdoors.

1. Wind

Wind will blow through any opening in a building. Some locations are much windier than others, which depends on climate and on how much the location is sheltered by trees or nearby buildings. For example, the top right of Page 166 shows a small ledge protecting many floors of a tall building from wind-blown rain. The ledge is able to do this because the building is located in downtown Chicago, where it is surrounded by many other tall buildings. Farmers in North America's open plains traditionally planted trees around their farmhouses to serve as a windbreak (and to provide shade). Most single-family houses get significant wind shelter from trees, bushes, and nearby houses. Coastal locations and hilltop locations are much more exposed to wind. The tops of buildings of any height are exposed to higher wind speed than lower parts because the wind is much slower near the ground.

2. Mechanical Equipment (Fans)

Many buildings are full of fans. Some, such as bathroom or kitchen exhaust fans, are intended to move stale air from indoors to outdoors to ventilate a building, while of course also pulling air in elsewhere to replace the removed air. Other fans, such as the fan in a furnace, are intended to move air only within a building but can also inadvertently move air between outdoors and indoors, as shown on Pages 483-487.

3. The Stack Effect

The "stack effect" is the mechanism that moves air through a building by convection, which is driven by differences in weight of indoor air versus outdoor air. Because warm air is lighter than cold air, the stack effect moves air up within heated buildings during the winter and down within air conditioned buildings during the summer. When the indoor and outdoor temperatures are equal, the stack effect does not move any air. In climates that get cold, the stack effect is stronger during the winter than during the summer because indoor-outdoor temperature differences are greatest during cold winters. In desert climates, the stack effect moves air down through a building during hot days and up through a building during cold nights.

The stack effect exists in buildings of any height, including one-story buildings, but is especially strong in tall buildings (or a tall stack of cardboard boxes with holes connecting the boxes). Revolving doors were invented to solve the problem of the stack effect pulling so much air in through the lobbies of tall buildings that it made it almost impossible to keep a lobby heated during the winter. They also solved the problem of the air pressure difference between indoors and outdoors making it almost impossible to open (or close) the front doors when the stack effect is moving large amounts of air through the doorway, in effect blowing the door open or closed.

When the stack effect is moving air through a building, there is a neutral pressure plane somewhere along the height of the building, where the indoor and outdoor air pressures are equal. If a window were opened at the neutral pressure plane, no air would flow through the window (assuming no wind and no fans running).

A properly airtightened multi-story building is a series of airtight compartments, with no significant stack effect, except small, disconnected stack effects within each floor.

The stack effect is one reason why windows or unintentional holes, such as leaks in walls, cannot be relied on to move the desired, or code-required, amount of air in the required direction through the required parts of a building at the required times. Stale air can easily move in the wrong direction. For example, on a cold day the stack effect will move fresh air in through an open kitchen window on the first floor of a two-story house. The incoming fresh air will push stale kitchen air through the rest of the house, which is presumably not what the person opening the window intended.

Wind, mechanical equipment, and the stack effect each move significant amounts of air. Which dominates air movement through a particular building depends on the speed and direction of the wind, what equipment is running, which interior doors are open, which exterior doors and windows are open, how leaky the building is, and the outdoor temperature. All these factors, except building leakiness, change continuously.

This photo, taken during cold weather, illustrates the stack effect. Temporary blue tarps cover window openings until new windows can be installed. The tarp near the bottom of the building is pulled in, showing that the building is sucking cold air in near the bottom. The tarps further up, especially the highest one, are pushed out, showing that air heated by the building's heating system is rising up through the building and leaving through any opening it can find near the top of the building because it is lighter than outdoor air. During the summer, the stack effect moves air down through a cool building. Cold winter air entering the bottom of a tall building during the winter can cause people inside the lower parts of a building to feel uncomfortable.

These photos, too, show that the stack effect is pulling the tarps in on the lower floors and pushing the tarps out at the top of the building where air is escaping. These photos were taken during cold weather, too.

Air Tells a Story as It Moves through a Building

The photo at right shows dark-colored dust on one edge of each fan blade, while the other edges are clean. The dust has been hitting the right edge of the blades (as viewed from below), which makes it clear which direction the fan has been turning: clockwise as viewed from below.

Dust has also accumulated on the textured ceiling where the fan has been blowing air along the surface of the ceiling. This makes it clear that air was being moved along the ceiling at the periphery of the fan.

In another building, dust has collected on the bumpy wall around the hole where the pipe penetrates the wall, proving that air has been leaking out of the hole, then skimming along the surface of the wall.

Neither one of these photos was taken in a particularly dusty building—air, especially in cities, normally contains more than enough dust to offer clues about air movement.

The photo at right shows dust streaks on the ceiling in the basement of a tall building in a cold climate. The stack effect is pulling air through the holes and up the stairway during cold weather.

The photo below shows black streaks on the ceiling above a steam pipe with metal fins on it, which is heating a basement. The streaks are the result of dust being heated and partially pyrolyzed (chemically broken down), and then moved by air currents. (Pyrolysis will be covered in Chapter 11: Fire - Basic Science.) The pattern on the ceiling reveals the air's path: up between the fins and along the ceiling.

The glass door at left is on the ground floor of a six-story building in a climate with cold winters. The stack effect pulls cold outdoor air through the length of the crack along the door. Then the airstream hits the wall, leaving dust streaks everywhere but at the hinge, which blocks the airflow.

The dust on the windowsill below was deposited by air leaking from outdoors to indoors through the crack between the windowsill and the sash.

The dust collected on these doorframes shows that **air has been flowing** through the gap between the door and the frame. The **location of the dust** shows the airflow direction: from the right side of the photo to the left side of the photo in each of the photos on this page.

The difference in density between the air and the dust (dust is denser) allows the air to make a sharp turn the dust does not make, just as an insect suspended in air gets separated out of the air when an approaching car suddenly moves the **air** up and over the windshield, leaving the **heavier insect** behind.

In each of the photos on this page, air has been flowing from the left side of the doorframe to the right side.

Some doorframes display dust that indicates that dust has been flowing in two directions. Sometimes the dust flowing in one direction is a different color or texture (fuzzy or not, etc.) than the dust flowing in the other direction. The top of the doorframe in the photo at left has some dust indicating air has sometimes been flowing in the other direction.

The doorframe at below left is an elevator doorframe. The white-colored dust is a hint that someone has been renovating on that floor, perhaps sandpapering joint compound or cutting gypsum board. The direction of flow (into the shaft) indicates that the stack effect has probably been moving air into the elevator shaft from a lower floor of the building in cold weather (or an upper floor of the building in warm weather).

The dust streaks in the photos at right and below right show that air has been flowing through the small crack between each door and its frame, and also show the direction air has been moving at least some of the time: toward the viewer in each of these photos.

The hinge shown at the top of Page 85 blocked the flow of air because it is a solid type of hinge. The hinge in the photo below left on this page has gaps between its parts, allowing air to sneak through in four places and then skim along the molding, where it left dirt streaks.

The black dust streak on the carpet in the photo above shows that a large amount of air has been leaking under the door when it is closed. The dust on the elevator door at left is white because someone was renovating, thereby adding white plaster or gypsum dust to the air, which traveled through the elevator shaft and out around the door. Below, air from the apartment is escaping out under the door and lifting the newspaper.

AIR LEAKS

Fiber Insulation Is Not an Air Barrier

In the photos on the right and bottom left, the fiberglass insulation is dark around the windows because air moving through the insulation left dust behind. This illustrates that there is not an airtight connection between the walls and the windows.

In the photo at bottom right, the fiberglass insulation between the wall and the insulated pipes is dark because dust has collected in it. This shows that air has been flowing through the fiberglass insulation—through the gap around the pipes.

These photos illustrate that fiberglass insulation, or any other material with holes through it, such as mineral wool, does not make an effective air barrier.

The photo at right, looking up into the ceiling where a light fixture was mounted, shows a pattern where air moved through holes in the light fixture, then through the fiberglass insulation, leaving telltale **dust spots** behind.

The photo below shows dust on fiberglass insulation in the facade above the window of a store in a cold climate. The four stories of apartments above the store pulled air in through leaks (the air moved in the direction away from the camera).

Rooms directly above stores can be cold because of construction defects (air leaks) around security gate mountings, behind signs, and between layers of construction done by different businesses over the years.

There is nothing wrong with the insulation shown on these two pages. But, because it is not protected by an air barrier, it is working as well as the sweater without a windbreaker described on Page 70.

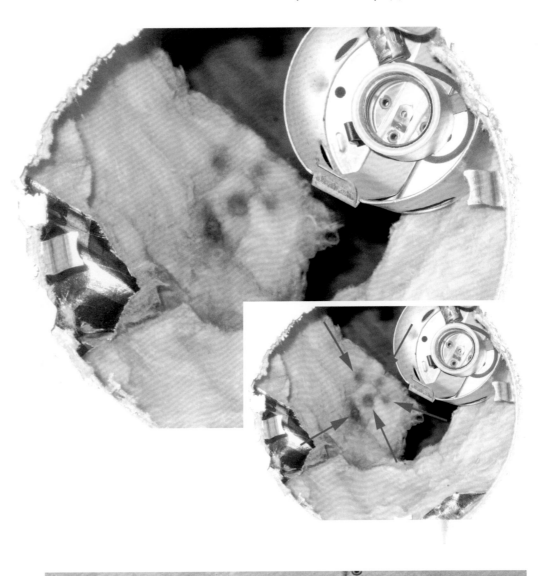

Beware of Gaps around Windows

The two windows in the photo below were ordered from the factory smaller than the opening in the brick wall—by a wide margin. This was done intentionally to make sure they would fit within the opening, with the gap filled in by various construction materials. Large gaps are difficult to make watertight or airtight, however, no matter how much product is used. When the gap is large enough to slip one's hand into, the material filling the gap will leak more air (and water), and start leaking much sooner in the life of the building, than a smaller gap would.

A better approach would be to measure more carefully and keep the gap as small as is practical.

Examples of much more skillful window installations are shown on Pages 109 and 112.

The window installations on this page are suboptimal. The windows at left were installed by removing the old wooden sashes and putting **new aluminum frames** within the original wood frames. The result is a mess: the old wood frame is rotted so badly that sunlight can be seen through **an opening**. A better approach would be to remove the old frames and install the new windows in the brick opening in the wall.

The windows in both photos below are too small for the openings in the walls. The gaps between the frames and the walls are filled with various materials. This installation is likely to allow air and water to leak.

Telecom-Related Air Leaks

Cable TV created new opportunities for entertainment and high-speed internet—and for air to leak into and through buildings. The cable TV wires in the photo at right are routed between apartments in a flexible metal conduit, which leaks air between apartments. It is connected to an electric box that also has many holes through which air can pass.

The photo below shows a gaping hole telecom installers cut into the firewall between two townhouse attics that nobody bothered to close up.

Yes, wires need holes so they can pass through buildings, but the holes should not be left open after the wires are installed. The smaller the holes are to begin with, the easier it will be to close them up later, and the more likely it will be that they will stay closed for a long time.

The wires in the photo at left will eventually be connected to the entertainment system in a house. Airtightening around all of them is a lot of work but must be done to make the house airtight. Because only a few wires might go between indoors and outdoors (to outdoor speakers?), airtightening around the wires mostly decreases air leaks within the house, which is critical to good soundproofing between rooms. Since sound travels through air, installing more speakers indoors and making holes to run more speaker wires can actually harm the acoustic properties of the house if the holes for the wires are not airtightened.

The recessed ceiling light fixture in the photo below has lots of holes in it. Airtight ceiling light fixtures are available, and simply buying one instead of this type is an easy way to reduce air leaks. They are slightly more expensive to buy but well worth the extra cost.

Note: Some light fixtures require airflow around them for cooling, and some are only approved for installation when they are not covered by insulation. Read and follow all manufacturer's instructions, and follow all codes.

Gaps around Pipes

The plumber who changed the drain pipe at right cut away some of the wall around the pipe, and nobody bothered to repair the gap. The gap allows fresh outdoor air to leak into the bathroom and pushes stale bathroom air into the rest of the house, which makes the bathroom uncomfortable during the winter and the rest of the house smelly year-round. The gap will also be a convenient pathway for cockroaches and rodents heading to the bathroom for a drink. (Techniques for discouraging pests will be covered in Chapter 13: Pests - Basic Science.)

The photo below shows holes cut in a concrete floor so pipes can pass through. The pipes are different sizes, but the holes are all the same size. Cutting smaller holes for smaller pipes would have kept the size of the gaps smaller and therefore easier to airtighten and fireproof. (Fireproofing will be covered in Chapter 12: Fire - Applied Science.)

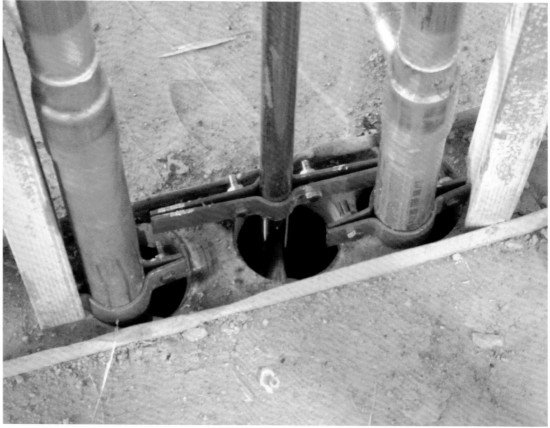

Gaps between Assemblies

An airtight material can serve as part of an air barrier, but many leaks occur between airtight materials or between assemblies, such as between walls and roofs or between walls and basements. The connection between roofs and walls is a notorious problem area in many types of buildings.

The infrared photo above left, taken during the winter, shows that the parapet (the wall around the edge of the roof) is mostly cold (dark). That is because there is no heated room on either side of it. The right end of the parapet is warm (white) because air is leaking from indoors through the parapet to outdoors at the connection between two assemblies: the roof and the wall. Heaters under the windows keep the window areas warm.

The building in the photo below is flat-roofed and two stories tall, with a roof structure made of **corrugated steel decking**. The decking's shape makes it difficult to make an airtight connection between the decking and the wall. The **spray foam insulation** shown in the small photo will probably help, although it is difficult to get the spray foam to cover the roof/wall junction because the junction is covered by **structural steel**.

When building a glass tower, such as the one in the photo at right, gaps between the **floor/ceiling assemblies** and the **glass** are particularly difficult to airtighten. The effects of air leaking at this junction are worsened by air pressure differences generated by fans in air-based heating, ventilating, and air conditioning (HVAC) systems. These air leaks make it difficult to control the temperature in a glass building because HVAC systems depend on each area of the building being reasonably airtight to help control the flow of large amounts of heating and cooling air. If enough air leaks between outdoors and in, HVAC systems sometimes lose control over indoor temperature.

"HVAC" usually refers to a system that uses air ducts to deliver all three services simultaneously by blowing a lot of air around a building. HVAC systems are typically found in office buildings in North America and aren't as commonly used in other building types or in other places.

The photo on the top of Page 99 is taken from the stairway of an apartment building that is being renovated. The **stairs** cover the connections between the **stairway walls** and the **floor/ceiling assembly** between apartments. The photo also shows **pipes** penetrating the floor/ceiling assembly, **electric boxes** penetrating the stairway wall, etc. This will need a carefully planned, carefully executed air barrier if each apartment is going to be an airtight, well-insulated box.

The photo on the bottom of Page 99 shows how a **bathtub** hides the **junction between the floor and wall**. There is no insulation and apparently no air barrier behind the bathtub, which can allow air to leak between the bathroom and the next room, the next floor, or outdoors. The exhaust fan in the bathroom will increase airflow through this junction. Creating an air barrier here requires coordination between the carpenters who build the floor and walls, and the plumbers.

In the future, someone sitting in the bathtub may wonder why the water cools off quickly. She may not first suspect cold outdoor air leaking into the house under the tub, but this is a common area for leaks, so perhaps she should.

The two photos on this page show how difficult it can be to create a continuous air barrier across assemblies.

Maintaining continuity can be especially difficult when access to the connection between two assemblies is blocked by something, such as the stairway in the photo at right or the bathtub in the photo below.

Intentional Holes Also Leak Air

The building at right has too many holes in the roof: plumbing vents, combustion exhaust vents (from water heaters, furnaces, or maybe fireplaces), and several others. Each of these holes is an opportunity for air to leak into or out of the building.

Better planning can eliminate the need for most of these holes, as will be discussed in later chapters.

The building at left dates back to a time when buildings were heated with a fireplace or stove in each room, as evidenced by the large number of chimneys. If the chimneys have not been closed up, they are moving huge amounts of air through the building.

The house at right has two large attic vents below the roof peaks. Codes specify the minimum size of attic vents, but these vents could probably be a lot smaller while still meeting code. Better yet, both the attic and the vents could be eliminated completely by making the space under the roof usable interior space. (This will be covered in Chapter 16: Building Enclosures.)

The house at left has an absurd number of vents on the front and the side. They probably increase airflow within the roof/ceiling assembly but at the cost of new problems, including reduced comfort, reduced building durability, and high energy bills.

Too Many Holes

The photo below shows a bathroom ceiling in a two-story apartment building. There are many places where air can leak from the building up into the attic and then outdoors through the attic vents (not shown), or from the attic down into the building.

Air can leak through the **non-airtight ceiling light fixture** (the **holes** are visible, making it clear it is not airtight). The **hollow interior of the bathroom wall** is not closed at the attic floor, which lets air leak into the attic from gaps around pipes, electric outlets, and medicine cabinets—and maybe even all the way up from the wet crawl space under the building (see Page 408). The bathroom **exhaust fan** is not connected to an air duct to exhausts stale air outdoors, instead venting humid bathroom air into the attic when it is operating. When the work was finished, the **insulation** was not reinstalled properly, leaving the bathroom ceiling cold during the winter and vulnerable to condensation.

The building has a new roof deck (the wood the shingles covering the roof are nailed to) because the old roof deck rotted away after a few decades of service. As a result of all these holes, all of which bring air containing water vapor from the house up into the attic, the new roof deck is starting to rot after just six months, as shown on Page 414. The new roof deck is rotting faster than the old one did because the bathroom fans used to be ducted to outdoors, but the ducts were eliminated when the deck was replaced.

Exhaust ducts to outdoors, an airtight light fixture, and some wood and caulk closing the gap at the top of the wall would stop most of the air (and water vapor) leaks and preserve the new roof deck.

Water vapor movement is covered in more detail in Chapters 5 and 6, and the interaction between air movement, heat movement, and water movement is covered in Chapter 16: Building Enclosures.

SOLUTION: AN AIR BARRIER

An air barrier between indoors and outdoors makes a building more comfortable, quieter, healthier for people, safer in fires, more durable, and more energy efficient than buildings without an air barrier. All buildings benefit from an air barrier between indoors and outdoors, and between parts of the building.

Codes in some places require buildings to be built with an air barrier. The amount of smoke that fire codes allow to pass through a fire-rated assembly is zero, which means that fire codes indirectly require an air barrier. Building codes that require soundproofing between apartments cannot be complied with without an air barrier either. This is explained in Chapter 10: Sound - Applied Science.

Because air barriers reduce sound transmission, they are especially important around bedrooms. Schools benefit from air barriers around each classroom. They prevent air from leaking between outdoors and classrooms, from classroom to classroom, and between classrooms and common areas such as hallways and basements. Office buildings benefit from having air barriers between floors and between sections of offices, and apartment buildings benefit from an air barrier around each apartment.

The less air that leaks through an air barrier the better. The saying "walls need to breathe" is just an excuse for carelessness, as explained on Page 379. Buildings do need ventilation, but construction defects (air leaks) are not a good strategy for protecting people's health.

Are Air Barriers Healthy for People?

Numerous people have gotten sick because of spending time in poorly ventilated buildings. Some office buildings built in the 1970s were especially problematic. But it wasn't air barriers that made people sick. Something else did.

In the 1970s, tile or wood floors were replaced with synthetic carpets that gave off nasty chemicals; wood and metal furniture was replaced with plastic or chipboard furniture, which off-gassed large quantities of formaldehyde and other chemicals; and carbon paper was replaced with mimeograph machines and blueprint machines, both of which used toxic chemicals. Together, these and other chemicals made office workers sick.

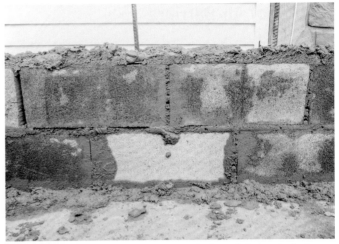

The photo above shows a concrete block wall being built by an experienced mason. The mortar in the horizontal ("bed") joints will probably fill the joints fairly completely. The vertical ("head") joints are much trickier, as the mortar tends to fall out as the wall is being built. Even if the mortar is perfect, the blocks themselves leak a lot of air, which can be demonstrated by putting your mouth on a block and blowing on it: air goes right through the block. One solution is to apply a coating on the block wall as shown on Page 107.

The buildings changed as well. Older office buildings had windows that opened. In the 1970s, office buildings were built with as many air leaks as ever but with more glass, and with large HVAC systems to meet the large heating and cooling loads associated with all the glass. Because HVAC systems depend on circulating huge amounts of air to specific parts of a building, they don't work with windows open. So, buildings were designed with inoperable windows. And, in many cases, the amount of ventilation air supplied was reduced to save energy.

It should be no surprise that people got sick when they started spending their days in poorly ventilated buildings filled with toxins. Ironically, if the walls of those 1970s buildings had been more airtight, the HVAC systems might have done a better job of delivering fresh air and removing stale air as intended.

The solution is to avoid putting toxins into buildings in the first place, remove toxins that are already in buildings, make buildings as airtight as practical, and ventilate. The chemical industry has made great strides in developing paints, adhesives, sealants, and other building materials that are less toxic. Today, most of the toxins in indoor air come from building contents, such as furniture, not from the building itself.

The following pages show different ways that air barriers have been included in walls over the years.

History of Air Barriers

The photo at right shows 50-year-old tarpaper that was installed behind shingles to act as a barrier to air. Tarpaper, also known as "asphalt-impregnated felt paper," has been commonly used since at least the early 1900s. Tarpaper also serves as a barrier to liquid water, as do all the other air barriers on this page and the following pages through Page 108.

Tarpaper typically overlaps at the seams but has no airtight connection at the seams, which limits its usefulness as an air barrier. Tarpaper is not used for walls as much as it used to be, but it is still used as a barrier to liquid water under roof shingles.

The photo at left shows a house under construction covered with Tyvek®, which has largely replaced tarpaper for use on walls. Tyvek® is a barrier to liquid water but not to water vapor, therefore it allows the wall to dry. How Tyvek® does this is explained on Page 132.

Tyvek® has several advantages over tarpaper. First, it comes in larger sheets than tarpaper, which means fewer seams that can leak air. Second, it is much stronger than tarpaper, which helps it resist damage during installation and from high winds after installation.

After Tyvek® started replacing tarpaper in the late 1900s, other companies started to offer similar products. The generic name for these products is "housewrap" or "homewrap."

The housewrap at right is shown overlapping the **tops of the windows and door** to help keep liquid water out of the wall at the connections between the windows and the wall, and the door and the wall. It is **taped** at the sides of the windows and the door, and the bottoms of the windows, to reduce leakage of air and liquid water.

By the early 2000s, increased interest in reducing air leaks resulted in the development of special adhesive tapes like those shown above that could stick to housewraps and connect them at the seams. However, this left housewraps vulnerable to wind during or after construction. The better the seams are connected, the more the air barrier acts like the sail of a boat. The photo at left shows Tyvek® connected with a "fully adhered membrane"—a thick rubber-like material with a peel-off backing and a strong adhesive, which can connect housewrap to other materials. One key advantage is that it comes in sheets larger than tape, reducing the sailboat problem.

Housewraps are becoming less popular in favor of covering the whole building with a fully adhered membrane. The photo at right shows a building covered with a fully adhered membrane that is a barrier to both air and liquid water. Some, but not all, fully adhered membranes are also barriers to water vapor. Because the entire surface of the membrane is coated with a strong adhesive, the whole membrane is fully adhered to the wall behind it. This transfers the wind load to the wall, which solves the problem of wind tearing the membrane or breaking the connections between the membrane and the windows or other parts of the building.

Photo: Phebe Horschel.

The photo at left shows a house that has been covered with a fully adhered membrane, which is being covered by foam insulation and then stone. The membrane is rolled back above the window opening so that after the window is installed it can be overlapped shingle-style on top of the window. This will keep water from leaking between the membrane and the window.

A fully adhered membrane is an especially durable and reliable air barrier technology.

Brush, roll, or spray-on materials are now becoming more popular. In the photo at right, a mason brushes a cement-based material onto a concrete block wall. When the material dries, it will form a barrier to air and to liquid water but will not be a barrier to water vapor. This will reduce wetting but still allow drying.

The **black material** is a fully adhered membrane. It is used where the wall assembly meets the floor/ceiling assembly because gaps in the masonry in that area might not be completely covered by the cement-based barrier used on the smoother parts of the wall.

In the photo below, a yellow material is being rolled onto a concrete block wall. The material will be a barrier to air and to liquid water but not a barrier to water vapor. It covers the **sides of the window openings** (called the "window returns"), too, where it can easily be connected to the windows, making the air barrier continuous across the windows and the wall. The photo below left shows where different materials and assemblies meet at the corners of the window openings. A thicker material is troweled onto fiberglass mesh, which adds physical strength to the air barrier in that area.

A more recent development, shown at right and below, is wall sheathing panels with a factory-applied material that is a barrier to air and to liquid water but not to water vapor. The panels do not form a barrier to air or to liquid water unless they are connected to each other in an airtight and watertight manner. The manufacturer makes a special tape that is designed to adhere to the seams, solving the problem of air leaks and liquid water leaks at the seams.

Sheathing is the wall layer on the outdoor side of the studs. It handles some structural load, transfers the wind load to the studs, and, depending on the material, is sometimes also a fire barrier.

In the photo at left, a brush-on or roll-on material has been applied to the seams between the yellow sheathing panels on the right side of the building. This material will make an airtight and watertight connection between panels. On the left side of the building, another layer is being applied to the wall. This will form an even better barrier to air and to liquid water.

Another recent innovation is very high-quality tapes. In the house under construction in the photos on this page, the connections between assemblies are airtightened with special tape.

The **roof** structure consists of "structural insulated panels," which are made by sandwiching a thick layer of foam insulation between two pieces of oriented strand board (chips of wood glued together). The structure of the walls is made of autoclaved, aerated concrete blocks (special concrete with tiny air pockets) with mortar between the blocks. The outdoor side of the blocks is covered with foam insulation and then shingles. A **layer of plaster** covers the indoor side of the wall, as shown below. The completed wall and roof are both effective airtight assemblies. The vulnerable places are the connections between assemblies: between the roof panels, between the roof panels and the wall, and between the wall and the windows and doors.

One way to airtighten these vulnerable connections is with special tape (see photo below). In the photo at left, a primer (adhesive) is being brushed onto the wall near a door, enabling the tape to make a permanent and airtight connection between the door and the wall.

Adding an Air Barrier to an Existing Building

The house on this and the next page is having a barrier to air and to liquid water applied.

First, as shown in the right side of the top photo, the old siding is removed.

Next, a yellow air barrier material is applied with a roller. Because the air barrier is applied to the outdoor side of the existing black sheathing panels (the flat sheets of material on the outdoor side of the wood studs in the wall), it is easy to make it continuous. If it were applied to the indoor side of the wall, not only would the indoor side of the walls need to be removed and replaced, but there would be interruptions because of pipes, wires, and intersecting walls. Because it is adhered to a rigid part of the wall (the sheathing), it is not vulnerable to being torn or loosened by wind, as a housewrap would be.

The photo at right shows fiberglass mesh being applied around the windows. Mesh increases the physical strength of the yellow barrier material at vulnerable connections, such as those around the windows.

Once the yellow barrier material has dried, a continuous layer of silver-colored foam insulation is applied to the outside of the house. (See photo, right.)

Last, as shown below, new siding is installed on top of the insulation.

This building now has a barrier to air, a barrier to liquid water, and, on the outdoor side of these barriers, a thin but continuous thermal barrier (insulation). On the outdoor side of the insulation is a new layer of siding, which protects the barrier layers from ultraviolet light (from the sun), wind, and rain, and makes the building aesthetically pleasing.

This sequence of layers is optimal and will be covered in more detail in Chapter 16: Building Enclosures.

Airtightening the Connection between the Windows and the Air Barrier

A bead of **white caulk** in the photo at right connects the window to a piece of flashing fabric that connects the indoor side of the window to the air barrier on the outdoor side of the concrete blocks. The photo at bottom left shows the **flashing fabric** visible on the outdoor side of the window opening. (It will be covered with bricks, as shown in the photo at right.) The flashing fabric adheres (with the help of some primer) to the brushed-on cement-based barrier to air and to liquid water (see top of Page 107). The caulk is on the indoor side of the wall, where it is protected from the sun's ultraviolet rays, rain, and fluctuating outdoor temperature (which causes materials to shrink and stretch). Because the caulk is so well protected, it can be expected to serve as an airtight connection for the life of the window.

In the photo below right, the gap between the window and the wall is airtightened with foam. Note that the wall was framed accurately, reducing the size of the space that needs to be filled with foam. The best way to close a gap is with an accurate measurement and very little filler.

Inoperable Windows Leak Less Air

The photo at right shows new windows in a two-story-tall loft. Most of the old double-hung (vertical sliding) windows were never opened during the decades they were in place because they were installed high above the floor. Most of the new windows (pictured) were fixed in place in their frames at the factory, which makes them much more airtight. Because they have no hinges, sliding mechanisms, or latches, they were also much less expensive to buy than operable windows.

When the new windows were ordered, the owner asked for operable windows in a few locations where he remembered opening windows in the past, plus a few more locations where he guessed someone might want to open windows in the future. He ordered the rest as fixed windows. The windows that do open are casement windows (hinged), which are much more airtight than the double-hung windows they replaced (see Windows Glossary on Page 69).

After the new windows were installed with airtight connections to the walls, cold drafts were eliminated, street noise was almost entirely eliminated, and dry indoor air during the winter was greatly reduced. (Dry indoor air during the winter will be explained in Chapter 5: Water - Basic Science.)

Photo: Phebe Horschel.

In the house at left, the windows high up are too high to reach without a ladder, thus the owner chose to have them fixed in place. Two **windows** down low are casement windows, and the two larger windows down low are fixed in place. With only two windows that open, both casements, the house will leak less air (and noise) than it would if more windows were operable.

Air flowing in one window and out the other provides good ventilation. A larger area of the room would be ventilated if the operable windows were located **further from each other**.

Air Barriers in Interior Walls

Modern gypsum board walls can leak much more air than old plaster walls such as those shown on Page 327. Plaster makes a reasonably airtight connection to floors, window frames, electric boxes, and other parts of buildings. Gypsum board does not make an airtight connection to floors, window frames, electric boxes, or other parts of a building unless care is taken to create an air barrier.

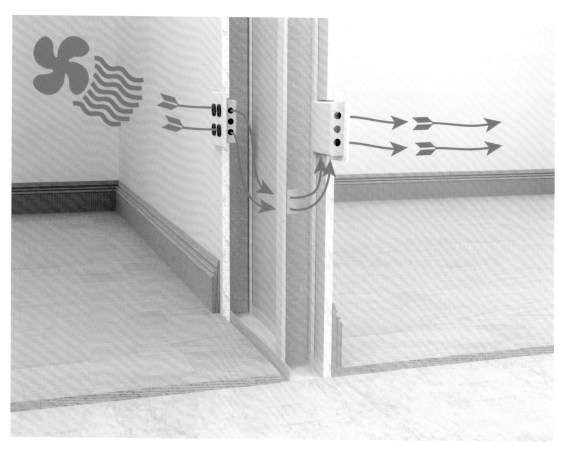

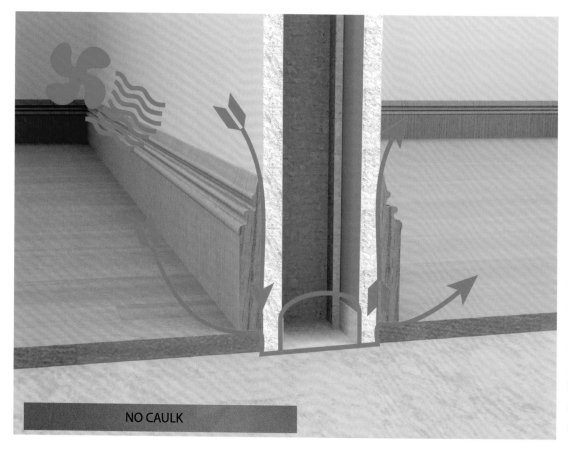

NO CAULK

The drawing above, of a wall cut open, shows air leaking into an electric box on the left side of the wall, traveling through the wall, and continuing back out another electric box on the other side of the wall.

The drawing at left shows air leaking under and behind the baseboard, under and over the floor track (the metal channel the wall studs are connected to at the bottom of the wall), and back out the other side of the wall.

The drawing at right shows a wall under construction. On one side of the floor track is a bead of yellow caulk. Though it will adhere to the gypsum board, the caulk will not form a barrier to air passing under the gypsum board and then under the track, as shown in the drawing below.

Described another way, the caulk has not been applied in a way that will stop air from leaking from one side of the wall to the other.

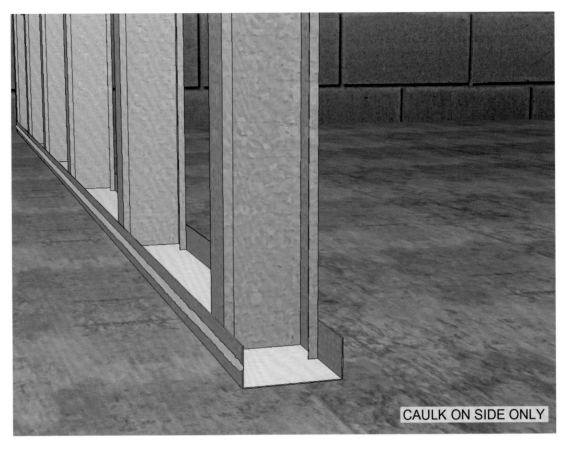

CAULK ON SIDE ONLY

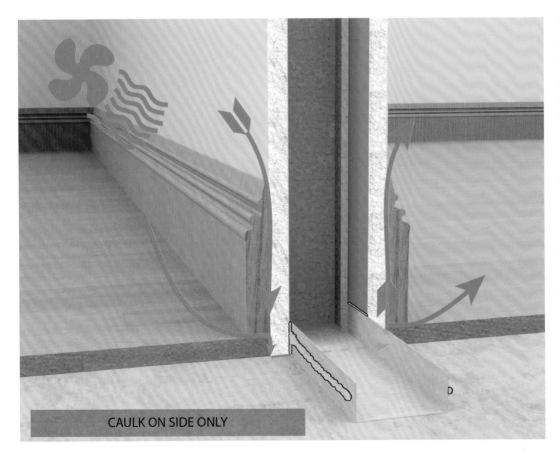

CAULK ON SIDE ONLY

The gap between the wall and the subfloor is narrow, but it is as long as the wall and therefore allows a lot of air to leak through.

This long-but-narrow gap also allows whole sound waves of a relatively long wavelength through the wall. This allows the wall to transmit sound waves that carry voices and other distracting sounds. Smaller holes can only transmit shorter-wavelength sounds, which are more likely to be perceived as random noise.

The drawing at right shows another wall that has been built with caulk improperly applied, this time in a different way.

The caulk underneath the floor track does keep air from passing underneath the track, but it does not form a barrier against air passing over the top of the track.

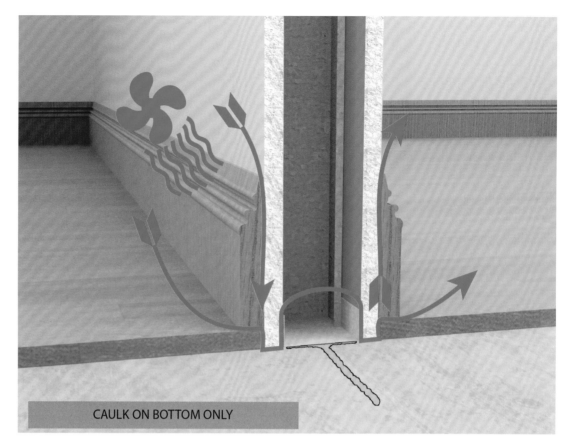

CAULK ON BOTTOM ONLY

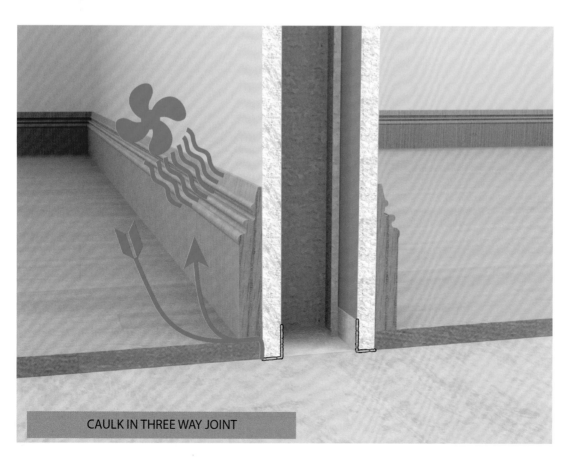

CAULK IN THREE WAY JOINT

The drawing at left shows the right place to put the caulk: in the three-way joint between the floor, the track, and the gypsum board, where it can form an effective barrier against air passing from one side of the wall to the other.

As shown on the next page, the caulk must be applied to the entire length of the wall. These drawings show the steps involved in creating an airtight connection between the wall and the floor. The same caulk joint needs to be applied where the wall meets the ceiling.

Airtight Connection between Floor and Gypsum Board Wall: ① The floor is swept clean, or dirt will cause a gap between the bottom of the wall and the floor. ② Track and studs are assembled. ③ The floor is swept again—dirt is continuously generated on a construction site, and chemists have not yet invented caulk that sticks to dirt. ④ A thick bead of caulk goes at the intersection of the track and the floor. ⑤ Gypsum board is set into the wet caulk, forming a three-way connection between the board, subfloor, and track. ⑥ The finish floor and baseboard molding are installed.

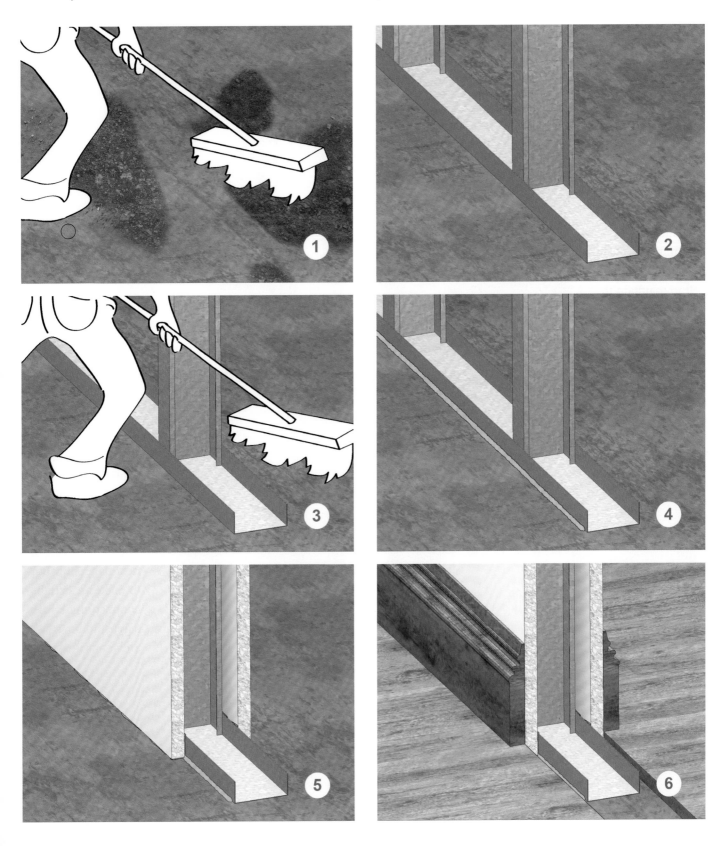

The photo at right shows a **bead of black caulk** applied where the ceiling track meets the concrete ceiling. One piece of gypsum board has been set into the caulk.

The photo below shows caulk applied where the track meets the concrete floor, with a gap left at the end of the track to allow gypsum board to run continuously past the intersecting wall at left to maintain the air barrier and fire separation.

The drawings on Pages 330-333 show how to use these gaps to make the gypsum board continuous in a wall that is intended to serve as a fire barrier.

The drawings on the next page show how to make an airtight connection between a gypsum board wall and a masonry wall.

Airtight Gypsum Board Wall Intersecting an Airtight Masonry Wall: ① The floor and ceiling tracks are installed with gaps for the gypsum board to continue to the masonry wall (the ceiling track is not shown). ② The studs are put in place, but the last stud on either side of the intersection is left loose. ③ Caulk is applied to the gypsum board wall's floor track, ceiling track, and end stud. ④ Boards are installed into the caulk, making an airtight three-way joint between the gypsum board, the track or end stud, and the floor, ceiling, or wall. ⑤ The loose studs are screwed into place. ⑥ Gypsum boards are installed over the masonry wall.

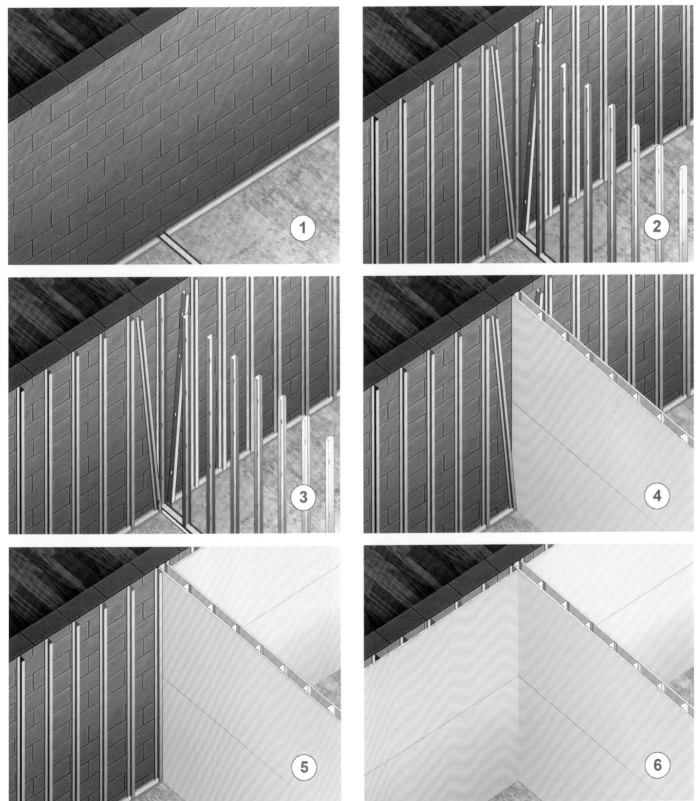

Airtightening Electric Boxes

Electric boxes can leak a lot of air. However, they can be airtightened with duct mastic. Duct mastic is a sticky, gooey material when it comes out of the can but hardens into a durable and slightly flexible coating. It fills the holes in the box.

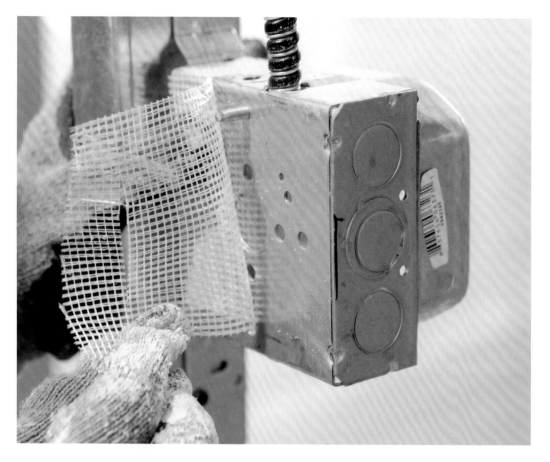

The photo at right shows fiberglass mesh being applied to an electric box. The mesh and mastic help hold each other in place and help bridge across holes. Below, duct mastic is being brushed on after the mesh is in place.

Water-based duct mastic is less toxic than other types. This will keep the air in the building healthier both during and after construction.

In the photo at left, duct mastic is being brushed onto the top of the box, filling in holes at the connection between the box and the flexible metal electric conduit containing wires.

Check electric codes before closing up the holes in an electric box. Some codes require boxes to have holes that air can flow through to remove built-up heat.

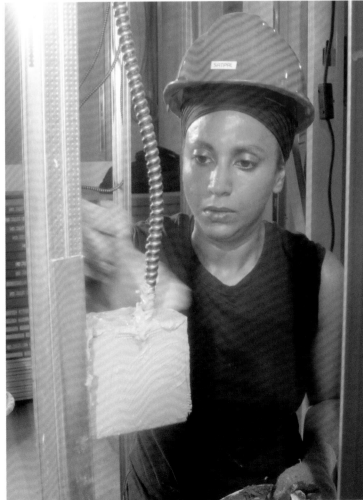

Model: Satpal Kaur.

After airtightening the back and sides of an electric box, caulk can make a good airtight connection between the front of an electric box and the gypsum board, as shown in the photos on this page.

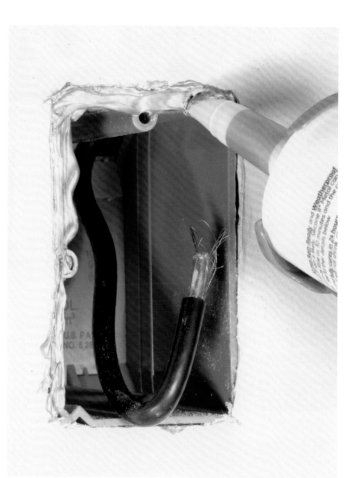

In the photo at right, the electric box behind the gypsum board will be covered with a telephone jack, which will be connected to the wire in the box. Sometimes telephone wires penetrate walls without going through a box. It is best to terminate wires for telephones, cable, intercoms, thermostats, internet, and sound (as well as whatever will be invented next) in boxes. This is because boxes can be airtightened more thoroughly than a simple hole in the wall. Another advantage is that a box offers something more solid than gypsum board to mount whatever is connected to the wire and avoids the need to make more holes in the gypsum board to mount it.

For example, if a thermostat is connected to a wire and mounted on the gypsum board, it might come loose and pull on the wire and the airtight connection. Holes around thermostat wires are especially problematic because they allow air from somewhere else to get to a thermostat, fooling it into thinking the temperature in the room is different than it actually is. Mounting a thermostat securely on an airtight box prevents this problem.

Airtightening Holes

Airtightening holes where pipes and wires pass through air barriers is critical to making a building airtight.

The gaps around the radiant floor heating tubes in the photo at right are filled with orange spray foam. Very little, if any, air will leak through those holes.

The photo at left shows pipes and flexible electric conduits passing through a wall above where a ceiling will be installed. The gaps are filled with red fire caulk (also called firestop compound) because they are passing through a fire wall that divides one part of an apartment building from another.

Fire caulk is a sophisticated material that stands up to a fire. When applied properly, it forms part of an air barrier.

The photo at right shows one way to properly firestop (and airtighten) the connection between a wall and a floor/ceiling assembly. **Wood joists** support the plywood subfloor for the room above, metal channels will support a ceiling, and gypsum board is part of a firewall that extends up past the ceiling to the subfloor. Instead of trying to cut a single piece of gypsum board to fit closely around the joists, the gypsum board is cut below the joists, and then smaller leftover scraps of gypsum board are used to fill the gaps between the joists. White caulk continues the air barrier between the pieces of gypsum board, while red firestopping compound firestops and airtightens around a penetration for electric wires.

The pipes in the photo at left run vertically through a floor/ceiling assembly inside a wall.

The holes where they penetrate the floor/ceiling assembly are covered with red firestopping compound, which of course also serves as part of an air barrier.

Airtightening Gaps around Doors

The door in the photo at left has three built-in airseals, also called weatherstrips. One is enough if the airseal, the door, and the frame are in perfect condition, are perfectly aligned, and stay that way. For very good airsealing expected to last a long time, three are better than two, which are much better than one.

The hotel doorway below has a **weatherstrip** along the side and a high-quality "**sweep**" on the bottom, both of which will substantially reduce air leaks and sound transmission. Choosing good products and installing them correctly can greatly reduce air leakage around doors, both in new construction and in existing buildings. The most durable and effective weatherstripping products are usually designed to be compressed by the face of the door as the door closes.

The bottom of a door is more challenging because along the bottom there is no doorframe for the door to compress a weatherstrip against. The challenge of airsealing along the bottom of a door is made easier by installing a raised "saddle," or threshold, which gives an airseal something to press against. Some good methods of airtightening at the bottom of a door are shown on the next two pages.

The door saddle above has a **compressible rubber strip** along one side. This is a simple way to achieve a good air barrier, as closing the door compresses the rubber strip.

The mechanism below has a **button** that gets pushed by the doorframe when the door closes. When the button is pushed, a piece of **weatherstripping** slides down against the floor. This is more complicated than other approaches but has the advantage of not requiring a door saddle.

The saddle on the next page has a groove that receives a J-shaped metal strip attached to the bottom of the door, which is more rodent-resistant than anything made of rubber or plastic.

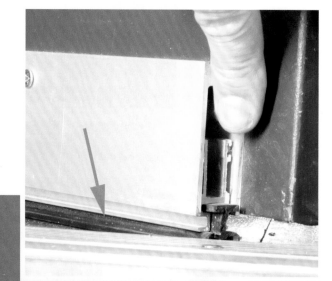

Airtightening Between Buildings

The photo below shows an "accordion strip" type of air barrier material being installed between two apartment buildings. Before it was installed, outdoor air would blow freely between the two buildings, greatly increasing the surface area of the buildings that lost heat during the winter and gained heat during the summer. During the summer, warm humid air would get into the gap, be cooled by the shade (and by contact with the air conditioned buildings), and condense water onto the buildings. The accordion strip will greatly reduce both of these problems.

Model: Chris Benedict, R. A.

Measuring Air Leakage

The photo above right shows an architect using a blower door to measure the airtightness of an apartment. The blower door has an electric-powered fan that is creating an air pressure difference between the inside of an apartment and the hallway. The building's front door is open so the blower door can reference outdoor air pressure. The instruments are measuring the air pressure difference, as well as how much air is passing through the fan. This reveals how leaky the apartment is. The blower door is also helpful in finding where the air leaks are, so they can be fixed. Large leaks make a rushing air noise, and, if the temperature of the outdoor air is very different from the temperature of the indoor air, the leaking air can be felt on a person's skin or can be found with an infrared camera.

People started building blower doors for their own use in the late 1970s, but it wasn't until the early 1980s that they became commercially available—an illustration of just how young the field of building science is. Though the first people who built telescopes and microscopes are long dead, the first people who built blower doors are not only very much alive—they are still making important contributions to the field today.

SUMMARY

Build it airtight; ventilate it right.

Chapter 5 **WATER** Basic Science

WHAT IS WATER?

Water in its liquid form is the substance that fills the oceans and flows through our bodies. Water sometimes takes the form of a solid: ice. Water also takes the form of a gas, called water vapor, which is part of the air we breathe. A gas containing only water vapor is called steam. Whichever of these forms it comes in, water is still H_2O: a molecule made of two hydrogen atoms and one oxygen atom.

WATER: THE ULTIMATE DESTROYER OF BUILDINGS

More damage is done to buildings by water than probably all other destructive forces combined. Water can destroy buildings slowly and steadily, or suddenly. Any building, from a log cabin to a modern house, will be destroyed if it is not protected from water. Floods from broken pipes are probably second only to rainwater as a cause of water damage to buildings and may even do more damage than fire. Insurance companies track the numbers, which have many zeroes after them, and track the percentages, which point to water as the main cause of lawsuits related to construction defects. The better a building design protects a building from water, the fewer repairs the building will need and the longer it will last.

FOUR WAYS WATER MOVES THROUGH A BUILDING

Understanding how to control the flow of water through a building requires understanding how water enters a building, how it is stored in a building's materials, and how it eventually leaves. Understanding all of this first requires understanding the different ways water moves within, or through, a building. (Wherever there might be any confusion about what form of water is being discussed, this book calls water in its liquid form "liquid water" to distinguish it from ice or water vapor.)

There are approximately four ways water moves through a building, or through parts of a building, each of them important to building science. The four are listed below in no particular order, categorized by the mechanism that moves the water and then by the form the water takes.

Mechanism that moves water through a building	Form water takes as it moves through a building
1. Gravity	Liquid water
2. Capillary suction	Absorbed liquid water
3. Diffusion driven by vapor pressure difference between areas of high concentration and areas of low concentration	Water vapor (water in its gas state)
4. Whatever mechanism moves the air the water vapor is part of, such as wind	Water vapor (water in its gas state)

One exception to these four ways is liquid water pushed through a hole in a building by an air pressure difference. (See Pages 168 and 169.) Another exception is liquid water pushed through a crack in a basement by water pressure.

Because each of these mechanisms contributes to both wetting and drying a building, none of them is only "good" or "bad" for a building. They are all governed by the laws of nature, which are "good" if they are understood and taken into consideration when making decisions, but the same laws also govern the problems that will occur if they are misunderstood or ignored.

Understanding how water moves through a building also requires understanding the sometimes strange ways water behaves as a liquid, as well as the mostly ordinary ways water behaves as a gas.

BEHAVIOR OF WATER AS A LIQUID

Electromagnetic attraction between water molecules explains much of the behavior of liquid water. Water molecules have a small positive charge on one end and a small negative charge on the other end, which makes them behave like small magnets. Picture a pile of magnets on the counter near the cash register in a toy store—the attraction they have for each other causes them to cling together in a lump. The closer they get to each other, the more energy it takes to pull them apart. The magnets in the middle of the pile are surrounded by other magnets on all sides, to which they are strongly attracted. Therefore, magnets near the middle require more energy to separate from the pile than magnets at the edge of the pile. A pile of magnets shaped to have the maximum number of magnets in the middle and the smallest possible number of magnets at the edge will require the maximum energy to pull apart. A sphere (see drawing below) has the smallest surface area of any other shape with the same volume, and therefore more energy is required to pull it apart than is required for any other possible shape.

Triangular or pyramid-shaped water drops are not found in nature, because any shape other than a sphere increases the number of water molecules that are on the surface, where their forces of magnetic attraction will not be satisfied as well as if they were in the middle of the drop. Any shape other than round has fewer molecules in the middle and more molecules at the surface than a round drop would have, making it a higher-energy shape than a round drop.

The magnets in a lump will cling together until energy is "used" to force them apart. Energy used to force magnets apart is analogous to adding heat to ice to turn it into liquid or adding heat to liquid water to turn it into individual gas molecules. Energy is used to overcome the magnetic forces holding the toy store magnets together, just as latent heat is added to overcome the forces holding water molecules together in ice crystals or holding water molecules together in drops.

In the other direction, the latent heat released when water vapor condenses into liquid water, or liquid water freezes into ice, is analogous to the energy released when magnetic forces pull the magnets together.

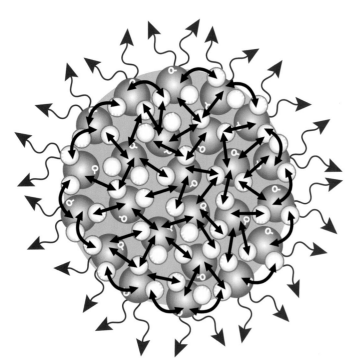

Water molecules tend to arrange themselves into a sphere because a sphere minimizes the number of molecules at the surface, where their forces of magnetic attraction will not be satisfied as well as if they were in the middle of the drop. Described another way, a round shape maximizes the number of molecules in the middle and minimizes the number of molecules at the surface, making it the lowest-energy state of any shape. Water drops are not perfect spheres due to gravity, wind, and their attraction to surfaces, but they still tend to be round.

A pile of magnets and a drop of water both tend to be round because of attraction between particles. The second law of thermodynamics implies that if someone puts some magnets into his pocket and walks around, the magnets will tumble around and arrange themselves into a shape that maximizes the number of magnetic forces holding the magnets together, leaving a minimum of unused magnetic forces (energy) still available. The second law also says that water flows down a mountain toward the ocean to minimize the energy stored in the water, and a pile of neatly sorted black and white marbles carried around in someone's pocket will mix themselves randomly—both the water flowing and the marbles mixing maximize the entropy, or randomness, in the system. The reason a drop of water tends toward a spherical shape is the same: to maximize the entropy, or randomness, in the system. Moving water uphill, sorting marbles, and making round drops of water triangular each require energy.

A sphere-shaped drop of water has a lower-energy state than any other shape because the maximum number of molecules are completely surrounded by other molecules they are attracted to, and the minimum number of molecules are at the surface of the drop, where they still have available magnetic energy. The second law says that all systems progress toward lower-energy states, which in the case of a drop of water means becoming round.

Surface Tension

Another way of looking at the characteristics of water that cause a drop to be round is to consider surface tension. The molecules at the edge of a drop of water are surrounded by molecules on only one side, with an open side waiting to cling to something else, thus they have potential to do work, which means they are in a higher-energy state than the molecules in the middle of the drop. With nothing else to cling to, they are strongly attracted to each other. This attraction provides the force to pull the water into as round a shape as conditions permit. But a drop of water (or a pile of magnets) lying on a table will not be a perfectly round sphere because there are other factors influencing its shape.

One factor is gravity, which pulls the clump of water molecules downward, changing the shape to look more like a chocolate-chip cookie: round at the edges and higher in the middle.[1] Another factor is water molecules acting like small magnets, which causes water to cling to, or "wet," surfaces to a greater or lesser extent depending on its attraction to particular surfaces.

Liquid Water Clings to Surfaces

Liquid water is attracted to almost anything it touches. How well the water is attracted to, or "wets," a surface

1   Cookies are actually shaped by similar forces: the stickiness of the butter and eggs in the batter, which could be thought of as the attraction between cookie dough "molecules," and gravity.

The drop on the right is on a waxed part of a car roof. The drop on the left is the same size, "measured" with an eye dropper, but is on an unwaxed part of the roof. Water's magnetic attraction causes it to cling more strongly to the roof than to wax, therefore the drop on the left is more spread out, with more molecules clinging to the car. The drop on the right is pulled upward and more round, closer to a sphere shape, because the water molecules are not as strongly attracted to the wax.

determines the shape and behavior of drops of water on surfaces, which influences how water moves through a building.

Liquid water's tendency to cling to surfaces can make it maddeningly difficult to find a roof leak because, when liquid water travels through a building, it usually clings to one surface, then to another, on and on down through the building, sometimes never dripping through open air. This characteristic of water needs to be kept in mind when designing buildings to shed rainwater, which will be discussed in Chapter 6: Water - Applied Science.

A drop of water will only take the shape of a sphere in the middle of a spaceship, where there is no gravity to pull it out of a round shape and no surface for it to cling to. After a water drop floats around in a spaceship for a while, it will eventually find a surface to cling to and will no longer be a sphere. A drop of water falling as rain is shaped by a battle between surface tension making it round and wind forcing it into countless other shapes.

A water drop on a waxed car will be round with high edges because water is not very attracted to a waxed surface. A drop on a surface that water is more attracted to, such as an unwaxed car, will be spread out wider and flatter because water is more attracted to the unwaxed surface. On both the waxed car and the unwaxed car, the different shapes represent the lowest-energy state of the water because both shapes best satisfy the force of gravity, the forces of attraction between the water molecules and other water molecules, and the forces of attraction between the water molecules and the molecules of surrounding objects (car or wax).

Is Liquid Water Really Still H$_2$O?

When water molecules get close enough to each other to become liquid, the magnetic attraction between molecules causes water to form groups with a minimum size of about 50 H$_2$O molecules, which could be thought of as H$_{100}$O$_{50}$. Every drop of water contains a vast number of H$_{100}$O$_{50}$ groups.[2] Therefore, it is accurate but potentially misleading to describe liquid water molecules as H$_2$O. The main implication of liquid water taking the form of H$_{100}$O$_{50}$ is that liquid water behaves as if its molecules are larger than water vapor molecules.

Liquid water's larger group size explains how a raincoat made of Gore-Tex® fabric is "waterproof" to water falling as rain yet allows a person's sweat to evaporate right through the fabric. The fabric is made with countless holes that are each too small for H$_{100}$O$_{50}$ liquid water groups to pass through but are large enough for individual H$_2$O water vapor molecules to pass through because water vapor molecules do not travel in groups—they travel alone

2   It is probably best not to describe water this way on a chemistry exam.

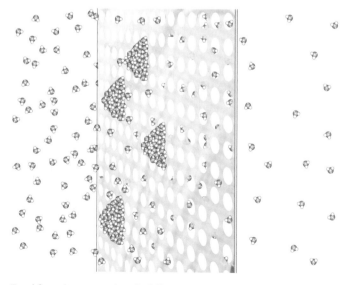

Tyvek® and many other building wrap products have holes large enough for individual water vapor molecules to pass through (in either direction) but too small for liquid water molecule groups to pass through. This makes them a barrier to liquid water but not a barrier to water vapor.

as individual H$_2$O molecules. Tyvek® and other building wrap materials work the same way. This is amazingly simple—holes just the right size, also called a "selective barrier," select what forms of water can fit through. It is like a spaghetti strainer with holes too small for spaghetti to get through but large enough for water to fit through. It is a filter that liquid water cannot fit through but water vapor can fit through. In building science terminology, this makes Tyvek® a barrier to liquid water but not a barrier to water vapor.

In summary, liquid water is pulled into a round drop by surface tension, clings more tightly to some surfaces than to others, and does not fit through some of the tiny holes water vapor can fit through.

Water vapor, also known as water in its gas state, does not exhibit any of these behaviors.

The following pages describe in more detail the four ways water moves through a building.

1. LIQUID WATER MOVED BY GRAVITY

Gravity moves liquid water downhill, ever closer to the ocean, in satisfaction of the second law of thermodynamics. This can be seen by noticing that water stays in the bottom of a bucket or watching how the water behaves if it is dumped on the ground. Liquid water molecules behave differently from individual marbles in a bucket of marbles, however. If a bucket of marbles is dumped on the ground, some marbles will roll off by themselves. If a bucket of water is dumped on the ground, no individual water molecules will flow anywhere alone.

2. LIQUID WATER MOVED BY CAPILLARY SUCTION

Because liquid water clings to surfaces, it exhibits another strange behavior: within materials with lots of small, interconnected holes, also known as porous materials, it is pulled in every direction, including uphill. Examples of porous materials include a kitchen sponge, wood, gypsum board, and concrete. This pull is called capillary suction. Capillary suction has nothing to do with the way capillaries in our bodies work. Water climbs some distance

A straw basket would not be good for use as a bucket to carry water because the pressure of the liquid water pushing on the gaps between the pieces of straw would cause water to leak through the gaps. But the thatched roof above keeps the inside of the building dry because the water clings to the straw fibers while gravity pulls the water down the steep slope of the roof. A thatched roof would not work if it were not steeply pitched because there are gaps between the pieces of straw.

up the holes in a porous material or up the sides of a glass of water because the water molecules' magnetic attraction causes them to cling to the surrounding material and to pull other water molecules up behind them.

The height water will climb up the sides of a container depends on the container's size and shape, and how much the water is attracted to the material the container is made of. A large container, such as a swimming pool, has many molecules in the middle pulled down by gravity and relatively few molecules clinging to the edges, while a thin tube such as a drinking straw has fewer molecules in the middle and relatively more molecules at the edges, where attraction to the sides of the straw pulls them upward. The smaller the diameter of the tube or container the water is in, the higher up capillary suction will lift it because there is relatively more surface for the water molecules to be attracted to.

Described another way, capillary suction lifts water higher up a small-diameter tube than a large-diameter tube because the small-diameter tube has proportionally less "middle" where water is pulled down by gravity and proportionally more wetted surface. The maximum height capillary suction can lift water in masonry building materials is higher than the tallest buildings ever built.

An everyday example of capillary suction: place an ordinary kitchen sponge on a puddle of water on a table, and the water will immediately move uphill into the many holes in the sponge, against gravity and against the water's attraction for the table. This is because the numerous small holes in the sponge have lots and lots of surface area for the water to wet.

After liquid water or water vapor is absorbed into a porous material, it behaves mostly as a liquid, and it can evaporate just as a puddle of water can. However, because many of the water molecules are clinging tightly to the porous material and less tightly to other water molecules, the latent heat of vaporization required to change absorbed water from a liquid to a gas is a little higher in this case than for liquid water that has not been absorbed into a material. Described another way, water absorbed into a porous material has a slightly lower energy state than liquid water that is not clinging to a porous material and will therefore require slightly more heat to evaporate.

Water absorbed into a porous material will spread within

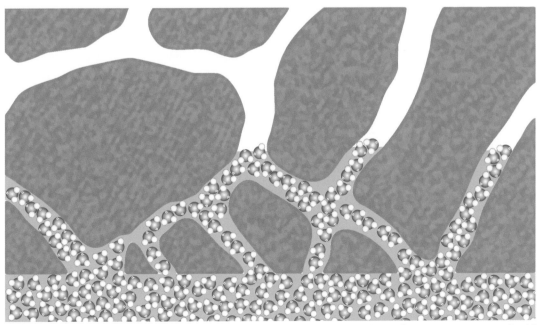

This drawing shows liquid water absorbed into the pores of a porous material. Capillary suction can move liquid water many kilometers up against gravity if the holes in a material are the right sizes and connect with each other.

the material in satisfaction of the second law. The second law not only dictates that the water will spread out to find surfaces to satisfy its attractive forces but also dictates that the water will spread from areas of high concentration to areas of low concentration (from wet areas to dry areas), just as black and white marbles will mix evenly throughout a bucket that is shaken or a drop of milk added to a cup of tea will spread itself out within the tea until it is evenly distributed throughout the cup.

Absorbed water's tendency to spread out by capillary suction can cause building materials to become either more wet or less wet. For example, if a little water leaks through a small hole in a roof shingle, and is absorbed by the wood underneath the shingle, capillary suction will spread the water to the drier wood surrounding the leak. This process simultaneously reduces the water content of the wood directly under the leak while increasing the water content of the surrounding wood. This spreading out of the water tends to keep all the wood, including the wood adjacent to the leak, too dry for mold to grow, which of course helps preserve the wood. In contrast, capillary suction moving water up from soil into a concrete foundation or basement of a building is one of the mechanisms that wets building materials and can

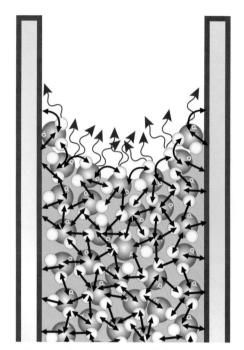

Capillary suction moves water higher in a narrow tube than in a wide tube because a narrow tube has proportionally more edge and less middle than a wide tube.

cause damage. Stopping the capillary suction would prevent the wetting. Therefore, it is not helpful to think of capillary suction as being either "good" or "bad" for a building—it is simply another process that needs to be understood in order to make smart decisions to protect buildings.

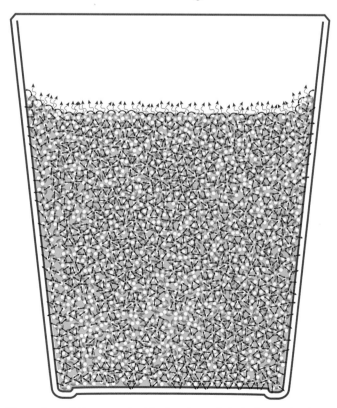

The surface of the water in this glass has relatively few molecules at the edges, where they cling to the sides of the glass, compared to the middle area, where there is no glass for them to cling to.

3. WATER VAPOR MOVED BY DIFFUSION (Without Airflow)

Water vapor, also known as water in its gas state (or, more commonly, "humidity" when there is a lot of it in the air around us—the amount in outdoor air depends on the weather), makes up about one to five percent of the air we breathe and a lower percentage at altitudes higher than where people live. Water vapor acts as just another one of the gases making up the mixture we call air. As with other gases, water vapor will move from an area of high concentration to an area of low concentration in a process called diffusion.

Each of the gases making up the air in a tire exerts its own pressure on the tire independent of the existence of the other gases in the tire. When a tire pressure gauge measures the difference in air pressure between the inside and the outside of a bicycle tire, it shows the sum of the individual pressures of all the gases in the tire, including the water vapor. Any difference in the air pressure between one part of the tire and another is quickly eliminated by air moving from the area of high pressure to the area of low pressure. This is required by the second law of thermodynamics, which would have to be violated for the air pressure to remain different in different parts of the tire. If a piece of glass cuts the tire, the large difference in air pressure between the inside and outside of the tire (higher inside the tire) causes the air to quickly rush out of the tire, again in satisfaction of the second law of thermodynamics.

The second law of thermodynamics also explains why each of the different gases in the tire mixes itself evenly throughout the tire. A higher concentration of nitrogen or oxygen or water vapor inside one part of the tire would soon be eliminated by that gas moving from the area of high pressure or high concentration (of that gas) to the area of low pressure or low concentration (of that gas).

Each of the gases in the tire contributes to the total air pressure within the tire. Water vapor's contribution to the total air pressure is proportional to the amount of water vapor mixed in with the air in the tire. This proportion is called "specific humidity." ("Relative humidity" will be explained later in this chapter.)

Water Vapor from the Shower

A shower adds a lot of water vapor to the air in a bathroom. Just as it is impossible for the water vapor pressure to be significantly different from one part of a tire to the other, it is impossible for water vapor pressure to stay different from one part of the house to the other (unless, like a bicycle tire, the bathroom has no openings large enough for water vapor molecules to pass through, which is highly unlikely except perhaps in a submarine). In obedience of the second law, the water vapor will eventually spread itself out until the vapor pressure is equal throughout the house. When molecules move from an area of high concentration to an area of low concentration, the process is called diffusion.

How Will Water Vapor Leave the Bathroom (without Air Movement)?

If the bathroom door is open, water vapor will diffuse through the air in the open doorway. But, even if the door is closed—depending on what the bathroom door is made of and how many times the door has been painted with what type of paint—some water vapor might move through small holes in the door, from an area of

Each of the gases mixed in the air in a tire distributes itself evenly throughout the tire, and exerts its own pressure on the tire, as if the other gases were not there. A tire pressure gauge measures the sum of the individual pressures of each of the gases making up the air in the tire, including the water vapor.

high concentration (the bathroom) to an area of low concentration (the next room, or the hallway).

Any building material with holes large enough to allow individual water vapor molecules to pass through it is called "water vapor permeable," and any material that does not have holes large enough to allow water vapor to pass through it is called "water vapor impermeable," or a "vapor barrier."

Vapor-permeable materials offer varying amounts of resistance to the diffusion of water vapor. An unpainted wood door offers less resistance than a painted door. More exact terminology would describe permeable materials as being partly water vapor permeable, which is a property that can be measured. Other common materials—glass, sheet metal, vinyl wallpaper, gloss paint, and many types of plastic—allow essentially no water vapor to pass through them and are therefore considered total barriers to water vapor diffusion.

Water vapor diffusion is an important mechanism to understand about buildings. If no new energy is added to a building, all the water vapor in a building will distribute itself through diffusion until the water vapor concentration is equal throughout the building (assuming it is not stopped by a water vapor barrier). The same thing would happen if the sun were to stop shining: all the liquid water on our planet would flow downhill to the same level, and all the water vapor in the atmosphere

As explained by the second law of thermodynamics, water molecules will diffuse from an area of high concentration, such as a bathroom with the shower running, to areas of low concentration, such as outdoors, the attic, and other rooms in the house. Materials with holes large enough for water vapor molecules to diffuse through, such as untiled walls, the ceiling, and the door (depending on how much of what type of paint is on these surfaces), are described as "water vapor permeable." Materials that do not have holes large enough for water vapor molecules to diffuse through, such as the glass in the windows and the glazed tiles on the walls and floor, are described as "water vapor impermeable" and are called "water vapor barriers."

would spread throughout the atmosphere to the same vapor pressure.[3] This is in obedience of the second law of thermodynamics, which would have to be violated for water to stay concentrated in one part of the planet.

The amount of water vapor moved through buildings by diffusion is usually small. It can be important, especially in assemblies that have large temperature or humidity differences across them. However, in most cases, adding a water vapor barrier to a wall to stop wetting by diffusion will do more harm than good. This is because diffusion is

typically more important as a drying mechanism than as a wetting mechanism in buildings.

The wetting of building materials is more effectively reduced by stopping water vapor that is moved with moving air.

4. WATER VAPOR MOVED WITH MOVING AIR

Whenever air moves, the water vapor mixed into the air moves with it. Picture putting a drop of milk into a lake. The milk will obey the second law and spread out evenly until it is completely mixed with the lake, just as

3   For all the water on the earth to level itself out, the earth would also have to stop revolving and the moon's gravitational pull would also have to go away, but if the sun were to stop shining these would be minor problems by comparison.

If the bathroom door is open, much more water vapor will diffuse through the air in the doorway than through the door or any other permeable materials (assuming no air movement).

it does in a cup of tea. Next, picture putting a drop of milk into a slowly flowing river. It will spread out at the same rate as in the lake, but because all the water in the river is slowly moving downstream, some of the milk will be spreading upstream slowly, while some will be spreading downstream more quickly. Last, picture putting a drop of milk into a quickly flowing river. Again, the milk will spread out evenly, but because all the water is flowing quickly downstream, all the milk will be moving downstream, including the milk that is spreading through the water in the upstream direction. The movement of water in the quickly flowing river overwhelms the spreading out of the milk upstream against the current. This is analogous to air currents overwhelming diffusion of water vapor by water vapor pressure differential.

Just as currents in this hypothetical river move milk, air

currents move water vapor. Wind moves water vapor across oceans and continents, opening a window moves water vapor in or out of a house, and breathing moves water vapor in and out of a person's lungs.

This brings up an important question. Which mechanism moves more water vapor: diffusion from areas of high concentration to areas of low concentration or air currents? The answer depends on how strong the vapor pressure difference is and how strong the air current is. But in terms of water vapor movement through buildings, even a gentle air current will overwhelm almost any vapor pressure difference.

One common example is taking a shower in a bathroom that has an exhaust fan. If the fan is not running, water vapor at a high concentration in the bathroom will diffuse

With the window open and the wind moving air in through the bathroom door and out the bathroom window, moving air and diffusion are both moving water vapor out of the bathroom, but moving air moves much, much more water vapor out of the bathroom than diffusion does.

out through the water-vapor-permeable wooden door, and much more water vapor will bypass the door and diffuse through the gaps around and under the bathroom door. This water vapor will move to areas of lower vapor pressure and keep moving until the vapor pressure is even on both sides of the bathroom door. If the fan is running, it will push air containing a lot of water vapor (humid air) through the exhaust duct to outdoors, while pulling air that probably (except on a hot, humid day) contains less water vapor into the house through leaks, then under the bathroom door. With a normal-sized bathroom fan, and a normal-sized crack around a bathroom door, essentially all the water vapor that leaves the bathroom will move with the air current out the fan's exhaust duct.[4] Almost

no water vapor will escape through the open door by diffusion because the air being drawn by the fan into the bathroom will be moving faster than diffusion can spread the water vapor upstream against the flow of air.

Diffusion evens out water vapor concentrations very slowly because it depends on molecular vibration, which takes place over extremely small distances.

The amount of water vapor moved by moving air is so much greater than the amount moved by vapor pressure diffusion that the "milk in tea" analogy can be misleading. Most of the spreading out of the milk in a real cup is actually caused by convection, driven partly by the milk starting out colder and therefore heavier than the tea and partly by the fat in the milk being lighter than tea. But even if the two fluids, tea and milk, were of equal density,

4   Hopefully, the fan's exhaust duct does not end in the attic or anywhere else inside the building as is sometimes the case. It should always be routed outdoors, so that it moves the air containing a high concentration of water vapor out of the building.

An exhaust fan quickly replaces the humid air in the bathroom with dry air from the house, drying the bathroom much faster than diffusion can.

currents caused by pouring the milk into the tea would be responsible for most of the mixing. Therefore, the milk analogy is good for understanding how diffusion from areas of high concentration to low concentration works. It is also useful for understanding how diffusion is a less important mechanism than it can appear at first glance. In buildings, vapor diffusion moves much less water vapor than air currents. The erroneous assumption that diffusion is the most important mechanism that moves water vapor often leads to the installation of unnecessary and potentially harmful vapor barriers.

Air currents also explain why a dehumidifier (a mechanical device that removes water vapor from air) in one corner of a basement can dry air throughout the basement. The dehumidifier adds heat to the air (from electricity and latent heat), which causes convection, and the dehumidifier's fan moves air. These air currents move

humid air to the dehumidifier and dry air away from the dehumidifier faster than diffusion can.

As air carries water vapor from place to place, changes in air temperature and pressure change the amount of water vapor that can be mixed with air.

Air pressure differences within buildings are not large enough to have a significant influence on how much water vapor air can contain. Therefore, in building science, it is reasonable to ignore air pressure and focus on temperature to determine how much water vapor air can contain.

The science of how much water vapor air can hold at various temperatures is called psychrometrics. (The word is pronounced "sy-cro-met-rics.")

PSYCHROMETRICS: HOW MUCH WATER VAPOR CAN THE AIR HOLD?

The word psychrometric comes from the Greek words "psuchron" (cold) and "metron" (means of measurement). The science of psychrometrics can be described with two simple concepts:

1: Cold air can't hold much water vapor.

2: Hot air can hold a lot of water vapor.

The difference is enormous: air deep inside a person's lungs—that is, at body temperature—can hold almost ten times as much water vapor as air at the freezing temperature of water. The amount of water vapor that air can hold at a specific temperature can be measured with great precision, or looked up on a chart. But in the early 1900s, even the best scientists had only a rough idea.

Much of the early theoretical work in the field of psychrometrics was done by an engineer named Willis Carrier. Carrier was born in 1876 and grew up on a farm, where his mother Elizabeth taught him how to work with his hands. He went to engineering school, where he learned the theoretical side of things, giving him that ever-powerful combination of blue collar (practical) and white collar (theoretical) knowledge. After he graduated in 1901, he got a job at a company called the Buffalo Forge Company, which manufactured blowers and heaters. In 1902, when he was about 25 years old, the company sent him to Brooklyn, New York, to solve a problem at the Sackett & Wilhelms Lithographing & Printing Company.

Sackett & Wilhelms was doing color printing, which required sending the paper through the presses multiple times, once for each color. Between colors, the paper absorbed moisture from the air, which caused the paper to swell. The change in paper size changed the location of each layer of ink enough to cause blurring or gaps between colors.

At the time, air conditioning equipment as we know it today did not exist. There had been a few pioneering attempts to cool air with blocks of ice in air ducts or with primitive refrigeration equipment, but all available options were crude and hard to control. When Carrier was assigned to solve the humidity problem in the printing plant, so little was known about dehumidifying air that he began studying weather charts in an attempt to grasp the theoretical aspects of dehumidification.

One night, as he was waiting on an outdoor railroad platform near Philadelphia, Pennsylvania, he had some time to think. The air that night was cold, just above freezing, and was full of fog (small drops of liquid water suspended in the air). Carrier knew that even though the air around him was so humid it was foggy, there couldn't be much water vapor mixed in the air because the air was so cold. At any temperature, air can be relatively humid or relatively dry, relative to how much water vapor the air can hold at that temperature. This property of air is called "relative humidity." Another measure of humidity, "specific humidity" (see Page 135), is the ratio of water vapor in the air to the mixture of air and water vapor by weight.[5] The relative humidity of the air that night was high—about 100 percent—but the specific humidity, the actual amount of water vapor in the air, was low. A good way to understand this is to think of different temperatures of air as buckets of different sizes.

Because cold air can't hold a lot of water vapor, it can be thought of as a small bucket, like the blue bucket at right.

Because hot air can hold a lot of water vapor, hot air can be thought of as a large bucket, like the red bucket at right.

Air at an intermediate temperature, such as room temperature, can hold more water vapor than cold air but not as much as hot air, so it could be thought of as a medium-sized bucket, which can hold a medium amount of water vapor, like the purple bucket at right. Buckets other than these three sizes and colors would not accurately represent the principle that warm air can hold a lot more water vapor than cold air can hold.

5   A similar measure of humidity is "absolute humidity," which is not used in this book because it is the ratio of the mass (weight) of water per volume of air, and air volume changes with temperature and pressure, which can lead to confusion.

The three buckets below represent air at different temperatures, each with the same amount of water vapor in them. Described another way, they each have the same specific humidity, but they each have a different relative humidity. The hot air on the left is relatively dry because it does not contain much water vapor compared to (relative to) how much water vapor it could hold at that temperature. In other words, its relative humidity is low. The bucket in the middle has the same amount of water vapor in it as the red bucket, but because it is at an intermediate temperature, it is a smaller bucket and therefore is more humid relative to how much water vapor it could hold at that temperature. Described another way, the bucket in the middle has a higher relative humidity than the bucket on the left, even though they have the same amount of water vapor in them. The cold bucket on the right contains the same amount of water vapor as the other two, but because it is a smaller bucket, its relative humidity is even higher.

The three buckets below also contain the same amount of water vapor as each other but have more water vapor in them than the buckets above. Each has a higher specific humidity than the same temperature (size) bucket above, and each also has a higher relative humidity than the same temperature bucket above. The cold bucket below is 100 percent full. Described another way, the cold bucket contains air that is at 100 percent relative humidity, also known as saturated air. If the hot air in the bucket at the left were cooled, the bucket in the middle would be the result, and if it were cooled more, the bucket at right would be the result. If, instead of being cooled, the air were heated, the air in the middle, and then the left, would be the result.

The red and purple buckets below contain the same amount of water vapor as each other. Each has a higher specific humidity than the same temperature bucket at the bottom of the column at left, and each also has a higher relative humidity than the same temperature bucket at the bottom of the column at left. If the hot air at left were cooled to the temperature at which the air becomes saturated (the temperature depends on the air's specific humidity), the saturated air in the middle would be the result. This temperature is called the dewpoint temperature, which is sometimes included in weather reports. If the air were cooled more (below its dewpoint temperature), the result would be the bucket on the right: the bucket would overflow. Because air can't be at over 100 percent relative humidity, some of the water vapor would turn into liquid water—for example, condensation on a bathroom mirror when the mirror cools the air or, in the case of the air Carrier saw on the Philadelphia railroad platform that night, drops of water in the air: fog.

Fog is visible because it is liquid water. Water vapor is invisible. On a day when the outdoor air is foggy, the drops are suspended in air that is about 100 percent humid, which prevents the liquid water drops from evaporating. Thus they stay suspended in the air until something changes, such as the sun warming the air to a point where it can absorb the droplets of water, which would then turn into invisible water vapor.

If very wet air, such as the "air" coming out of a chimney or a car exhaust pipe, mixes with air cold enough to cause some of the water vapor to condense into drops, and humid enough to delay evaporation, the drops take a second or two to evaporate. This is why exhaust stays visible for a few seconds on a cold and humid day.[6]

The same thing can happen when a person breathes on a cold and humid day: his breath forms fog, at least for a few seconds, until it mixes with enough of the surrounding air, which is not as humid.

6 Combustion creates new water that did not exist before, as described in Chapter 11: Fire - Basic Science.

The drawing below right shows what happens when someone breathes air that is cold and relatively humid. The air the person inhales is cold, as shown by a small blue bucket, and the bucket is relatively full, indicating high relative humidity. As the air enters the person's mouth and throat, it warms up. Warming the air reduces its relative humidity because warmer air, like a larger bucket, is able to hold more water vapor. The air absorbs water vapor from the mouth and throat and, after that, from the lungs. The large, warm, and wet surface of the lungs, as described on Page 7, further warms the air and adds more water vapor. As soon as the air is exhaled, it gets cooled by outdoor air, which causes the bucket to overflow: fog forms, and is visible for a second or two, until the saturated air mixes with enough of the drier surrounding air for the water droplets to disappear by evaporating. Air a person exhales holds about ten times as much water vapor as air that is at water's freezing temperature can hold. Therefore, the large bucket should be about ten times as large as the small bucket if the outdoor air in the drawing is at water's freezing temperature. (For space reasons the bucket isn't shown that large.)

Willis Carrier was probably watching this happen with his breath on the railroad platform that night. As he thought about how to control the humidity in the printing plant, he realized that he could reduce the specific humidity of air to any level he chose by cooling the air to whatever temperature would condense enough water out of the air—a breakthrough at the time. From this idea, he derived formulas for the relationships between humidity and temperature, which replaced the sloppy rules of thumb then used by engineers. His gift to the world was the Psychrometric Chart, which makes it easy to skip the formulas and look up anything about the relationship between air temperature and humidity.

The equipment he designed for Sackett & Wilhelms was a success. It dehumidified, and at the same time cooled, the production area, allowing accurate placement of the different colors of ink, eliminating problems with blurring or gaps between colors. This early equipment was still far too large, noisy, and expensive to go into the offices to keep people comfortable. Although comfort for people eventually became the air conditioner's most common application, most early systems were used to stabilize humidity for quality control purposes in industries such as textiles, steelmaking, and film manufacturing.

When the start of World War One slowed business at Buffalo Forge, Carrier and six other engineers pooled their savings and started their own company: Carrier Engineering Corporation. They started out by designing cooling systems assembled from parts they selected from catalogues and then eventually started manufacturing their own equipment. In 1928, they installed experimental cooling equipment in the offices of their second manufacturing plant, in Newark, New Jersey. In 1937, they installed greatly improved (but still experimental) equipment when they moved their headquarters to Syracuse, New York. A few other office buildings were built with primitive cooling systems in the 1930s, but

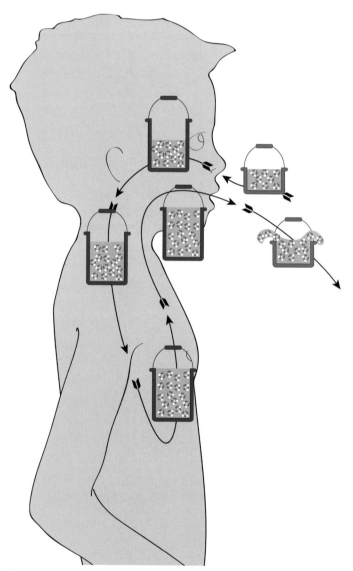

The air a person exhales is usually saturated with water vapor, which is another way of saying it is at 100 percent relative humidity. This is why exhaling onto a mirror condenses water out of a person's breath, even when the mirror is not very cold: the mirror is a good conductor of heat, and the person's breath is saturated, so cooling the breath even a little (to the temperature of the mirror, which at room temperature is colder than a person's lungs) will cause water to condense out of it.

the Depression and World War Two stopped most new building construction. The company was not idle during the war years, however. It produced cooling equipment for the munitions industry and the military.

After World War Two, the newly formed United Nations decided to build its headquarters in New York City. The architects chose to make it an almost all-glass building. Architects had long dreamed of all-glass buildings, but, until the 1940s, technology was not available to provide the large amounts of cooling that all-glass buildings require. (This was especially true of buildings built before the development of multi-pane glass with energy-saving coatings and tints.)

Willis Carrier himself designed the cooling system for the UN building in the late 1940s, just before he died in 1950. The company he formed went on to become the largest manufacturer of air conditioning equipment in the world, and soon the industry was producing equipment that would be recognizable today. Willis Carrier was one of the few people who succeeded at both science and founding and operating a successful business based on that science.

Today, removing water vapor from air with an air conditioning system or a dehumidifier is usually done the same way that Willis Carrier did it: by cooling the air to a temperature colder than its dewpoint temperature. (The dewpoint temperature is the temperature to which air needs to be cooled to start condensing water out of the

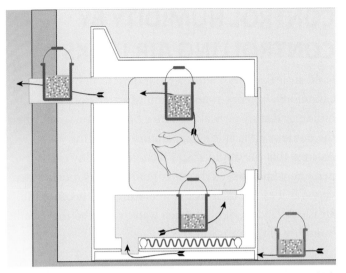

A clothing dryer removes water from clothing and adds it to air, which can absorb the water vapor because the dryer first heats the air, lowering its relative humidity. Heating air does not change its specific humidity.

air, which is the same temperature at which the relative humidity will be 100 percent.) Cooling the air below its dewpoint temperature will cause water to condense out of the air (usually onto the cold surface that is absorbing heat from the air), reducing its humidity. For example, when an air conditioner is cooling air, the cold part of the air conditioner cools the air below its dewpoint temperature, and water condenses on the cold part of the air conditioner, from where it runs down a drain pipe.

Hot air can hold a lot more water vapor than cold air, which can easily be proven by putting wet clothes into a clothes dryer on a very humid day and seeing that the dryer can remove water from clothing and put it in the air. The dryer first heats the air, so the air can hold more water vapor, and then tumbles the clothing through the air. The clothing dries because it is surrounded by air at low relative humidity—not low specific humidity—and because the hot air supplies the latent heat of evaporation.

Note that heating air does not dry air in the sense of removing water vapor. Heating air makes it dry relative to how much water vapor it can hold at the new temperature. This is why this property is called relative humidity. Cooling air increases its relative humidity, and heating air reduces its relative humidity. This is why the air inside so many heated buildings is so dry during the winter.

The original air ducts in the UN building in New York City are tapered. This reduces turbulence and associated energy "losses" caused by sudden transitions between different duct sizes and shapes. This level of quality is rare in modern ducts.

CONTROL HUMIDITY BY CONTROLLING AIR LEAKS

Cold air leaking into and then out of a warm building can remove an enormous amount of water from the building. Picture air leaking into a building on a day when the outdoor air is at the temperature of freezing water. Assume that the outdoor air's relative humidity is 50 percent, which means the air contains half as much water vapor as it can hold at that temperature. But because the air is cold, it cannot hold much water vapor, so the specific humidity of the air is low.

As the air leaks into the house, the heating system in the house heats the air. Because warm air can hold more water vapor than cold air can hold, the now-warm air can suddenly hold more water vapor. Described another way, heating the air as it comes indoors reduces its relative humidity, while its specific humidity stays the same.

If air at water's freezing temperature is at 50 percent relative humidity and gets heated to room temperature,

its relative humidity will be reduced to about 10 percent, which is drier than normally found in nature, except on hot afternoons in deserts. Described another way, heating the air allows it to hold five times as much water vapor as it held when it was outdoors. People living in houses that leak a lot of air are familiar with the symptoms of low wintertime relative humidity: dry lungs, throat, lips, skin, and eyes. The low-relative-humidity air also absorbs water from building components, such as wood floors, causing them to shrink, creating noticeable gaps between boards.

If air is entering a building, the same amount of air must be leaving the building through another opening, such as a chimney, a bathroom vent, or another leak. When the air goes back outdoors it brings with it whatever moisture it absorbed from people, wood floors, etc. The water vapor is mostly moved not by diffusion but with moving air.

The more air that leaks through a building, and the more heat the heating system adds to the air, the higher the rate of moisture removal from the building. Three factors determine how much water vapor gets removed from a

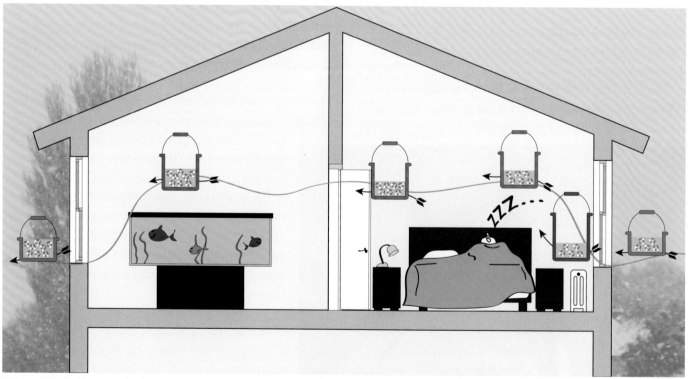

Winter air is leaking into the house through the window at right. The outdoor air that leaks in is cold (small blue bucket outdoors at right) and contains nearly as much water vapor as it can hold at that temperature (about 80 percent relative humidity), which is represented by the bucket being mostly full. As soon as the air comes into the house, it gets heated (large red bucket) by the radiator under the window. Because it is hot, it can hold much more water vapor, and therefore its relative humidity is low. This is shown by the large red bucket being mostly empty. (Note that its specific humidity has not changed—the amount of water in the bucket is the same as before the radiator heated it.) The incoming air mixes with the rest of the air in the room, shown as room-temperature air (medium-sized purple bucket), with a relative humidity that is still much lower than it was when it was outdoors. The room-temperature air absorbs water from the person breathing and from the fish tank, as well as water that has been absorbed by the materials the building is made of. This raises the relative and specific humidity of the air. The air then leaks back outdoors.

building by winter air moving through the building:

1. the amount of heat the heating system adds to the air,
2. the amount of water vapor in outdoor air, and
3. the quantity of air moving through the building.

The type of heating system has nothing to do with how much the relative humidity of the indoor air is reduced by heating it, although heating systems that move air around the building with fans can increase the amount of air moving through leaks, as shown on Pages 483-487.

The amount of heat the heating system adds to the air is mostly determined by the weather. The colder the outdoor temperature, the more heat the heating system adds to bring indoor air up to room temperature. Of course, people's individual preferences determine what "room temperature" actually is, but it doesn't vary as much as outdoor temperature. So, the quantity of heat a heating system adds to winter air entering a building is mostly determined by outdoor temperature—more heat as the outdoor temperature gets colder. The second factor, outdoor humidity, is also impossible to control, of course, other than by moving to a new climate.

The third factor, the quantity of air moving through a building, can be controlled. Reducing air leakage was discussed in Chapter 4: Air - Applied Science. But, even if someone managed to design and build a building with zero air leaks, any building with people in it should be ventilated. Ventilation systems that are well designed and properly built deliver and remove enough air, but not too much air, and move it to and from strategic locations in the building. Some ventilation systems also control the humidity of the ventilation air. Ventilation systems will be discussed in detail in Chapter 17: Indoor Air Quality.

During the summer, if the outdoor air is humid and enters a building and gets cooled by an air conditioner, its relative humidity increases. Some of the water vapor in the air might be removed by the air conditioning system, depending on how well the system dehumidifies. The amount of water added to the building during the summer is determined by the same three factors that control winter drying: outdoor temperature, outdoor humidity, and the amount of air moving through the building. It is impossible to control outdoor temperature or humidity, but summertime wetting of a building can be reduced by limiting the flow of outdoor air through a building.

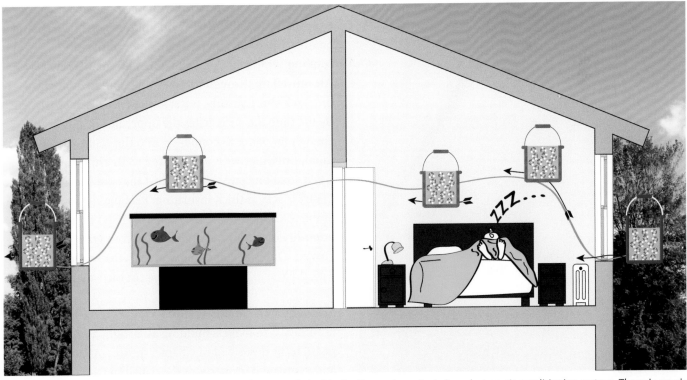

Hot, humid summer air is leaking through a house that is cooled with shading and good windows but no air conditioning system. There is no air conditioner or dehumidifier removing water vapor from the air inside the house. The outdoor air (at right) is hot (shown as a red bucket) and has a relative humidity of about 80 percent (shown as an 80 percent full bucket). When the outdoor air leaks into the house, it mixes with the rest of the air in the room (shown as a purple bucket). But its lower temperature (smaller bucket) means it cannot hold as much water vapor as the hot outdoor air (larger bucket), therefore its relative humidity is about 100 percent, represented by the bucket being full. The air moves through the house, not absorbing water from the person or the fish tank, leaving the person's skin feeling wet. Then the air leaks back outdoors.

Specific humidity indoors has nothing to do with how well a building's walls are insulated, and it has little to do with the presence or absence of a water vapor barrier in the walls. Indoor humidity during the summer is the result of a never-ending race between water vapor removed by air conditioning or dehumidifying equipment and water vapor added by air moving through the building, as well as by internal sources such as showering, cooking, people breathing and sweating, and evaporation from plants and fish tanks. Similarly, indoor humidity during the winter is the result of a race between water vapor removed by air moving through the building and water vapor added by these same internal sources. A heated building that leaks a lot of air will be very dry during the winter because the leaks will remove water vapor faster than internal sources can replace it. A heated building that does not leak much air will retain more humidity from internal sources.

Mirror Quiz: Why is part of this hotel bathroom mirror not fogging when the rest of the mirror is? Turn to Page 560 for the answer.

Dry indoor air can also be prevented by using a mechanical device called a humidifier to add humidity to the air, but adding too much can easily cause mold growth. (Also, adding humidity requires a lot of energy: the latent heat of evaporation of the liquid water.)

Some buildings—even buildings with lots of air leaks— get too damp during the winter because of large internal moisture sources combined with insufficient ventilation. A typical case is a tall apartment building occupied by large families who add a lot of water vapor to the indoor air by cooking, showering, and exhaling in a small living area. Air moved up through one apartment after another by the stack effect absorbs water vapor from each apartment. By the time the air reaches the upper floors, it is humid enough for water to condense onto the walls, which causes mold. Buildings with uninsulated walls are vulnerable when someone puts a bed against the wall because the mattress acts as thick insulation, keeping the indoor side of the wall cold during the winter, which raises the relative humidity of the air near the wall, encouraging mold growth. Described another way, with the mattress in the way, the warm indoor air can't warm the wall in that area.

Mold grows on this bathroom ceiling because a lot of water vapor has been added to the air from regular showers and not enough water vapor has been removed by ventilation. Most building codes recognize a window as a form of ventilation, but apparently the residents do not make a habit of opening the window when they shower. This is understandable: the house is in a cold climate.

The safest and healthiest approach to controlling indoor humidity is to make a building as airtight as practically possible, as described in Chapter 4: Air - Applied Science, and ventilate it properly, as described in Chapter 17: Indoor Air Quality. Most existing and new buildings are not very airtight and would do a much better job of keeping people comfortable and healthy if they were retrofitted with a good air barrier.

The vast majority of buildings, both old and new, leak enough air to make the indoor air dry during the winter. One of the reasons flu season occurs during the winter is that, in most buildings, indoor air is dry during the winter.

Winter Flu Season Is Caused by Dry Air

The World Health Organization estimates that each annual flu season results in three to five million cases of severe illness and about 250,000 to 500,000 deaths worldwide. The 1918 flu was especially virulent and killed at least 25 million people around the world. It has long been known that the flu peaks in cold weather, sometimes reaching infection levels ten times higher than in warm weather, and that these higher infection levels are related to lower indoor humidity.[7] The mechanism was recently investigated thoroughly.

In 2007, researchers at the Mt. Sinai School of Medicine in New York City measured transmission of a human strain of flu virus between infected guinea pigs and uninfected guinea pigs at different air temperatures and humidity levels. At each temperature and humidity level, the researchers measured how many viral particles were sneezed out by sick pigs, how many pigs got infected, and the reaction of the pigs' immune systems, as indicated by innate immune mediators in their mouths and noses.

In their summary, the researchers said, "Our data implicate low relative humidities produced by indoor heating and cold temperatures as features of winter that favor influenza virus spread."[8] They found that indoor temperature did not determine how many viral particles a sick guinea pig sneezed out but that guinea pigs living at warm temperatures sneezed out viral particles for about eight days, while guinea pigs living at cold temperatures sneezed out viral particles for about ten days. They also discovered that temperature did not change the strength of a guinea pig's immune response. The biggest discovery was that most of the guinea pigs living in dry air, regardless of air temperature, caught the flu from nearby infected guinea pigs, while none of the pigs living in humid air (again regardless of air temperature) got sick.

Dry air has absorbed water from this wood door, exposing a brown strip of **unpainted wood**. Wood-panel doors are actually designed to accommodate changing humidity because when wood shrinks (as it dries out) it does not shrink evenly in all directions. The grain of the long pieces of wood (which determine the size of the door) is oriented in the direction that minimizes change in length, allowing the width of those pieces to change, which has a minimal affect on the overall dimensions of the door. As the large panels in the middle of the door expand when they absorb water from humid summer air and shrink in dry winter air, they slide harmlessly in and out of grooves in the wood around them, occasionally exposing unpainted wood.

Viral particles are small pieces of genetic material, which when sneezed out are surrounded by a few molecules of water. The research found that the water evaporates quickly in dry air, making the viral particles lighter, helping them stay airborne. In humid air, the particles will be pulled by gravity to the floor, where they will not infect anyone. The research also found that dry air has an effect on respiratory systems that makes a host more vulnerable to catching the flu. Therefore, other than the flu vaccine, the best way to prevent catching the flu during the winter is to stay out of heated buildings that leak a lot of air because the indoor air in leaky buildings gets too dry. Running a humidifier can also help.

The pig mechanism was demonstrated when thermostats were installed in every room in a New York City high school one summer. The next winter, the school principal, who got an attendance report on his desk twice each day, saw that the absence rate had dropped to about half of what it had been the previous winter. He concluded, probably[9] correctly, that many of the absences in prior years were caused by poor air quality in the school. Before the thermostats were installed, most classrooms were

7   G.H. Green, "Positive and Negative Effects of Building Humidification," <u>ASHRAE Transactions</u> Vol. 88, no. 1 (1982): Pages 1049-1061.

8   A.C. Lowen, S. Mubareka, J. Steel, and P. Palese, "Influenza virus transmission is dependent on relative humidity and temperature," <u>PLoS Pathogens</u> Vol. 3, no. 10 (2007): Page 1471.

9   Because the number of absences is highly variable from year to year, comparing rates from only two years is not conclusive.

overheated, so teachers would simply open the windows. The open windows allowed the free flow of cold outdoor air, which made the indoor air very dry. The resulting low-relative-humidity air helped the water molecules evaporate from around flu virus particles, allowing them to stay airborne longer, and presumably also made the students' respiratory systems more vulnerable to catching the flu. After thermostats were installed, the teachers were able to keep the windows closed because the thermostats controlled the heaters, keeping the classrooms at a comfortable temperature. The school's ventilation system moved enough fresh air through each classroom but not too much. This reduced the drying effect of cold outdoor air. Water evaporating from the students' lungs and skin was able to maintain a reasonable humidity level in the classrooms, which reduced the sickness rate.

Summertime Psychrometric Adventures

During the summer, the challenge is reversed. The difficulty is keeping indoor air from becoming too humid. This is because the indoor-outdoor temperature relationship is reversed during the summer: indoor air is usually colder than outdoor air and therefore cannot hold as much water vapor as outdoor air.

When hot, humid summer air comes into a building via leaks and gets cooled down, its relative humidity goes up, sometimes up to 100 percent. Maybe the air gets cooled to its dewpoint temperature, and cooled further, causing moisture to condense out of the air. The warm, humid outdoor air can treat the cool indoor surfaces of a building

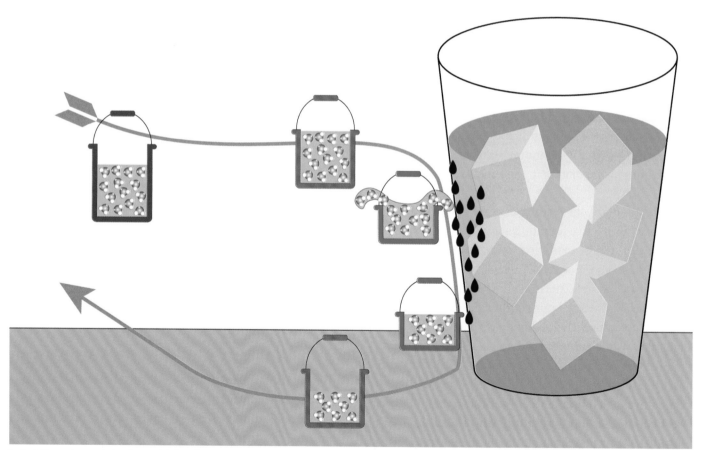

In building science, it is often said that "water moves toward cold." This drawing of a glass of ice water shows how that can happen. Hot, humid summer air surrounds the glass. The air near the glass is cooled by conduction, which makes the air heavier, creating a convective current of air, which pulls air downward along the sides of the glass as it cools and then pushes the air out away from the bottom of the glass. As the air starts to cool near the top of the glass, its specific humidity remains unchanged, while its temperature drops. As the glass continues to absorb heat from the downward-moving air, the air gets cold, signified by a blue bucket, which is too small to hold all the water vapor, so some of the water vapor condenses out of the air, forming liquid on the glass. As the air moves away from the glass at the bottom, it warms up by mixing with other air, resulting in a mixture with lower specific humidity than the rest of the air in the room. The difference in the specific humidity of water vapor in the air—lower in the air next to the glass and higher in the rest of the room—creates a "water vapor pressure gradient." This difference in water vapor concentration moves water vapor by diffusion from an area of high concentration (the rest of the room) to an area of low concentration (near the glass). Diffusion won't even out the water vapor concentration as quickly as convection, but it is correct to understand that condensing water out of the air does create a water vapor concentration difference (gradient) that will move water vapor toward the area of lower concentration.

as a giant bathroom mirror: one big surface to condense water onto.

This is why car windows fog up when it is raining. Air leaking into the car through cracks or via the ventilation system is very humid, and people add even more water vapor to the air by breathing. Rain keeps the window glass cool, so when humid air inside the car touches the glass, it gets cooled below its dewpoint temperature, and moisture condenses out of the air onto the glass.

The same thing happens when a bathroom mirror fogs up during showering. The glass is a better conductor of heat than the walls and ceiling, therefore it cools the warm, humid air more quickly than the other surfaces. The glass is also dense enough for its thermal mass to be

more concentrated than the thermal mass of the tile or the walls and ceilings, which helps keep it cool longer. The bathroom air is heated and humidified by the hot shower, and when it touches the mirror it gets cooled below its dewpoint temperature, and moisture condenses out of the air onto the mirror. The tiles condense less water than the mirror but more water than the walls because they are a better conductor of heat than the walls but not as conductive as the mirror. A quick shower might not condense any water onto the tiles, maybe only on the mirror, but a longer shower will start to condense water onto the tiles. Depending on the humidity in the house and how many people take showers around the same time, water might or might not condense on the bathroom walls and on the ceiling, too.

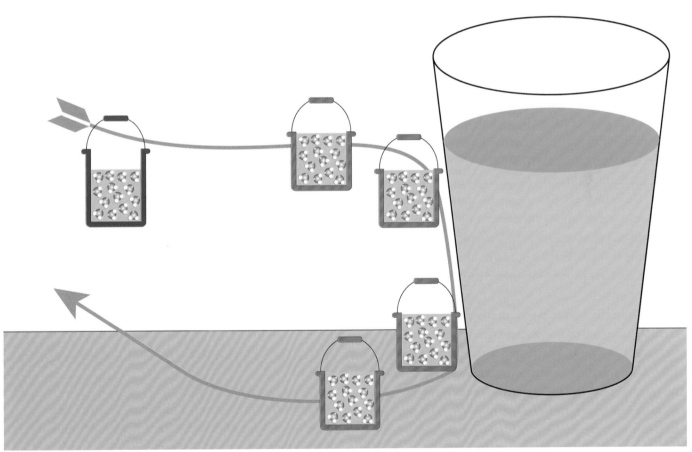

The situation is critically different if the water is cool but not cold enough to cool the air below its dewpoint temperature. Without ice in the glass, the hot, humid summer air surrounding this glass of water is cooled but not cooled below its dewpoint temperature. The air near the glass is cooled by conduction, which makes the air heavier. This creates a convective current of air that pulls warm humid air downward along the sides of the glass as it cools and then pushes the air out away from the bottom of the glass. As the air cools near the glass, its specific humidity remains unchanged, while its relative humidity increases. As the air moves away from the glass at the bottom, it warms up by mixing with other air, resulting in a mixture with the same specific humidity as the rest of the air in the room. Because the glass did not remove any water vapor from the air, there is no vapor pressure gradient between the air near the glass and the air in the rest of the room. It is true that the air near the glass has a higher relative humidity than the rest of the air in the room because the air there is cooler. Therefore, only under some circumstances is it correct to say that "water moves toward cold." A vapor pressure gradient is set up if a cold surface condenses water vapor out of the air, as shown on Page 148. But in the drawing above, no vapor pressure gradient is created. If a situation similar to above were to exist in a building, such as air being cooled by a window, the air would have high relative humidity, materials would not dry well, and mold might grow, but water vapor would still not be moving toward the cold.

Bathrooms are usually ventilated well enough that the walls and ceilings have a chance to dry out between showers, which prevents mold growth. Cars usually dry out between rainstorms, also denying mold a chance to grow. Basements are another story.

Basements tend to be problematic when they are uninsulated and therefore "thermally coupled" to the earth. Described another way, heat conducted freely between an uninsulated basement and the soil around and under it can cause problems. Soil near the surface changes temperature with weather, but about two meters (six feet) below the surface, soil stays at about the same temperature all year round. The soil temperature depends on the geographic location, but in climates with a winter, the soil under the surface is warmer than outdoor air during the winter and colder than both indoor and outdoor air during the summer. Because the soil is colder than both indoor and outdoor air during the summer, uninsulated basement walls and floors will also be colder than summer air, which can cause stubborn moisture problems.

When warm, humid summer air leaks into an uninsulated basement, it gets cooled by the basement's concrete or stone walls and floors. Cooling the air any amount, even a little bit, raises its relative humidity. Cooling it below its dewpoint temperature will cause water to condense out of the air. Unfortunately, basements are not like bathrooms, which have water vapor added intermittently, and which usually have a chance to dry out between showers. Basements stay colder than outdoor air all summer long and therefore are prone to moisture problems, many of which are unfairly blamed on liquid water supposedly leaking from surrounding soil. In reality, the water might be condensing out of the air onto the cool concrete or stone walls and floor. Ventilating a basement can get rid of the moldy smell, but whenever outdoor air is humid and warmer than the soil it makes the problem worse by bringing in a near-infinite supply of water vapor that is likely to condense on the cool basement walls and floor.

Fortunately, with an understanding of building science, curing basement humidity problems is straightforward. Chapter 16: Building Enclosures explains how to do this.

As already discussed, too many air leaks (or too much untreated ventilation air entering a building) will make the air inside the building humid if the outdoor air is warm and humid. High humidity in a building can make people uncomfortable and cause mold growth. Therefore, controlling air leaks is critical to maintaining healthy indoor humidity during the summer.

Because controlling air leaks helps maintain wintertime humidity at healthy levels, too, controlling air leaks is key to maintaining indoor humidity at comfortable and safe levels throughout the whole year. This is true even in maritime climates, where winter air can be humid enough to make houses damp: controlling leaks reduces how much water vapor is brought in by outdoor air.

Psychrometric Problem Areas: Basements, Attics, and Crawl Spaces

As mentioned earlier, uninsulated basements are problematic because the soil keeps floors and walls colder than summer outdoor air in most climates.

A typical attic is partly indoors and partly outdoors, which can also be problematic. In an attic, flows of air, heat, and water vapor from indoors and outdoors intersect. At some point, these flows will combine in a way that will be very damaging to the building. The only thing worse than an attic is a crawl space.

In this book, the term "crawl space" describes a space underneath the building that is not conditioned (heated, cooled, ventilated, dehumidified), typically has no air barrier or insulation isolating it from outdoor air or the soil, and typically is too low to stand up in. In a typical crawl space, flows of air, heat, and water vapor from indoors, outdoors, and the soil, plus liquid water from the soil, all interact with each other. In far too many crawl spaces, these flows combine in a way that is damaging to the building.

Remedies for problems with basements, attics, and crawl spaces are all described in Chapter 16: Building Enclosures. After the quiz photos at right, the photos on the next three pages show how to look for signs of water movement and its results.

Water Quizzes

Water Quiz #1: Why did water vapor condense out of the air overnight as liquid water ("morning dew") on the rear window, and as ice on the roof, but not on the side or front windows of this car? Clue: It has nothing to do with heat from the car's engine, and nothing to do with the sun, which just came up. Turn to Page 560 for the answer.

Water Quiz #2: How did some tea get into the saucer under the cup? What will happen next? Clue: Nobody spilled any tea. Turn to Page 561 for the answer.

Water Quiz #3: Why, a few minutes after someone mopped this tile floor, are the floor tiles wet in the middle but not around the edges? This is an apartment building hallway, with a hallway below that is the same temperature. Turn to Page 562 for the answer.

Water Quiz #4: Why is water vapor condensing onto only one of the windows? And why in the middle of the pane only? And which surface of which pane is the water condensing on? Clue: The photo was taken during the winter. Turn to Page 563 for the answer.

EFFLORESCENCE: A RECORD OF WATER'S MOVEMENT

The photo at right shows **efflorescence** on bricks that were delivered recently. Rain dissolved salts that were in the bricks and flowed to the bottom of the bricks, taking the salts with it. Salts remain on the surface where the rain evaporated. Efflorescence is formed when salts are dissolved out of bricks, mortar, concrete, soil, or other materials and left behind on the surface the water evaporates from. In the first year or two of a brick building's life, efflorescence is often spread somewhat randomly over the face of a wall. On older buildings, it shows where water has been evaporating from a surface, which can give clues as to where water got into the wall.

The photo below shows **light-colored streaks** running down below horizontal cracks on the face of the mountain. Rain falling on top of the mountain dissolved salts from the mountain, carried the salts out the cracks, and evaporated, leaving the light-colored salts behind. Note that the streaks are similar in color to the upper part of the mountain, a clue that they are maybe made from salts in that part of the mountain. Also note that there are no streaks below the same cracks on the right side of the mountain, perhaps because in that area the top of the mountain is too pitched (sloped), which keeps water from soaking into that area.

The **efflorescence pattern** on this highway retaining wall (right and below) shows where water leaked through **joints in the coping** (the material forming the top of a wall) and **holes for railing posts** and how far it got before it evaporated, leaving white salt behind. The lower part of the wall shows a **damage pattern** that is probably caused by differences in the concentration of road salt in the wall. Perhaps the salt caused additional freeze-thaw cycles (water in the wall froze and thawed more times during a winter with salt than without salt); perhaps the salt reduced drying; perhaps the damage was caused by subflorescence. (Subflorescence is when salts accumulate within the bricks, as described on Page 206.) The damage is worse, and extends higher, where less rain leaked into the wall.

Efflorescence patterns on buildings show where water has been evaporating from the surface, which can offer clues as to where water has been leaking into a building. The salts are often washed off by the next rain, making them a good guide for what has been happening recently.

CONDENSATION CAUSED BY INSULATION

Why is the floor wet under the rug at right? This is a basement floor made of tile on top of concrete that is resting on soil, with no insulation under the floor. The climate is cold during the winter and hot and humid during the summer.

The temperature of the soil under the floor does not change significantly throughout the year, and neither does the temperature of the air in the basement. The soil under the house is significantly cooler than room temperature all year, which keeps the tile cooler than room temperature all year (remember: the floor is uninsulated). Throughout the whole year, heat is moved by radiation from the room-temperature basement walls and ceiling to the surface of the tile, and by conduction from the room-temperature basement air to the surface of the tile. Heat is conducted continuously all year from the tile floor to the concrete under the tile, then to the soil under the house.

Insulating something makes one side of it colder. The rug's small insulating value reduces the heating of the floor under the rug, while conduction from the floor to the soil cools the floor under the rug to a temperature lower than the dewpoint temperature of the humid summer air. This photo was taken during the summer, when humid outdoor air leaked into the house, and water condensed out of this humid air onto the floor under the rug. The reason the uncovered floor is dry is that the lack of insulation (no rug) kept that area of the floor warmer than the dewpoint temperature of the air. If the rug were moved to a different part of the floor, the wet spot would soon dry, and the floor under the rug's new location would soon get wet for the same reason.

Books, cardboard boxes, walls, or anything else with significant insulating value covering the floor will cause the same problem. Possible solutions include not using a rug, running a dehumidifier in the basement constantly throughout the summer, or airtightening the house and running the dehumidifier just a few hours per day during the summer. Airtightening the house will reduce the problem regardless of what else is done. Insulating between the floor and the soil is disruptive and expensive but will permanently stop the problem. (Insulating on the outdoor side of an assembly is covered in Chapter 16: Building Enclosures.)

SUMMARY

The movement of water through buildings has a huge influence on people's comfort and health, as well as on a building's durability. Therefore, its movement through buildings needs to be carefully controlled. Movement of liquid water tends to get all the attention, but water vapor that is moved with air can lead to buildings getting too dry during the winter and too humid during the summer (in most climates). Airtightening buildings, therefore, is critically important to solving problems with too much or too little water vapor in indoor air.

Chapter 6 **WATER** Applied Science

WHY IS IT IMPORTANT TO UNDERSTAND WATER MOVEMENT THROUGH BUILDINGS?

Water is the enemy of buildings. This is why buildings need to be protected from water.

Buildings are expected to protect people from water coming from the sky (rain or snow), from the soil beneath us, or from floods. And, buildings should also protect people from water in its gas state. For example, in places where summers are humid, buildings should keep out much of the humidity in outdoor summer air. Too little water can also be a problem. For that reason, buildings should also provide protection from too little water vapor in indoor air, also known as dry air.

Building interiors are usually made of water-vulnerable materials such as gypsum board and carpeting. If buildings were built entirely of waterproof materials,

Paint damaged by water leaking through the roof above.

and the interior of a building were allowed to get wet, the waterproof building materials would not help much, because nobody wants to sleep in a wet bed, wear wet clothing, or read wet books. If parts of buildings or the contents of buildings stay wet enough for long enough, pests move in, metal parts rust, bricks can be damaged by freeze-thaw, and mold will damage the building and its contents. Instead of trying to keep every part of a building dry forever, it is safer to assume every part of a building will get wet at some point, and think about how the building will dry.

How Wet for How Long?

Water damage to a building is not simply a question of a building material being wet or dry but a question of how wet for how long. Some parts of a building, such as a gypsum board wall or ceiling, will be damaged by a relatively small amount of water. A wood floor can withstand getting some water spilled on it and then drying out in a reasonable amount of time. If a wood floor stays wet long enough, however, the wood will absorb water and swell up, causing floorboards to buckle up and pull the nails out. Other materials, such as bricks and roofing paper, are usually thought of as

Mold is growing on the painted gypsum board ceiling, caused by water that leaked from above. There is probably much more mold growing on the upper side of the gypsum board, because that is the side the water leaked onto.

Removing part of a wall revealed this screw, which accidently punctured a water pipe when the building was being renovated. Nobody noticed the problem until months later, when the screw rusted enough for water to start leaking.

being "waterproof," or invulnerable to damage by water. However, even those materials will be damaged if they stay wet enough for long enough, especially if they get so cold that the absorbed water freezes. The less wet a material gets, the better, and the more quickly a material dries, the better. How wet a material gets and how long it stays wet both depend on three mechanisms: wetting, storage, and drying.

Three Water Questions

Many parts of buildings eventually get wet, which makes it unrealistic to try to keep an entire building perfectly dry forever. It is more realistic to consider these three questions:

1. How often will the building materials get wet, and how wet will those materials get?

2. How well can those building materials store water?

3. How long will the materials stay wet? Or, alternatively, how quickly will these materials dry?

WETTING, STORAGE, AND DRYING

Each of these three mechanisms needs to be considered when determining how water affects a building. Ignoring any one of them is asking for trouble. Reducing wetting and damage from wetting is described on Pages 157-215. Storage of water in building materials is described next, on Pages 216-217. Drying is covered starting on Page 218.

Wetting

The two main mechanisms that wet buildings are rain and leaking pipes. Some experts say that leaking pipes cause floods more often than rain. Leaking pipes can never be completely eliminated, but a few smart strategies will greatly reduce problems. One strategy, locating water pipes where they are less prone to freezing, is described on Page 228.

Storage

Most building materials can absorb water and dry later without being damaged. For example, brick and stone exposed to rain absorb water, which then evaporates after the rain stops. Water vapor from cooking or showering gets absorbed into a gypsum board or plaster wall, and then the wall dries out later, after showering or cooking is finished. When a building gets flooded, even indoor materials such as gypsum board and wood flooring can survive if the building is dried out quickly enough.

Water leaking through a brick facade to the next layer of a building might do damage, or it might not. If the next layer is concrete blocks, the blocks can absorb and store the water until the water evaporates. If the next layer is plywood backed up by wood studs, the wood cannot store as much water as the concrete blocks and is therefore more vulnerable to becoming saturated, which will lead to mold growth. And because saturated wood cannot absorb more water, water is therefore more likely to penetrate farther into the wall, to the interior, where it can do more damage and maybe take longer to dry. If the material behind the bricks is gypsum board backed by metal studs, the studs absorb zero water, and the gypsum board can only absorb a little before being damaged.

Drying

Water usually wets building materials as a liquid but dries as a gas. This is similar to a bathroom towel: it sometimes absorbs some water vapor from the air as a person showers but mostly gets wet by liquid, and unless somebody squeezes water out of it, the only way it dries is by evaporation. Building materials are often wetted by water vapor, but regardless of how a building gets wet, absorbed water does not leave as a liquid—nobody squeezes water out of a building—it always leaves as water vapor. Changing liquid water into water vapor requires energy (latent heat), which is why drying a building requires heat. Insulating an assembly makes one side of it colder. As newer buildings get insulated better, less heat is available for drying the outside of a building in cold weather, which is why it is so important to pay attention to how a building will dry. And for water vapor to leave an assembly, it needs a path that is not blocked by a vapor barrier. This will be covered in Chapter 16: Building Enclosures.

WETTING, STORAGE, AND DRYING: HOW MUCH WETTING?

Good design and construction can go a long way toward reducing the amount of wetting a building experiences. The following sections will discuss how to reduce wetting from rain.

First Line of Defense: A Properly Pitched Roof

Keeping rain out of buildings has been a challenge since people started living indoors. Roofing materials and methods are always changing, which does not make decisions easier. But the basic principles stay the same.

A "flat" roof, which would be more accurately called a "low slope" or "low pitch" roof, is usually designed to be pitched (sloped) toward the drain. The design for this building asked for only a little pitch, which can be hard to achieve in practice. A less than optimal design and an imperfect installation have combined to cause water to pond (gather) in an area that is vulnerable to leaks: the connection between the roof assembly and the wall assembly. Ponding is also a problem because constant exposure to water can deteriorate roofing materials. Instead of depending on perfect installation, a more realistic solution is to design the roof with more pitch.

This house has a flat roof that is completely flat, with no roof drains or gutters. The reason? It is in Egypt, where it gets only a little rain every ten years or so.

The roof receives more rain than any other part of a building. This is why a roof should be designed with the old roofer's saying—"Keep the water moving"—in mind. All the rain that lands on the roof should move quickly downhill to a drain that removes the water from the building.

Many buildings have roofs that look flat but are actually pitched (sloped) toward a drain. How much pitch is important, as is the direction of the pitch. More pitch is usually better, with the limit being the point at which the roofing materials might slide downhill.

The roof shown at right is pitched toward a valley where the **drain** is installed. This is not good enough to prevent water from ponding in a vulnerable area: near the stairway bulkhead (the enclosure around the top of the stairway) at left. This area is vulnerable, because it is located at the intersection of two assemblies: the roof and the wall. Worse, there is a door there, where water can leak into the connection between the doorframe and the wall, or between the doorframe and the roof. The roof would drain better if it were pitched in an "X" shape that directed all water toward the central drain. (See the next page for examples of this.)

Pitch on a "flat" roof is commonly accomplished by angling the structure of the roof, as in the photo above, and/or by using tapered pieces of foam underneath the waterproof layer. The foam "tapers" in the photo at left are left over from a roof installation. When installed on the roof and covered with a layer of waterproof material, they create pitch in the desired direction.

In the photo at right, the roof structure is angled to create **pitch from left to right** (see colored areas in inset below). Placing foam tapers under the black waterproof roofing material creates **pitch toward a valley leading to the drain** and **pitch away from the wall at the edge of the roof**. The result is a "flat" roof pitched toward the **drain** in multiple directions, preventing water from collecting anyplace, especially along walls or other vulnerable areas.

The photo at left shows rain running toward **roof drains** thanks to **"X"-shaped patterns** created by tapers.

Both of the roofs on this page are well designed. Neither gives water a chance to sit still, especially near walls.

The "flat" roof at right is on a house built in the 1800s. It is pitched more steeply than most modern flat roofs. It had to be, because the roofing materials available in those days were not nearly as good as those available today. Leak prevention then depended more on gravity than on good materials. Now, modern materials are so leak resistant that "flat" roofs can be built with less pitch than this roof has. (Some modern roofs have no pitch at all.) But gravity is free, and lasts longer than any material, so it should be used to maximum advantage, even when the best materials are available.

More pitch equals fewer leaks and fewer roof repairs.

The 1800s tenement building at the right side of the photo at left has a steeply pitched **stairway bulkhead**. The apartment building at the far left, built in the 1990s, has an **elevator machine room** with a completely flat roof, which depends on very good materials for waterproofing. The **elevator machine room** and **boiler room** roofs of the building in the middle, built in 2007, are pitched more steeply than most modern "flat" roofs, which provides extra protection against leaks and will help the roofing material last longer.

Roof Overhangs Protecting Walls

The less water wets a wall, the less water can get into it and cause damage. Roof overhangs, also known as eaves, can protect walls by reducing wetting.

Short roof overhangs can only protect the upper part of a wall, usually less than one story. A wider overhang gives more protection and extends the protection further down the wall.

Two stories is about the practical limit of how much wall can be protected by a roof overhang. The tops of taller buildings are exposed to too much wind-blown rain for an overhang to work, and the lower floors are too far away from the roof overhang to be adequately protected.

A building taller than two stories that is not sheltered by a nearby building will get significant wetting regardless of the width of the roof overhang and needs to be designed with increased wetting in mind. This also means that wall materials and designs that have proven durable on one- or two-story buildings might not work on taller buildings.

This building has had **repairs** done around the windows on the lower floor but not on the upper floor. Apparently the roof overhangs protected the upper floor windows from rain but not the lower floor windows.

The other side of the same building shows the same pattern: repairs around the windows on the lower floor but not on the upper floor. The fading pattern on the end wall shows the extent of the protection provided by the roof overhang: relatively dry at the height of the upper-floor windows, little or no protection lower down.

The photo at right, taken on a rainy day, shows how roof overhangs reduce the amount of wetting on the walls—especially higher up.

The front wall of the tiny house at left would have been protected from **water damage** if the roof extended out to protect the wall. The side wall has almost no protection either.

The door does have a little roof over it, which seems to be doing a good job of protecting it.

Most of the wood siding on the right side of the garage at right has turned grey because of wetting from rain. The upper part of the right side of the wall has kept its original color, because it is protected by the roof overhang.

The roof overhang below is wide enough to provide good protection for the wall of the one-story house, even with no rain gutter. But when it rains, water splashes off the step onto the wall around the door and wets the bottom of the door and the doorframe.

One of the close-ups at the bottom of this page shows how much the doorframe has rotted in two years.

Before

After two years

The pattern of colors on the wall below shows how even a very short roof overhang can protect the upper parts of a wall. The original light wood color of the shingles is visible at the top. Lower down, much of the wall has turned darker, with the lower parts that get wettest turning grey.

Not All Rain Is Equal

Seattle, Washington, is located in the Pacific Northwest of North America, an area known for frequent rain during the winter. Among architects, builders, building owners, and insurance companies, it is also known for walls that rot away and have to be replaced at great expense. But, surprisingly, it is not the amount of rain that causes the problem. Miami, Florida, and Houston, Texas, each get approximately 50 percent more rain per year than Seattle. Yet neither of those cities is known for their rainfall or for rotting walls. Why is that?

The answer is simple. In Seattle, rain falls more days out of the year. The issue is not just how much wetting occurs but how much drying a climate allows for.

A climate like Miami's or Houston's gets a day or two of heavy rain followed by some dry days. The first drops of rain wet the outside of a building, and once the outside is wet, much of the additional rain falling on the building drains off as a liquid, because the wall is already wet. When the rain stops, the sun comes out and the building has a few days to dry.

Picture walking home through a heavy rainstorm that soaks your shoes completely. You get home, pour the water out of your shoes, and walk around barefoot while your shoes dry. Even if you do this every day, your feet are dry most hours of most days. But if your feet got a little wet and never had a chance to dry—for example, if you put plastic bags on your feet instead of socks, or if you stepped in a puddle every morning but did not take your shoes off all day—your feet would spend most days mostly wet, which would cause "interesting" things to happen to them.

In Seattle, after a light rain wets the building, the next day often another light rain wets the building a little more, and the next day another light rain wets the building a little more. The building does not typically get wet enough for rain to drain off as a liquid, so a high percentage of the rain that falls in Seattle is absorbed by the building. The problem is worse, because Seattle gets a lot of rain during the winter, when the outdoor side of the building is cold. The building might go weeks without a few dry days, which creates ideal conditions for mold.

New buildings are getting more insulation. The more insulation a wall has, the smaller the amount of heat available from indoors to dry the outdoor side of a wall during the winter, and the more important preventing wetting becomes. This is especially true in places like Seattle, where there are fewer drying days. Rain is always a liquid when it wets a building. In Miami, a lot of rain leaves a building as a liquid draining off a wet wall, but, in Seattle, much more of the water leaves as a gas (water vapor). Converting the liquid water (rain) to gas requires heat—the latent heat of vaporization.

Reducing insulation levels raises the temperature of the outdoor side of a building during cold weather, because, with less insulation, more heat moves from inside the building to the outdoor side of the wall. This makes more heat available to dry the outdoor side of a building. Eliminating insulation completely makes a lot of heat available to dry a building. No insulation means no durability problems but also no comfort and no money left after buying all the heating equipment and paying the energy bills. Reducing wetting is a much more energy-efficient way of making a building durable than adding heat.

A roof overhang, especially a wide overhang, can help protect a wall from rain. This overhang is protecting a wall in Seattle, Washington.

Wind-Blown Rain (and Snow)

A roof overhang will reduce wetting. But not all rain falls straight down. Buildings have to be designed to withstand wind-blown rain that "falls" sideways. Corners of buildings get more wetting than other parts of a building, because wind direction changes at the corner of a building, separating out rain and snow and depositing them on the walls the way a moving car separates bugs (and rain) out of air and leaves both behind on the windshield (see car at right). This is true for both horizontal corners where a roof meets a wall and vertical corners formed by the intersection of two walls.

At horizontal corners, cornices, like the one at right, provide shelter for walls the way overhangs do but also help by covering the wettest part of the wall: the top.

Vertical corners protrude unsheltered into the wind, causing extra wetting at the corner. An outside corner is not only wetter than other parts of a wall, but during the winter it is also colder than the rest of the wall, because there is less indoor surface than outdoor surface at an outside corner. A parapet wall (the wall around the edge of a "flat" roof) is even colder, because both sides—the side facing the roof and the side facing outdoors—are exposed to outdoor air.

A moving car pushes air up and over its roof. Insects are heavier than air, so the sudden acceleration of the air leaves them behind, in the path of the car's windshield. The same thing happens if the car is standing still and a strong wind is blowing toward the front of the car; the air makes a sudden turn to go up and over the car, separating out insects, which hit the windshield.

The building on the left has no cornice, whereas the building on the right does. The cornice is more than decorative. It splits the wind into two windstreams: one that flows straight over the roof and another that hits the cornice, which directs it down the face of the building. The cornice covers the wettest part of the wall with metal. When the airstream that hits the cornice makes a sudden turn downward, the water in that air keeps going horizontally, hitting the cornice, not the facade of the building. Air approaching the unprotected building at left splits into one airstream that turns suddenly upward to go over the building and one airstream that goes down the front of the building. Water that keeps going horizontally out of both of these airstreams wets the masonry at the top of the building. The building on the right will experience less wetting, and much of the water that does wet it will wet the cornice, not the masonry wall. Reduced wetting of the masonry will cause the building on the right to last much longer.

The lighter-colored parts of the building at right have gotten more wetting over the years. Some much lighter color at the corner is evidence of repairs. The lower left has been sheltered by a narrow ledge, thus it is darker, except for the light-colored areas under the windows, which are larger lower down. The ledge doesn't protrude far, yet it provides protection for six stories of wall, because the building is surrounded by other tall buildings, which help shelter it from the wind. The wall below the wider ledge (higher up) is much lighter, probably because that area of the building is not as sheltered by nearby buildings.

The building below left has no cornice on its side wall, and wind-blown rain is wetting the top of the wall.

In the photo below right, snow has separated out from air and collected on the vertical outside corner of the building. That corner experiences more wetting and less heat for drying than the rest of the wall. The combination of extra wetting and less heat for drying might cause freeze-thaw damage to the masonry at the corner.

Unfortunately, there is no way to prevent extra wetting at vertical corners. Reduced insulation could provide heat for drying but at the cost of increased energy use and slightly reduced comfort. Other approaches include increasing the thickness of the barrier to liquid water at the corner or using different building materials there.

The photo at right, which was taken during the winter, shows the top of a building that is wet from wind-blown rain. Heat conducted through the walls is drying the wall below the **parapet** (see inset photo). Because the parapet has no heated space behind it, it is not drying as quickly as the wall below it. The wall below the parapet at the right is dry, while the wall below the parapet on the left of the building is not dry. The difference between the two sides is probably due to a difference in wetting because of more rain blown onto the left side of the building.

What parts of the building at left are being repaired? The parts that get the wettest: the top and the corner.

This building has no cornice. If the building had been built with a cornice, the top would have been protected and probably wouldn't have needed repairs.

Wind Blowing Water through Cracks

The drawings on this page show what happens at a small **gap** between a window frame and a window sash when rain is falling on a day without wind: nothing. Because there is no wind, no air will leak through the gap.

The stack effect or mechanical system fans might be moving some air, but neither of them creates air pressure differences as large as a strong wind.

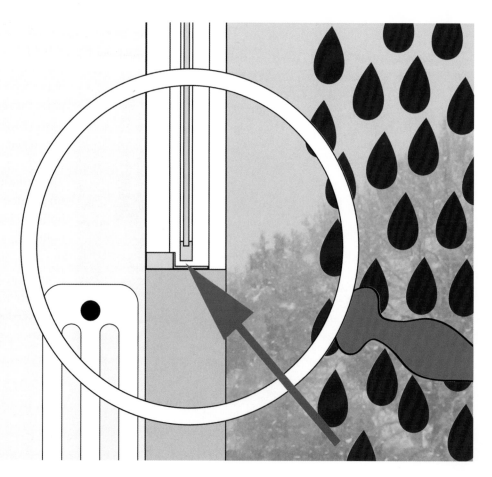

The magnifying glass view at left shows a close-up of the **gap**. Normal double-hung windows in decent condition have gaps that can easily be this large.

On a windy, rainy day, the air that leaks through this same **gap** can move liquid water with it, even though the water has to move against gravity to pass through the gap.

Wind can create a pressure difference between outdoors (higher) and indoors (lower) that moves air through any small gap or hole. (Remember those boxes in Chapter 3: Air - Basic Science.) If the wind blows the other direction, and moves air out through the crack, the moving air would not move liquid water into the building.

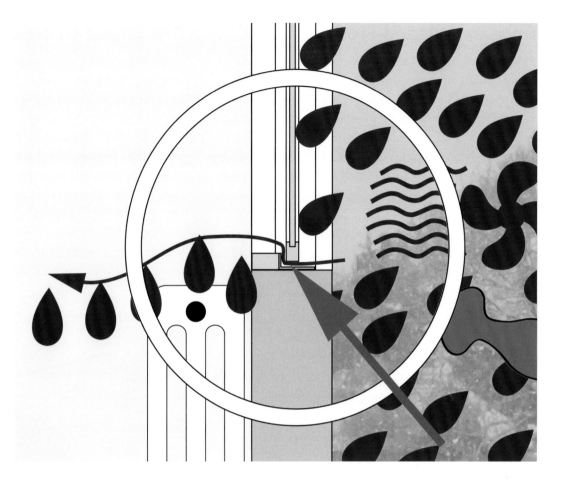

The pressure difference can also move liquid water through holes in a building's walls. Therefore, any **air leak** is a potential water leak. Liquid water blown through holes by wind is an exception to the four main ways water moves through a building listed on Page 129.

Insulation that does not reduce air leakage does nothing to stop this wetting mechanism. A good air barrier between indoors and outdoors can reduce or prevent wetting caused by wind blowing water through holes.

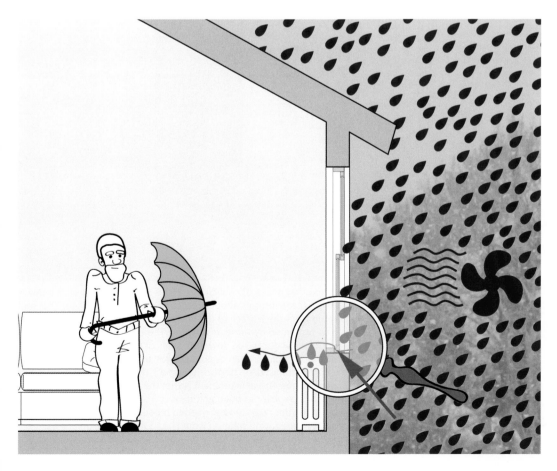

Door and Window Protection

Even if materials don't leak water, gaps at connections between materials are vulnerable to leaking, and gaps at connections between assemblies are even more vulnerable. Connections between walls and doorframes and between walls and window frames are especially vulnerable. Gaps at these places connect outdoors directly to indoors, where any difference in air pressure can push liquid water directly indoors. Gaps between windows and windowsills are especially vulnerable, because gravity can help move liquid water through them. All these gaps should be protected by an air barrier. Otherwise, wind can move liquid water toward the indoor side of a wall, even if the water has to go up against gravity, as shown in the drawings on Page 169.

Recessed Doors and Windows

The first line of defense is always to reduce wetting, which can be done by mounting doors and windows closer to the indoor side of the wall. This protects doors and windows from wind-blown rain, as well as from water draining down the surface of the wall above.

Designers of older buildings had a lot of incentive to do this, because they had no materials good enough to make long-lasting waterproof connections. The doorway at right, from a castle built in the 1500s, and the old doorway below, are great examples of this technique.

This arch not only protects the wooden door, it also protects incandescent light bulbs so well that they survive outdoors.

Drip Edges: An Ingenious Technology

Water drains down the surface of a wall, because its magnetic attraction causes it to cling to the wall and because gravity moves it downward.

A groove that's cut into a downward-facing surface creates an obstacle for water, because water can't run up the uphill side of the groove. This groove creates an isolated edge called a drip edge, which is an effective way to reduce wetting of doors, windows, and other parts of walls. A drip edge will stop water from running further down a wall, forcing it to fall off the building and maybe all the way to the ground without touching the building again.

This doorway of a castle built in the 1500s shows someone was thinking ahead a few centuries about protecting the door from rain. The door is set in from the surface of the wall, which reduces wetting. The door is also protected by three drip edges. The curved top of the doorway encourages water to run down the sides of the doorway, which moves water more quickly than encouraging it to drip straight down, while also preventing water from dripping off the doorway and splashing onto the door. The only problem is that the masonry at the bottom of the door opening has been getting wet from water running down the sides of the doorway and has needed repairs that the surrounding wall has not needed. One solution would be to slope the ground away from the door (this castle, like many, was built on top of a hill, which makes this practical).

Drip edges are still a good idea, and are used in many buildings today. In the photos above, the **grooves** cut into the window lintels (horizontal supports above a window) create drip edges. The grooves must be at least 10 mm (3/8") deep and wide to prevent a drop from crossing. Water can be seen forming into **drops** on the drip edges. The drops will fall off as soon as they are large enough. In the photo below, the concrete coping is nicely pitched on top to reduce the amount of water that would otherwise sit on top of the wall, soaking into the coping and the joints between coping stones. The coping has two **grooves**, which form drip edges to reduce wetting of the wall below. The coping is wide enough to overhang the wall sufficiently so that water dripping off the coping will fall clear of the wall. Every protected surface shown in each of the photos on this page will get wet but not nearly as wet as it would without these smart design features. The grooves forming the drip edges on this page are not nearly as deep as those on Page 170, but they work the same way and are deep enough and wide enough to prevent water from dripping across them.

The masonry in the photo at right has **grooves** on the undersides of some surfaces, but they are not deep or wide enough to force water to drip off. The stain pattern on the masonry show streaks continuing down the surface, which shows that the grooves are not creating effective drip edges.

The windowsill in the photo at left came from the factory with a groove that was not deep and wide enough to create an effective drip edge, so a mason is cutting a deeper (10 mm, or 3/8") and wider (also 10 mm, or 3/8") groove before installing the sill.

Drip Edges Needed!

The photos on this page show horrible lintel design. The undersides of all of them slope in toward the windows, actually directing water onto the windows. The stains on the wall in the photo at left show that the water runs down onto the window and then continues onto the wall below.

The wall in the photo above is even worse, because there are no stains below the windows, indicating that water has apparently leaked into the wall.

The wall in the photo at left should be called a "second chance" design, because if the water does not get into the wall near the first window, it gets a second chance at the window below. Being set back into the wall cannot protect the windows from the poorly angled lintels. When the windows in these photos leak water, the windows are not the problem. A bead of high-quality caulk, carefully applied to a clean and dry exterior surface, where it will be exposed to rain, ultraviolet light from the sun, and the window expanding and contracting, is not a long-term solution. This is not the fault of caulk manufacturers or the people applying it. The long-term solution is a drip edge or lintels that are angled away from the windows.

Decorative Details That Make It Worse

The decorative details shown on this page allow rain that falls on them to wet the wall below. This makes parts of the wall wetter than they would have been without the decorative details.

Better design would include drip edges, which force the water to drip away from the wall into open air.

Centuries before anyone knew that water was H_2O, designers knew how to keep it from destroying a building. The photo of the castle at left is evidence of this: **drain spouts** extend far enough away from the wall to prevent water from wetting it further down.

Roof Overhang Quiz

The roof overhang in the photo below has been protecting the **upper part of the wall** from rain. Because it stays relatively dry, the wood has kept its original light color. But why has the same width of roof overhang not been protecting **the part of the wall above the porch**? Turn to Page 563 for the answer.

If These Walls Could Talk

Actually, they are talking, but few people have learned to listen.

Both of the walls on the right side of this page show white efflorescence patterns that reveal the movement of water.

The photo at right shows that water has been running from the roof of the small building on the right onto the front walls of both buildings. Perhaps a gutter is missing or clogged with leaves, or a downspout (vertical drain pipe) that is supposed to carry water to the next pipe is leaking.

The efflorescence in the photo below right shows that the ornate masonry lintels above the windows are pitched toward the wall. Therefore, when rain falls, it will run toward the wall. A better design would have the lintels pitched slightly away from the building, so the water would drip onto the street below instead.

The wall in the photo below would experience much less wetting if it were protected by windowsills with drip edges or lintels that extended out past the windowsills, or both.

The wall at right shows efflorescence in a "W" pattern. Just as on the highway retaining wall on Page 153, water leaking through joints in the coping at the top of the wall wets the wall under the joints and leaves the white efflorescence behind when it dries. The joints in the terracotta coping in the photo below left have a similar vulnerability: gravity pushes water into the joints, which require caulking for protection.

The joints in the terracotta coping stone below right are overlapping. This discourages gravity from moving water through them. The mortar in the joints slows down whatever water does get into the joints long enough for most of it to run down to the bottom of the coping. The coping overlaps the parapet on both sides, forming, in effect, two drip edges—one on each side of the wall—that force water to drip free into the air.

Connections between parts of buildings leak less water when they do not depend on sealants such as caulk. Connections designed to use gravity to move water away from the joints are more reliable. The less caulk a building needs, the less maintenance it will need in the future and the more durable it will be.

Leaking Windowsills, Expensive Wall Repairs

The photos on this page show how leaks at windowsills are not just a minor annoyance; they can cause severe damage. The photo below shows a wall damaged by water leaking in around the windowsills. The close-up, below left, shows a windowsill on the same wall that is partly backpitched—water runs back toward the window, instead of away from the building. The water drains into the wall below the windowsill, causing the damage visible in the photo below and likely also damaging the indoor side.

Repairing the wall without first solving the pitch of the windowsill would be a waste of time and money.

The photo below right shows a wall that was damaged by water leaking between a windowsill and a wall, then down inside the wall.

Gravity helps water get into walls at the edges of windowsills. It therefore is worth paying extra attention to how windowsills are designed and built.

Both of the masonry walls on this page have been repaired where the walls got the most wetting: below the edges of the windowsills, where water ran off the sill edges and onto or into the walls. The triangular white areas on the wall at right are where damaged stone was removed and new stone or concrete was used as a replacement. In the photo below, the darker-colored strips under each window are where new stucco was applied to the wall.

If the sills in both of these photos had been modified to reduce future wetting, the walls wouldn't have needed to be repaired and wouldn't need to be repaired again in the near future.

A good solution for both buildings on this page would be to pitch the sills away from the windows, extend them further out from the wall, cut a groove to form a drip edge, and turn the ends of the sills up where they meet the walls (as explained on the next two pages).

The windowsill at right is not sufficiently pitched toward the outdoor side of the wall and depends on caulk to prevent water from entering the wall. The caulk is in a vulnerable location: it is exposed to sunlight and rain. Ultraviolet light is very destructive to many building materials, and constant wetting shortens the life of the caulk. In addition, the windowsill is made of metal, which expands more than masonry does with heat. The constant thermal expansion and contraction of the metal windowsill has pulled the caulk joint apart. Once again, the "failure" of the caulk joint is not a failure of the caulk. It is caused by asking the caulk to do the impossible.

The windowsill below is designed better than the one at right—it has lots of pitch away from the window, and has **upturned ends**, which keep water from spilling over the ends of the sill and into the wall. But it could be better. The wall does not cover the upturned end, but is behind it, which allows water to run down the wall and perhaps get into **the crack between the sill and the wall.**

The sill at right is properly pitched, which encourages water to run away from the building. It also extends past the wall below it, which encourages water to drip off instead of running down the wall. An **upturned edge** on the end of the sill prevents water from running off the edge of the sill into the wall. But **part of the wall** extends down and touches the sill, allowing capillary suction to spread water running down the sill up into the wall. The solution is to end the wall above the upturned edge of the windowsill, as shown in the photo below.

The **uphill end of the sill** in the photo above extends under the window, therefore it does not depend on caulk to keep water out. Caulk for airtightening purposes, which also helps keep out wind-blown rain, can be applied on the indoor side of the wall, where it will be protected from damage from sun, rain, and the worst of the thermal expansion of the sill and the window.

The **uphill end of the sill** in the photo at left is in front of the window, rather than tucked under it. This could let water into the wall. Above the sill there is an **overhang**, which directs at least some water dripping off the window out past the upturned edge of the sill.

Proper Flashing Sequencing

When liquid water leaks into a building, as it inevitably will, it should be made to flow back out of the building immediately. Flashing—either a flat sheet material or a sprayed-, rolled-, or brushed-on material (as shown on Pages 110 and 111)—will help do that, but it has to be installed properly.

Successful flashing installation depends on layering the materials in the correct sequence, so that when rain falls on the building or is blown into leaks in the building, flashing takes advantage of gravity and moves water out of the building, not deeper inside it. As always, gravity is more reliable than any product or connection between products. Therefore, successful and durable flashing depends more on correct layer sequencing than on perfect connections between materials.

The raincoat example below shows that properly layered water-control materials can be quite effective at reducing wetting of either a person or a building. Proper sequencing works even if the connections between materials are not perfectly waterproof but merely overlap the way a raincoat should overlap rainpants or rainpants should overlap boots.

Unsuccessful layering. Rain will cling to the model's hair, and gravity will pull it down under her collar, inside her raincoat. Rain falling on her raincoat will cling to her raincoat and—because it is tucked in—will run down into her rainpants, and rain falling on her rainpaints (also tucked in) will run into her boots. The waistband of her pants is closed tightly around the bottom of her raincoat, which also prevents air from passing under her raincoat and drying the water that gets under it. Model: Mina Agarabi, P. E.

Successful layering. Rain will cling to the model's hair, and gravity will pull it down outside of her collar and outside of her raincoat. Rain falling on her raincoat and rainpants will run down to the bottom edges of her raincoat and pants, where it will drip off. The open hemline of her raincoat will allow some air to pass through, helping to dry any water that manages to get under her raincoat. The model's long hair is like the decorative elements of a building's facade that can be used to help shed water.

The photos on this page show examples of properly and improperly sequenced flashing.

The photo at right shows a properly sequenced piece of metal flashing. The metal is under the shingles above it but layered on top of the shingles below it, which prevents water from getting under the flashing, from where it could wet the roof deck. The water drips onto the top of the shingles below the flashing, from where it will flow all the way down the shingles to the edge of the roof. The flashing shown below right is improperly sequenced: water will get under it and leak through the roof around the pipe.

In the photo below, the **copper under the windows** is pitched steeply enough to keep the water moving away from the window. It ends on top of a **piece of flashing** that overlaps the roof shingles below it. **Shingles** overlapping the ends of the flashing prevent water from getting under its ends. Correct sequencing keeps water flowing on top of one material and then another, all the way down to the edge of the roof, where it drips onto the ground or into the gutter without ever having a chance to leak into the building.

Flashing: Correctly Layered or Not?

In the photo below, one of the layers of flashing is sequenced incorrectly. Rain leaking through the cladding (the outermost layer of the wall, which is not installed yet) will run down the **barrier to liquid water (and air)** that was brushed onto the concrete block, then over the **sheet metal strip** inserted into a mortar joint during construction, then down the front of the **upper piece of green flashing**, and then down the front of the **lower piece of green flashing**. So far, so good. But then the rain will sneak back behind the white flashing surrounding the window opening, which will direct it further into the building. The backward sequencing occurs where the white flashing was installed. Instead of being on the outdoor side of the **lower piece of green flashing**, it should be tucked underneath (behind) it.

Note that the white flashing around the window opening cannot keep water from entering the wall above the window, even if all the flashing was layered properly, because it will not overlap the top of the window. In this design, the purpose of the white flashing above the window is to make the air barrier continuous between the exterior surface of the concrete block wall and the interior side of the window, not for diverting water out of the wall. The opening at the top of the window will be protected from water entry by having the lower piece of green flashing overlap the window. The following page shows the lower piece of green flashing sequenced properly, and overlapping the top of the installed window.

The green flashing has a peel-off back that exposes a strong adhesive. This type of flashing is sometimes called "a fully adhered membrane."

Rain leaking through the cladding that will be installed (and then through the insulation that will be installed behind the cladding) will run down the **barrier to liquid water (and air)** that was brushed onto the face of the concrete block, over the sheet metal strip, down the front of the upper piece of green flashing, and down the front of the lower piece of green flashing, which directs the water out above the window. The critical difference is the sequence of installation: the white flashing around the window was installed first (to connect the indoor side of the window to the exterior air barrier), then the green flashing above it, and then finally the upper piece of green flashing.

Note that the brackets for mounting the cladding are attached with fasteners that penetrate the flashing. This might allow water to leak through the flashing. However, these leaks are not expected to be a problem for several reasons. One

is that the cladding that will be installed later will protect the penetrations from wind-blown rain. Whatever small amount of water does leak through the flashing around the fasteners will be absorbed by the concrete blocks without damaging them. And finally, when water does leak into the wall, it can dry, because the wall has no water vapor barrier, except perhaps the green flashing, depending on which product is chosen. But because most of the wall (not visible in these photos) is not covered by flashing, the flashing does not inhibit drying much.

The design is robust enough to stand up to a few construction defects. Little wetting, high storage capacity, and almost nothing inhibiting drying combine to make this wall design resistant to water damage.

The photo above shows sheets of black flashing that were tucked into the mortar joints between the concrete blocks as the wall was built. The flashing is there to direct water that leaks through the bricks (which will be put up later) back out of the wall. The flashing is located where the wall is most vulnerable to water penetration: at the connection between the floor assembly and the wall assembly, and at the tops of the windows.

On the lower floors, the flashing is already partly torn off, probably by the wind, but maybe also weakened by ultraviolet light from the sun. The flashing on the top two floors is still intact, maybe because it was installed a few weeks after the flashing on the lower floors.

Exposure to ultraviolet light damages many materials, including many building materials, especially some types of plastic and other synthetic materials. One of the functions of cladding is to protect other layers of the wall from damage from ultraviolet light from the sun. Sometimes construction schedules need to be adjusted to make sure materials vulnerable to damage from UV light are covered in a timely fashion.

In the photo above, taken a few weeks later, bricks still haven't been installed and the flashing on the upper floors is now also damaged. The flashing on the top floor is almost completely gone, probably because the wind is strongest at the top of the building.

The bricks look nice in the photo above, but what do they hide? If the building leaks, repairs will be expensive.

One solution, shown in both photos at right, is to put a **strip of L-shaped sheet metal** into the mortar joint when the block wall is built. One leg of the sheet metal is visible, the other leg is inside the wall. Later, when the bricks are being laid, a **piece of flashing** is tucked under the sheet metal. This ensures water won't get behind the flashing. To a mason, installing a piece of sheet metal to direct water over flashing might be unheard of, but it would be familiar to a roofer. A roofer terminating a roof at a wall puts an L-shaped piece of metal called a "reglet" into the wall and calls the method "flashing and counterflashing." Metal strips like this can be seen terminating roofs in the photos on the tops of Pages 157, 158, and 159.

On the same wall, **plastic mesh** prevents wet mortar that squeezes out of brick joints from falling down behind the bricks where it could eventually stop water from draining out of the wall through strategically located **weep holes** (explained in more detail later in this chapter). The top of the mesh is cut in a zigzag shape, so any mortar that falls on top of it will not form a continuous barrier to water.

The photo at right shows another view of the house on the bottom of Page 106, which is covered by a fully adhered membrane. Note the piece of **fully adhered membrane** covering the metal flashing is shingled backwards. Described another way, the lower piece of membrane was installed later and overlaps the piece above it. This is a potential problem, because water running down the piece installed first could leak into the gap between the two pieces. The high-quality adhesive will probably prevent a problem, but it is always better to rely on gravity than on adhesive.

In the photo at left, the fully adhered membrane is temporarily rolled up above the window opening, so that it can overlap the top of the window after it is installed. This is an example of proper sequencing, which will prevent most water from leaking in at the top of the window.

The photo at right shows Tyvek® housewrap and black tarpaper flashing installed in the wrong sequence. The way the layers are sequenced, water that gets through the cladding can run down the housewrap, then sneak behind the black tarpaper into the wall.

The solution is simple. The Tyvek® housewrap should overlap the black tarpaper. It would also be better if the Tyvek® housewrap were to overlap both the tarpaper and the **step flashing**.

Step flashing will be explained on the next few pages.

The photo at left shows multiple repairs at a roof/wall connection, none of which apparently stopped the water leak. Water is probably leaking into the wall at the windowsill above and draining out of the indoor side of the wall near the roof/wall connection. The problem: nothing is diverting the water out on top of the roof shingles.

No amount of repairs to the exterior of the roof/wall intersection can prevent water that leaks in at the windowsill above from running down inside the wall. A proper repair requires removing the bricks and lapping the housewrap over the top of the step flashing. The drawings on the next three pages show how to do this.

Step Flashing Installed in the Correct Sequence

Step flashing is a type of flashing that goes between the edge of a row of roof shingles and a wall. It prevents water from escaping off the edge of the shingles, then leaking into the wall or under the shingles. The installation steps are as follows: ① First, tarpaper is installed on the roof deck starting at the bottom edge. ② Tarpaper is installed in sequence from the bottom up, so that the upper pieces overlap the lower pieces. ③ The whole roof is covered with a layer of tarpaper that overlaps at the seams (or a fully adhered membrane). ④ Shingles are installed starting from the bottom edge of the roof.

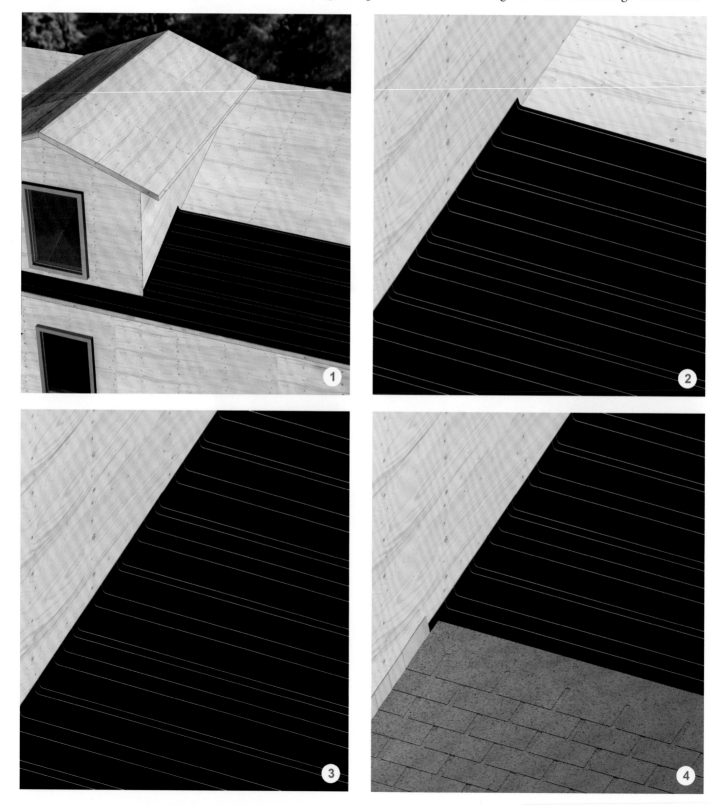

⑤ After each row of shingles is installed, one piece of **step flashing** is installed to prevent water from running off the edge of the next row of shingles. ⑥ Another row of shingles is installed. Note that the shingle at the left end of the row is layered on top of the piece of step flashing installed in Drawing 5. This keeps water from escaping off the edge of the row of shingles and running onto the wall or under the shingles, then further into the building. ⑦ Another piece of step flashing gets installed on top of the row of shingles installed in Drawing 6. ⑧ A row of shingles gets installed on top of the piece of step flashing installed in Drawing 7.

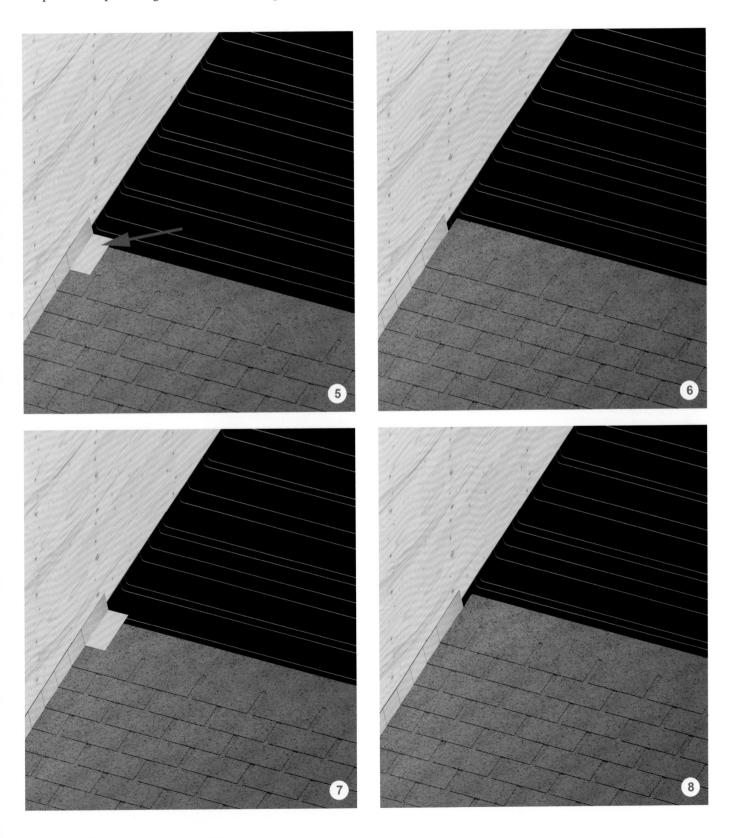

(9) A piece of step flashing gets installed on top of the edge of each row of shingles. (10) After all the shingles and all the pieces of step flashing are nailed down, housewrap is attached to the adjacent wall, overlapping on top of the step flashing. (This will prevent water from getting behind the step flashing.) Housewrap is a barrier to liquid water but not a barrier to water vapor, as explained on Page 132. (11) Vertical pieces of wood are nailed or screwed through the housewrap into the wall. The vertical pieces of wood reduce wetting of the wall by allowing any rain that gets behind the cladding a space to drain out. They are also for air circulation, which dries the wall as explained on Page 393. (12) The cladding (exterior siding—wood in this case) is attached.

Flashing was traditionally a flat material bought as rolls or sheets, but increasingly it is a gooey material sold in a can and applied by brushing, rolling, or spraying. One reason for this change is that installing sheets of flashing on the sides of large buildings high above the ground is very difficult. On tall buildings it is easier to apply flashing by brushing, rolling, or spraying. The greenish product in the photo at left and the yellow product in the photo below are both liquid-applied membranes. They come out of the can as a thick, paint-like liquid and dry into a tough, rubbery layer. Liquid-applied products are good for all sizes of buildings, including single-family houses like the one on Pages 110 and 111.

One advantage of liquid-applied products is that they can simultaneously serve as barriers to air and to liquid water. In theory, sheet products can do that also. But if a sheet product is not the type that adheres to the building (a fully adhered membrane) but is instead connected to the building with tape or with pieces of fully adhered membrane (as was done with the house on the bottom of Page 105), it is subjected to a wind load similar to the one wind puts on the sail of a boat. One strong gust of wind can tear a sheet product loose inside a wall, even after the building is completed and the walls are closed in, when nobody can see the problem.

Weeps to Make You Cry

"Weep" holes are intentional holes in a wall (or window) to let water drain out. Flashing inside the wall is usually arranged to direct water out the weep holes. Weep holes must be properly located to insure that they will actually drain water from the wall as intended.

Weep holes are sometimes positioned with some of them slightly above the bottom section of a wall. The theory is that if the lowest ones clog, water can still drain from the weep holes above. However, if the bottom weep holes do clog, water will usually build up high enough to leak into the building before it drains out the higher weep holes.

Most of the weep holes in the photo at right are far too high to be useful.

The white efflorescence on the bricks in the photo at left shows that water has been leaving the wall below the **weep hole**. Maybe water building up inside the wall also caused it to leak toward the inside of the wall. This could be avoided if the weep holes were located at the bottom of the wall.

In the photo at right, the **white plastic insert** in the weep hole is perforated with holes that are large enough for water to drain through but small enough to keep insects out. Unfortunately, the plastic insert is located too high in the wall to serve as an effective drain. The masons first laid a "bed" of mortar on the metal flashing, then laid bricks on top. This positioned the weeps on top of the mortar. Some water will leak through the mortar—but it will accumulate behind the mortar and probably leak into the building before it builds up high enough to drain through the weep.

At left, the masons corrected their mistake before the mortar set by lowering the insert down onto the metal flashing. The gap on top of the insert should, of course, also be filled with mortar.

Now water that gets behind the bricks will drain out through the weep holes.

Weeps That Work

The photos on this page show where water is draining out of brick walls at regularly spaced intervals—apparently from weep holes that work. After the water leaves the weeps, it runs down the surface of the wall. Efflorescence streaks are visible where the water evaporates.

In the photo at right, flashing directs water out of the building through weeps located where the floor/ceiling assembly meets the wall. There is more efflorescence at the top of the building, because rain wets the upper part of the building more.

The photo below shows efflorescence streaks below weeps located at floor level. There is more efflorescence below the weeps near the balcony, because more water is leaking into (and therefore draining out of) the wall in that area. Perhaps more water is leaking in there because of water ponding on the balcony, or because it gets in where the balcony supports penetrate the wall. Or, perhaps that part of the wall simply gets wetter because it is at the corner of the building, where wind-blown rain is separated from air as the air turns the corner.

One possible explanation for why more water is leaving the weeps at the right end of the wall is that the wall is noticeably wetter in the **area above those weeps**.

Reduce Mistakes—and Their Cost—by Building a Test Section

Building a test section of a wall helps catch mistakes in design or construction as early and inexpensively as possible.

The section in the photo at right was built inside an apartment building when it was under construction. It includes a section of a brick facade, an **expansion joint**, **weep holes**, some **precast masonry**, and **flashing**.

The two-story wall below is a test section built in the parking lot next to a large building under construction. It includes representative samples of doors, windows, a balcony, and each type of wall.

This is time and money spent wisely.

Divert Water away from the Door

The front porch in the photo at right is pitched away from the door, which will send any rain that blows in under the roof back out to the front lawn, extending the life of the door (and the wood around the door).

The sidewalk in front of the stores below is pitched away from the doors in two directions. First, it is pitched away to the left and right of each door, directing the water to low spots between the doors. Second, the whole sidewalk is pitched toward the parking lot. This shows a skillful use of gravity to move water away from the doors and the wall.

Don't Fight Gravity

The yard between the two buildings at right is sloped away from the buildings, and the roof drain pipes from both buildings extend to the lowest part of the yard, directing water away from the buildings.

In the photo below, the building to the right had flood problems, so the ground was sloped into a valley. The valley is also pitched a little, so on rainy days like this one, the water moves past the fence, from where it runs downhill away from the building.

The photos on Page 355 also show how small improvements encourage water to move away from buildings.

Keeping water away from buildings also discourages pests, as will be discussed in Chapter 14: Pests - Applied Science.

The next few pages will discuss another source of wetting: condensation forming on cold pipes.

Water Condensing on Cold Pipes

Cold pipes both inside and outside of walls should be insulated to prevent condensation from forming on them and wetting nearby building materials (and also providing cool, refreshing drinking water to pests).

It is common to insulate main cold water pipes but less common to insulate all the smaller pipes branching off to sinks, toilets, showers, and tubs. A cold water branch pipe going to a faucet gets cold when water flows through the pipe, then warms up after the flow stops. This reduces the need for insulation, because branches usually warm up before they condense much, or any, water vapor out of the air. A main cold water pipe supplying many fixtures, however, such as the pipe shown on Page 3, has cold water flowing through it so frequently that it condenses a lot of water out of the air. Cold water mains should always be insulated for this reason. Because water flowing through main pipes cools part of each branch pipe, the beginning of each branch pipe should also be insulated.

Even roof drains should be insulated. Snow or cold rain can cool a roof drain below the dewpoint temperature of indoor air, condensing water out of the air onto the pipe.

Because water spends a longer time in a horizontal drain pipe than in a vertical drain pipe, it is most important to insulate roof drains where they run horizontally.

Insulation does not need to be thick to prevent condensation on cold pipes, but it needs to fit the pipe snugly. Insulation of the wrong size will leave gaps for air to get past the insulation and touch the cold pipe.

In all cases, insulation intended to prevent condensation on cold pipes needs to incorporate barriers to air and water vapor on the warm side of the insulation. The air barrier prevents warm humid air from getting through the insulation and contacting the cold surface of the pipe. The water vapor barrier prevents water vapor diffusion from transporting water vapor from warm air near the surface of the insulation to the surface of the pipe. If pipe insulation does not include a continuous air barrier and a continuous vapor barrier, condensation on the surface of the pipe will wet the insulation, rendering it useless. The insulation in the photo below is covered with a white material that is a barrier to water vapor and air.

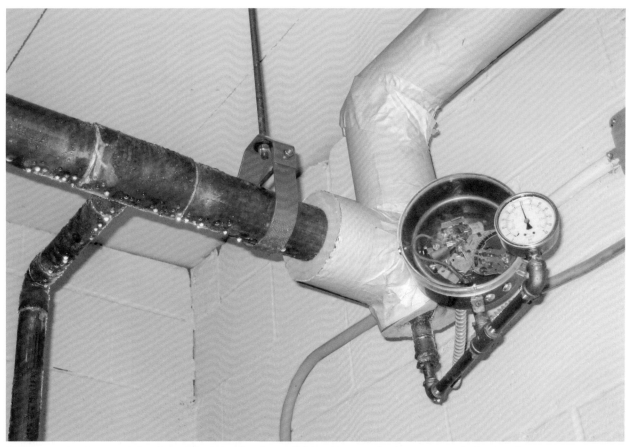

Water is condensing out of the air onto the uninsulated part of this cold water pipe but not onto the insulated part.

Insulating Cooling System Pipes

Air conditioning pipes are another type of pipe that needs insulation to prevent water from condensing out of the air onto the cold surface of the pipe. Air conditioning systems use pipes filled with cold refrigerant (see Page 511) or very cold water, both of which get colder than the cold water going to faucets. The lower temperature causes condensation at lower specific humidity (lower dewpoint temperature) than regular cold water pipes. Described another way, the low temperature of air conditioning pipes causes them to condense water out of drier air than cold water pipes would.

As with cold water pipes, air conditioning pipes need a barrier to air on the warm side of the insulation to prevent humid air from moving to the cold surface of the pipe. The insulation also needs a barrier to water vapor on the warm side of the insulation, which will prevent diffusion from transporting water vapor to the surface of the pipe. (The warm side is always the outer side of insulation on a cold pipe.) Pipe insulation is usually manufactured with one material that serves as both barriers.

Unless the barriers to water vapor and air are perfect, vapor pressure difference combined with any small air leaks through the insulation will move water vapor to the surface of the pipe, where it will condense into liquid water. Condensing water out of the air lowers the vapor pressure of the air near the pipe, which creates a vapor pressure difference that moves more water vapor toward the pipe. Normal fiberglass insulation would soon be completely wet. And because the pipe is part of a cooling system, the pipe stays cold for long periods of time without warming up, which wouldn't give the insulation any chance to dry out. When the type of fiberglass insulation normally used on hot pipes is used on a cold pipe, it can eventually get wet enough to start dripping water on nearby parts of the building.

One solution is to use foam insulation, as shown in the photo below. The foam is the "closed cell" type, meaning the small holes in the foam are not connected to each other, making the foam a good barrier to air and to water vapor. (A kitchen sponge, by contrast, is "open cell" foam—it can absorb a lot of water.) This solution works well with cooling systems that move refrigerant from one part of a building to another, because those types of cooling systems usually have long, continuous runs of copper tubing going from one part of a building to another with no elbows, tees, or valves, which are difficult to insulate with foam. (Elbows in the pipe runs are avoided by using soft-temper copper tubing, which is easily bent by hand to go around corners.)

Cooling system pipes that transport very cold water are more difficult to insulate, because they usually include many elbows, tees, and valves. These are hard to insulate with foam, and hard to cover with fiberglass covered by continuous and perfectly uninterrupted barriers to water vapor and air. Fortunately, a type of insulation has been developed that does not require perfect barriers to keep very cold piping dry: wicking insulation. See the next page for a description of this type of insulation.

Black foam insulation is perfect for insulating copper tubing that transports refrigerant in air conditioning systems.

Keeping Very Cold Pipes Dry with Wicking Insulation

Understanding how wicking insulation works is helpful to understanding all water movement through buildings because two of the four main water movement mechanisms (see Page 129) wet wicking insulation, and the other two dry it out.

Two mechanisms move water toward the pipe: water vapor moving with air leaking through the insulation, and water vapor diffusion from an area of high concentration (air around the insulation) to an area of low concentration (air at the surface of the cold pipe, after the pipe has condensed water out of the air). The insulation has a **cloth wick** wrapped around the pipe, which absorbs any liquid water that condenses on the pipe. If the pipe is horizontal, as is the pipe in the photo at right, the wick is **draped down from the pipe** and **spreads behind a series of holes** in the plastic cover.

Two mechanisms move water away from the pipe: capillary suction moving liquid water through the wick from an area of high concentration to an area of low concentration, and gravity moving liquid water downhill. Capillary suction moves water through the wick from wetter areas (near the pipe) to drier areas (further from the pipe) where the wick is exposed to air outside the insulation. Because the air outside the insulation is warmer than the air near the cold pipe, its relative humidity is lower, and therefore it absorbs water from the wick. In effect, the wick transports liquid water from a cold place (on one side of the insulation) with high relative humidity to a warm place (on the other side of the insulation) with lower relative humidity, where it evaporates. Because the holes are on the bottom of the insulation, gravity helps move liquid water to the holes. If the pipe is vertical, a plastic cover without holes is used, and, at joints between pieces of cover, the wick extends out through the joint and is draped out over the lower piece of cover about once per floor over the length of the pipe.

As long as the pipe stays colder than the dewpont temperature of the surrounding air, water will continue to move toward the pipe. As long as the relative humidity of the surrounding air is lower than 100 percent, water will continue to evaporate back into the surrounding air and not drip onto nearby parts of the building.

The photo at the top of Page 104 shows a similar drying technology. Before the siding was removed, the narrow strips of tarpaper hanging down from the wall extended into the gaps between rows of shingles. Capillary suction and gravity moved water down along each strip to the end where it would evaporate into the air in the small gaps between shingles, which was drier than the air in the cavity between the shingles and the tarpaper. These strips kept the wall drier than it would have been without them.

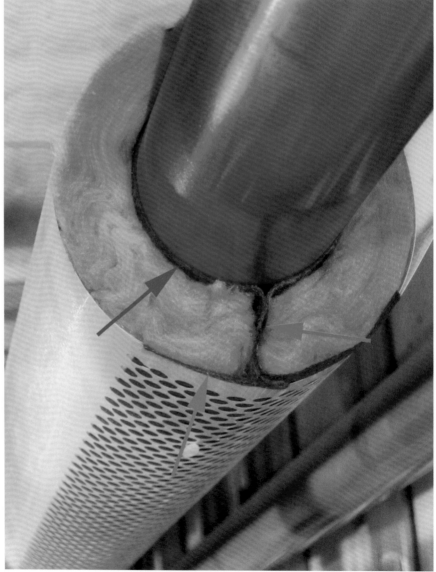

Wetting by Capillary Suction

Capillary suction can damage buildings by moving water into and through buildings.

The photo at right shows mold on the paper face of gypsum board covering a basement wall. The gypsum board absorbed water by capillary suction, which brings water up the wall. The water might have moved by capillary suction from the soil underneath and then through the concrete floor to the gypsum board. Or, water might have condensed out of the air onto the floor and then moved into the gypsum board. It is likely that both mechanisms contributed to wetting the gypsum board.

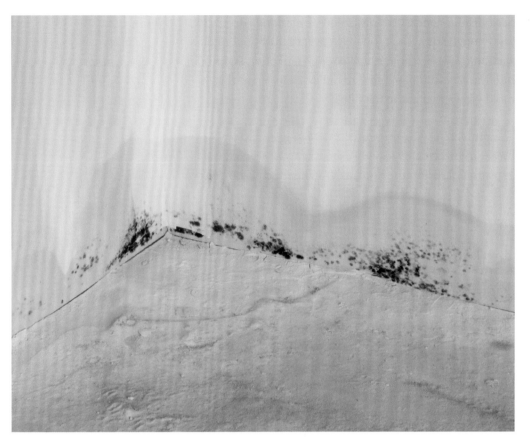

The photo at left shows water from a flood in a building under construction moving upwards via capillary suction into a concrete wall and a piece of gypsum board. Because the wall studs are steel, they are not porous enough to move water by capillary suction, but if they were wood, capillary suction would wet them, too.

The photos at right and below right show mold growing on the paper face of gypsum board in a basement that periodically floods. This basement never floods deeply, just enough so that water barely covers the floor. Capillary suction transports water high enough and often enough into the core and paper face of the gypsum board that mold grows well above the floor.

The problem can be prevented by creating a capillary break, in this case by leaving a **small gap** between the gypsum board and the floor, as shown in the photo below.

A **high water mark from a flood** is visible in the photo below, but that flood apparently did not cause any mold. The only place mold is growing on the gypsum board is above **where the gypsum board touches the concrete floor**. Elsewhere the **small gap** between the gypsum board and the concrete floor protected the gypsum board from getting wet by capillary suction and prevented mold, even where the board got wet in a flood. This shows that wetting from periodic floods has not caused mold growth, but the more constant wetting from capillary suction has.

The lowest part of the wall in the photo at right is faced with "tile backer board," which is not easily damaged by water, because it is made of fiberglass and cement.

Tile backer board was used because, during construction, someone smart noticed that this part of the building tended to get wet when the adjoining courtyard flooded after a heavy rain. Though any future flooding will still cause some damage, the wall will not be damaged as easily as if it were made of gypsum board.

In the photo at left, the light brown stucco wall is an exterior wall in a desert climate. The outermost layer of the wall is built with a gap to keep it above the outdoor walkway, creating a capillary break that will prevent capillary suction from pulling water up into the wall.

There is no gap under the wall next to the blue doorframe, but the doorway is set back into the wall, which reduces wetting in this area.

Subflorescence Damage

Subflorescence is the formation of efflorescence just below the surface of a material. Unlike efflorescence, subflorescence is damaging to masonry, as shown on the next few pages. The mechanism is explained in detail on Pages 209-211.

The brick pier in the photo at right is in the basement of a 1909 brownstone in Brooklyn, New York. The photo was taken in 2011, just after the building was gut renovated. It shows extensive damage to the mortar between the bricks near the bottom of the pier. The **pile of sand** on the floor in front of the pier is too neat and tidy to have been sitting there for 102 years. Therefore, much of the damage likely happened more recently.

Water in the soil under the building absorbed salts from the soil and traveled by capillary suction up into the pier. Apparently, during the renovation, the doors between the basement and outdoors were left open, offering a continuous supply of cold, dry air for the first time since the building was built. The dry air absorbed water from the surface of the pier, which was replaced by new water moved by capillary suction up from the soil. As the water evaporated, it left the salts behind in the pores of the masonry. The damage mechanism is associated with salts filling pores in the masonry, and is probably caused by salt crystals expanding and contracting with temperature changes (which does not require freeze-thaw cycles). A similar mechanism damaged the white finish **further up the pier**. Without the new supply of dry air, most of the water would have stayed in the masonry, and little or no damage would have occurred.

The pier in the photo at right supports a 100-year-old brick apartment building. **Pieces of brick on the floor** around the pier indicate recent and rapid damage. The owner had installed heating and air conditioning in the basement, both of which dried the basement air, causing water to evaporate from the masonry, leaving damaging salts behind and causing the bricks to crumble.

Even though both of the piers on this page rest on soil far from the edges of the buildings—meaning no rain has fallen on the soil directly under the piers for over 100 years—capillary suction keeps the soil wet enough to cause this damage. This demonstrates that all soil should be considered wet all the time.

The mortar on the lower part of the wall at right was crumbling, so it was replaced. The new mortar looks good, but now bricks are crumbling: one piece has fallen to the ground. This problem is often erroneously blamed on the new mortar being stronger than the old mortar. The real cause is that the new mortar mix is less vulnerable to subflorescence damage than the brick. This shifts the damage to the brick. The solution is to replace the new mortar with mortar that is similar to the original mortar.

The building below is in central Europe, where the specific humidity of the air is low (speeding up evaporation) and many buildings are old enough for subflorescence damage to be severe.

The damage to both of the walls on this page may have been worsened by the masonry absorbing water that contained ice-melting salt from the sidewalk, which is a more concentrated source of salt than normal soil.

Learn from History or Repeat It

The photo at right shows the remaining portion of a
building abandoned many years ago in a cold, mountainous
climate where freeze-thaw cycles are tough on masonry
that gets wet and stays wet.

The damage is the worst at the top and bottom. The middle
portion of the wall, which gets less wetting than the top
or bottom, is in okay condition. Note that the wall is on a
steep hill, so water pooling at the bottom of the building
cannot be blamed for keeping the soil wet. Capillary
suction generally keeps most soil in most climates saturated
enough to serve as an infinite source of water for walls.

The top gets wet from rain and snow, so the damage
mechanism at the top is probably freeze-thaw of the water
in the pores of the masonry. (Water fills pores in the bricks
and mortar, then freezes. The ice crystals expand with
enough pressure to break the bricks and mortar, thaw when
the sun comes out, and freeze again the very same night.)

The damage mechanism at the bottom of the wall might be
freeze-thaw, or it might be salts crystallizing in the pores of
the masonry (subflorescence), or both. Note that the stone
part of the wall is relatively undamaged, because the stone
is not nearly as porous as the bricks.

Wall Damage Quiz: Why is this wall damaged in this strange pattern? The dark-colored stone on the
bottom of the wall is a thin layer covering a thick brick wall behind it. Answer on Page 564.

Damaged bricks and mortar in a boiler
room far from the sidewalk show that
subflorescence damage can happen
without freeze-thaw cycles and far from
ice-melting salts.

How Subflorescence Damages a Building

① First, water dissolves salts that are in the soil, or already in the masonry (for example the bricks on Page 152). The drawings on this page show table salt (sodium chloride) ② dissolving in water, ③ forming **ions**—individual charged atoms of sodium (purple) or chlorine (green)—which stay suspended in the **water**, ④ binding to water molecules (see **red** and **blue** arrows in Drawing 3 below).

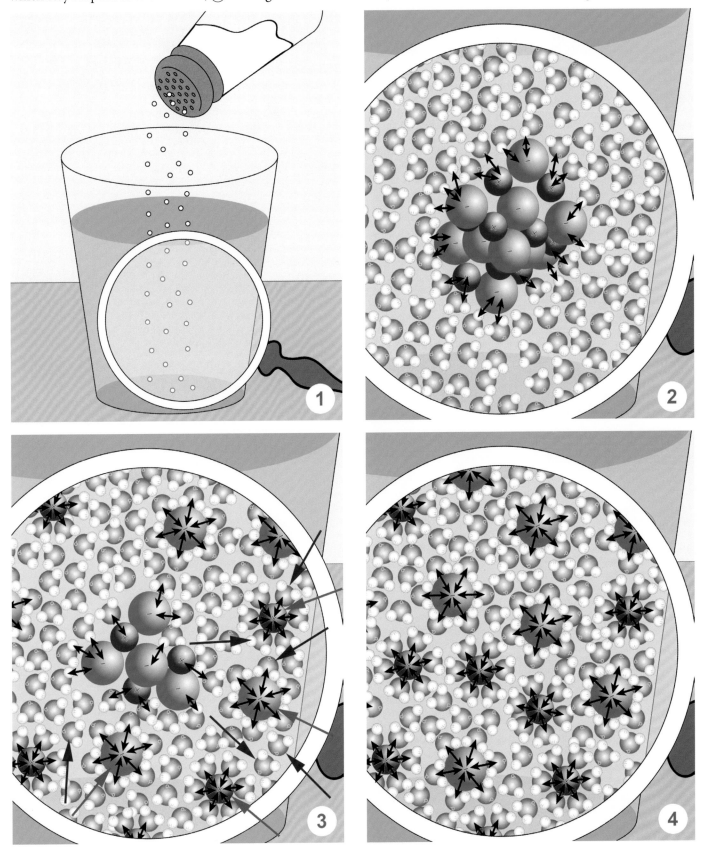

⑤ - ⑧ Capillary suction moves the water (see colored arrows in Drawing 8) containing the dissolved **salt ions** up through the building's foundation into **masonry** above the level of the soil, where it is exposed to air. Water evaporates from the masonry, leaving behind the salt ions, which re-combine as salt crystals within the pores at the surface of the masonry. Note that this is a mechanism which only operates at surfaces, where water can evaporate.

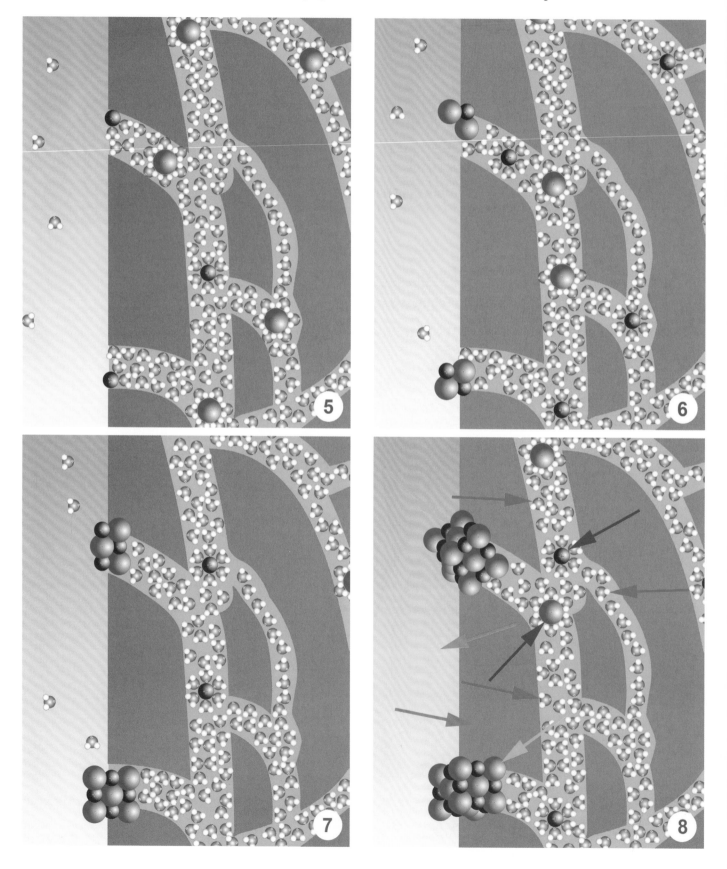

⑨ - ⑫ The salt crystals cause **pieces of the wall** to break off. Either bricks or mortar—or both—are destroyed, depending on their vulnerability. The exact mechanism may have to do with crystals expanding as they are formed, crystals expanding and contracting with changes in temperature, or a water pressure difference across the crystals. Different types of masonry have different pore structures, each of which is more complicated than can be shown in these two-dimensional drawings. The mechanism is called "salt wedging," "crystal growth wedging," or "haloclasty" in geology.

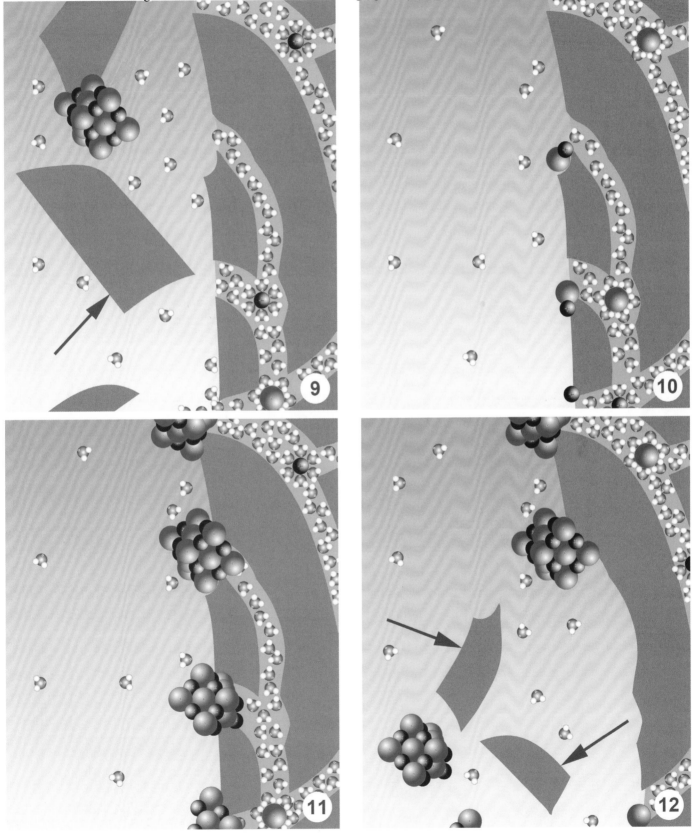

Prevent Damage with a Sacrificial Mortar Layer

In Europe, centuries of experience with subflorescence, where it is sometimes called "rising damp," have led to widespread use of a sacrificial mortar layer along the bottom meter (three feet) of the exposed wall. The sacrificial mortar layer, which is being applied in Drawing 3, does not stop or even slow down the capillary transport of water, or the salts dissolved in it. Rather, it protects the surface of the building from destruction.

The sacrificial mortar layer (Portland Cement and sand with some lime and maybe other additives) will slowly be destroyed by subflorescence. At that point, it is time to put on another sacrificial mortar layer (Drawing 7), which will protect the building for many more years, until it is time to put on another layer (Drawing 11). The sacrificial mortar layer should not merely move the damage further up the wall, as in Photo 12, but should have a pore structure that insures the sacrificial mortar layer will be destroyed, thus preserving the building.

When Building a New Building, Prevent Subflorescence with a Capillary Break

① Capillary suction pulls water from the soil up into a concrete **footing**, **floor**, and **wall**. ② Dig a ditch to undisturbed soil below any frost line. ③ Pour a reinforced concrete footing with a groove ("key") to hold the wall. ④ Trowel on a product similar to roofing tar to make a capillary break, or ⑤ apply a sheet-type capillary break product (blue in photo) on top of the footing. ⑥ Build the concrete foundation wall on top of the capillary break.

⑦ Protect the outdoor side of the wall with either a troweled-on capillary break product or a sheet product similar to the one shown in Photo 5. ⑧ Protect the floor slab (slab-on-grade) with stones large enough (19 mm [3/4"]) for the spaces between them to not be capillary pathways. ⑨ Use a plastic barrier to prevent soil gases, including water vapor, from coming up through cracks in the floor. ⑩ Pour the concrete floor slab. ⑪ Replace the soil on the outdoor side. ⑫ The capillary break protects the building from damage by capillary suction.

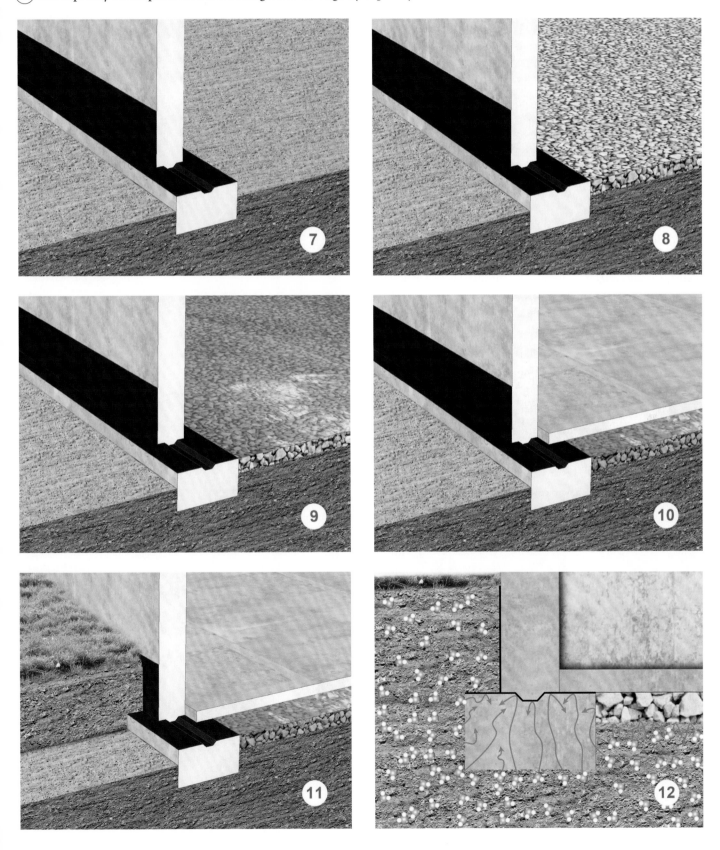

WETTING, STORAGE, AND DRYING: HOW MUCH STORAGE?

After reducing wetting as much as possible, the next consideration is the capacity of building materials to store water. Some walls, such as the thick brick walls which many buildings were built with in the 1800s, survive by storing water until they dry out later. Walls that work by storage have such a high water storage capacity that liquid water does not reach the indoor side of the wall in sufficient quantity to cause damage, despite the wall not having any barrier to liquid water. The wall in the photo at the top of Page 208, for example, apparently worked by storage until either people stopped heating the building, which took away the latent heat necessary to dry the walls, or the roof no longer protected it.

The photo at right shows a glass and steel office building. Except for the spray-on fireproofing on the structural steel, none of the materials visible have any significant water storage capacity. Therefore, any small water leak can result in damage to the indoor side of the wall.

The wall being built in the photo below is partly wood, partly steel. The part of the wall built from wood might be more durable than the part built from steel, because the wood can store water from a small leak until it dries later. The steel cannot store any water; therefore, a small amount of water might make the steel rust or might cause damage to a water-sensitive part of the wall (gypsum board, wood trim, etc.) backed up with steel studs.

An extension is being added onto the top of the building in the photo at right. The extension is built with less masonry and more glass than the older part, below. This makes it more vulnerable to water damage, because glass cannot store any water.

Both of the photos on this page show the underside of roofs in buildings under construction. Both have concrete block walls and "flat" (slightly pitched) roofs.

The **roof deck** in the photo at right is made of concrete. Therefore, any small leak in the roof can be absorbed by the concrete and will dry out later.

The **roof deck** in the photo below is made of steel and therefore cannot store any water. Any small leak can result in damage to the steel (rusting) or to the water-sensitive ceiling materials that will be installed, such as gypsum board or acoustic tiles.

Understanding water storage is critical to understanding building durability. But maximizing a building's water storage capacity by building massive fortress-like walls of brick or wood is not an economically viable strategy for building a durable building. (Building that way requires too much time, money, and space.)

As the building industry increasingly relies on materials that cannot store much water, designs must change to reduce wetting and encourage drying.

WETTING, STORAGE, AND DRYING: HOW MUCH DRYING?

Everything gets wet. The question is: How wet, and for how long?

Reducing wetting is critical, as explained earlier in this chapter. Storage can prevent damage when water spreads throughout enough material to keep the water concentration reasonably low when it is absorbed within a material that is relatively resistant to water damage. But building materials eventually need to dry out, or they will either be destroyed by water or covered with mold.

Drying takes energy: the latent heat of evaporation. If a building is not insulated, and is heated during the winter in a cold climate, its walls and roof have a warm side and a warm side. The outdoor side is not as warm as the indoor side, and the indoor side is not as warm as it would be if the wall were insulated, but the indoor side and the outdoor side are both warm, because heat from the heating system is going from the indoor side to the outdoor side and warming the outdoor side of the wall or roof, as well. During the summer, uninsulated walls and roofs have a warm side and a warm side, too, because heat is going from the outdoor side to the indoor side and warming the indoor side of the wall or roof, even with air conditioning. But nobody is comfortable in an uninsulated building, and nobody wants to pay the energy costs of living in an uninsulated building. Modern buildings in most climates get insulated, which causes the walls and roof to have a warm side and a cold side during the winter, as well as during the summer.

The more insulation an assembly has, the colder the cold side of the assembly gets. This is one reason modern buildings can have durability problems older buildings didn't have: one side of the walls and roof are colder and therefore wetter. The problem is worse at outside corners, where a wall is even colder, because it has more outdoor surface than indoor surface. In the future, as buildings become insulated even better, the cold side of building enclosures will keep getting colder.

Buildings need to be able to dry, and drying must be accomplished with ever smaller amounts of heat passing through walls. One way to help buildings

dry is to make sure walls can dry in both directions: toward indoors or toward outdoors. Many factors determine the direction water will move through a wall as it dries, including temperature, relative humidity, sun, wind, rain, air pressure differences, and other factors.

Knowing the direction of drying is not as important as making sure water can leave in both directions. If there is something in the wall that stops the drying in one direction or another, damage could result.

Walls are often built with a water vapor barrier, such as a sheet of clear plastic, with the intention of preventing wetting by water vapor diffusion. Some wall coverings added after construction, such as vinyl wallpaper, mirrors, and plastic classroom blackboards, are barriers to water vapor, too. In the case of roofs, the roofing material that is a barrier to liquid water is usually also a barrier to water vapor. Because a vapor barrier reduces drying, it is usually not a good idea to include or add a vapor barrier. The wisdom of deliberately adding vapor barriers versus building without them will be discussed in more detail in Chapter 16: Building Enclosures.

This building is located in a climate with hot summers and cold winters. Why are the bricks at the right side of the photo deteriorating, while the same bricks at the left side of the photo are fine? Wetting, storage, or drying? The bricks at the right side of the photo get more wetting than the bricks on the left, because they are on a one-story wall surrounding a garden, with no building above them sheltering them from rain. Also the garden wall is unheated, while the bricks at the left side of the photo are backed up by a heated building. Heat available to dry the bricks on the left probably makes the biggest difference in lifespan, but the difference in wetting is also a factor, as evidenced by more damage to bricks higher up on the garden wall.

The photo at top right shows a piece of foam insulation that will be attached to the outdoor side of a wall with a cement-based adhesive.

The trowel used to apply the adhesive, shown in the photo at middle right, has notches to create grooves that will allow water to drain out if it leaks past the foam when it rains. The grooves also allow a little air to circulate behind the insulation to dry water that has been absorbed into the building materials. The adhesive at top right, however, has been applied incorrectly: the circular pattern will not allow water to drain, nor will it allow much air to circulate.

The photo below shows adhesive that has been applied correctly: the straight, vertical grooves will maximize drying.

Because air can hold a lot of water vapor, but not a lot of heat, the energy penalty for allowing a small amount of air to leak behind the insulation is minimal. Described another way, a small amount of air leaking behind the insulation will not move much heat but can remove a lot of water.

Allowing a small amount of air to leak from outdoors into a wall—but not through it—and then back outdoors yields such an increase in building durability that it is well worth the small energy penalty. That said, it is always important for building durability to reduce—or, if possible, eliminate—air leaks that go all the way through a wall.

Drying with Outdoor Air

The two drawings on this page show the mechanism of cold outdoor air drying an indoor "flood." The drawing at right shows water spilled indoors on a cold winter day.

The drawing below shows cold outdoor air leaking in under the window at right. The outdoor air has a high relative humidity, shown by the bucket being almost full, but does not hold much water, because it is cold air (symbolized by the small bucket).

The air is heated by the heating system when it enters the house, shown by a large red bucket. The hot air mixes with indoor air that is not close to the radiator, and therefore is not as hot, which cools the hot air (symbolized by the purple bucket). The warm air still has the capacity to absorb much more water vapor (the purple bucket is not full). As the air passes by the small flood, it absorbs the water vapor that has evaporated from the floor, and the level of water in the purple buckets rises. Even a small amount of air leaking in and getting warmed is capable of absorbing a lot of water vapor.

The air leaks back outdoors, via another window, where it will have higher relative humidity and higher specific humidity than it did before it entered the house.

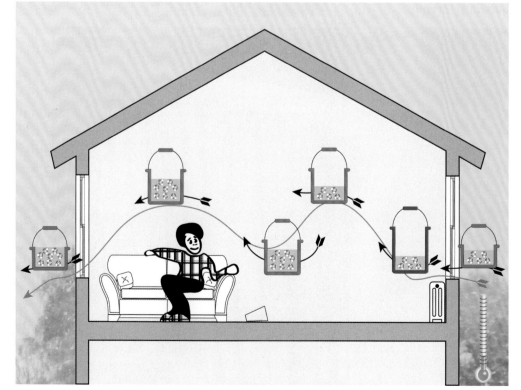

Outdoor air that is warmer than indoor air is not useful for drying a flood unless it is extremely dry and is only a little warmer than indoor air.

In the two drawings on this page, the outdoor summer air leaking in under the window at right is hot (large red bucket) and relatively humid (almost full bucket).

The air is cooled by the cooling system when it enters the house, shown by a purple bucket that holds the same amount of water as the red bucket but is now full—and therefore not able to absorb any more water than it already holds. Because the bucket (air) is full, water will not evaporate into it.

Opening windows to allow a large amount of outdoor air through the house might help absorb a little water vapor (the small remaining space in the red bucket at right) but at the risk of encouraging mold growth. (The air conditioning system can't cool and dry all the outdoor air, which will raise both the indoor temperature and the relative humidity, both of which encourage mold growth.) A better strategy would be to reduce air leaks as much as possible (best done before a flood), and run the air conditioning system until the building dries, while maybe also operating the heating system to keep the cooling system from turning off.

Four Steps for Drying a Flooded Building

Instead of drying a flooded building after a flood, it is better to prevent flooding in the first place. But floods happen. The following four steps should be kept in mind when drying out a building after a flood.

1. Prevent Mold Growth above the Flood Level

A flooded building's high indoor humidity makes it vulnerable to mold growth. Time is critical. One to three days of high indoor humidity is usually all it takes to cause significant visible mold growth. Depending on temperature and the type of building material available as food, mold generally requires a minimum of 85 percent relative humidity at a surface, and grows faster at higher humidity levels. Mold growth inside a building during and after a flood can be more expensive and time consuming to repair than any other damage from a flood, but it is often preventable. Steps to prevent mold growth should be taken as soon as possible, even if the lower part of the building is still submerged in flood water.

Before understanding how to prevent mold growth, it is important to understand a bit about mold and how it grows. The mold that grows inside buildings is really various species of fungi, which also grow outdoors and whose spores (microscopic seeds) are in the air around us all the time. Preventing mold growth by removing every fungus spore from the air is not realistic, except for in special rooms such as laboratories, which use very large filters and very large, noisy, energy-intensive fans.

Preventing mold growth by removing all mold food from a building is not realistic either, because mold can eat the dust in the air when the dust sticks to a wet or damp surface, such as tile grout. But mold favors some types of food over others, and it needs high relative humidity to grow, so it is realistic to control mold growth by preventing high relative humidity, especially where the foods mold prefers are present.

Each of the countless types of mold lives by digesting organic matter, just as people do. But mold has no teeth, so instead of biting off a piece of food, chewing it into smaller pieces, and then adding stomach acids to digest it, mold digests its food externally. It excretes digestive enzymes onto food, the enzymes break down the food, and then the mold eats the resulting mixture. Some of the chemicals excreted are poisonous to other species of mold, which explains why mold growth typically only involves a limited number of species growing on one part of a building. The antibiotic penicillin is a chemical excreted by Penicillium fungi. The word antibiotic literally means "anti-life." The ability to secrete an anti-life chemical is a handy superpower for an organism to have. But penicillin not only kills other microorganisms, it can also cause severe allergic reactions in people, which is why doctors and nurses ask people if they are allergic to penicillin.

It should be no surprise that people can also be allergic to other chemicals that various types of mold excrete. Mold exposure symptoms include sneezing, itchy eyes, coughing, runny nose, and increased incidence of asthma. People who are not initially allergic to fungi and the chemicals they produce can easily become allergic after

Though the flooding in this office is not deep, water is evaporating from the entire surface of the big puddle, adding enough water vapor to the air to put everything—carpet, walls, furniture—at risk of growing mold.

exposure. Sensitivity depends on previous exposure—how much and for how long—and also depends on an individual person's genetic predisposition, age, overall health, and sensitivity to other strains of fungi present at the same time. Unlike exposure to pathogens such as bacteria, to which the human body can build up an immunity, repeated exposure to chemicals generally worsens a person's sensitivity. It is virtually impossible to measure a person's sensitivity to all the possible combinations of different chemicals produced by all the different strains of fungi, or combinations of them. Instead of trying to find out which mold strains a person is allergic to, it is smarter and safer to eliminate conditions favorable to indoor growth of any mold.

Mold can digest dead wood, which is why forest floors are not covered with all the trees that have ever died. (Live plants have defense mechanisms.) But because mold does not have teeth, it is easier for mold to digest wood after it has been shaved into thin layers to make plywood. Even easier is wood chopped up into smaller pieces and glued together as chipboard. The easiest form of wood for mold to eat is paper, which is finely shredded wood. On the outdoor side of a building, wood can last for many years but plywood not as long. Paper-faced gypsum board should never be exposed to rain, even during construction. In a flooded building, the paper facing on gypsum board is often the first place mold grows.

Different species of mold prefer different humidity levels, and the preferred humidity level depends on temperature. Most species, however, require 85 percent or higher relative humidity. Note that air at 50 percent relative humidity in the middle of a room can easily be at 90 percent or higher relative humidity near a cold surface within the same room.

Lower temperatures generally slow biological activity, including mold growth. At lower temperatures, mold generally requires higher relative humidity levels, which is why people put food in refrigerators. Food in a refrigerator will still grow mold; it just takes longer. People do not like to live at temperatures found inside refrigerators, so preventing mold growth in buildings depends mainly on controlling humidity.

Most types of mold will not grow underwater, so the parts of the building covered by flood water are temporarily protected. A short distance above the flood level, the part of the walls wet by capillary suction can also be too wet to grow mold. Of course, when the flood waters recede, the wet materials can dry to levels ideal for mold growth. The greatest mold risk to a flooded building is above the parts of the building submerged by the flood or wet by capillary suction. When flood water submerges the first floor of a tall building, it is not unusual for the resulting high humidity to cause mold to grow throughout every other floor of the building, requiring the walls, doors, ceilings, carpets, and furniture to be replaced throughout the whole building.

Mold will usually not grow on a basement floor made of concrete or basement walls made of concrete, stone, or brick, because the chemistry of the masonry (very alkaline) resists mold. But if a flooded basement has a gypsum board ceiling, the paper on the gypsum board will often be the first place mold grows, because the water on the floor will keep the air in the basement humid.

During the winter, the easiest way to lower both the temperature and the humidity of the air in a flooded building is to open doors and windows to let cold air into the building. This will work even on a rainy or snowy day. If the flooded building has a basement, basement doors and windows should be opened, even if the basement is not flooded. Opening one or more doors or windows high up in the building, such as on the top floor, will also help prevent mold growth. This is because it helps move a lot of air via the stack effect, as described on Page 80.

A window in a flooded building opened a little during the winter. Water vapor has condensed out of the air onto the glass as **liquid** and onto the windowsill as **frost**. Condensation on the windows can be a guide to how far to open the windows: open further if water is condensing on the windows. The heating system is running full, while outdoor air colder than freezing is keeping the air in the building cold and much drier than a mechanical dehumidifier can achieve.

Because the outdoor air is cold, it is a psychrometric fact that its specific humidity is low. Therefore, when it enters the building and warms up, its relative humidity drops as shown on Pages 144 and 220, usually far below levels mold will tolerate. Cold outdoor air will warm up when it enters almost any building, including a building with a heating system destroyed by a flood, because solar gain through windows and thermal coupling with the soil under the building will keep almost any building warmer than the outdoor air during the winter. Cold winter air entering an unheated building will be warmed enough to lower its relative humidity—but not warmed enough to encourage biological activity such as mold growth.

The faster cold air is moved into the building and heated, the lower the humidity in the indoor air will be, and the faster the air will absorb water vapor. This will speed up the rate at which the building will dry, preventing mold growth. If the heating system is working, drying can be done even faster by turning the heating system on while the windows are open or using fans to blow cold outdoor air through the heated building. The energy bills will also rise quickly, but that will be much cheaper than replacing moldy walls and carpets. If the heating system is not working, turning on the lights will add a significant amount of heat. (Although, as lighting technologies become more energy efficient, this is becoming less true.)

Because winter air is cold, it can, in effect, refrigerate all the mold food in the building. This delays the growth of mold just as a refrigerator does.

Cold outdoor air is conveniently available after floods caused by frozen pipes, but it is not available after summer hurricanes. Moving hot and humid summer air through the building can increase the relative humidity, which will do more harm than good. A fast way to dry a wet building surrounded by hot and humid air is to close the windows to keep the hot and humid air out and turn on the air conditioning (cooling) system. As the humid air passes over the cold part of the cooling system, water will condense out of the air and go down the drain pipe connected to the air

conditioning system. At the same time, the cooling system will delay the growth of mold by cooling the building.

If the cooling system cools the building so much that there is no cooling load on the system (not enough heat in the building), the cooling system will turn off. Figuring out how to operate a cooling system and a heating system simultaneously, which is how some car windshield defoggers work, is one thing that can be done when preparing ahead for a flood. Kerosene- or propane-fired heaters, often used on construction sites, should not be used, because combustion adds water vapor to the air, as explained in Chapter 11: Fire - Basic Science. Portable electric heaters are a better choice, because they will add heat without adding water vapor to the air. A gas- or oil-fired heating system does produce water vapor as part of the combustion process, but these types of heating systems usually vent their exhaust to outdoors and therefore do not increase the humidity indoors.

If the outdoor air is hot and dry, opening doors and windows might help, or might not. A hygrometer (a device that measures humidity) and a thermometer can measure outdoor and indoor humidity and temperature, and a psychrometric chart can show if the outdoor air contains less water vapor than the indoor air. Warm outdoor air should be used with caution because, even if it is dry, it involves the risk of increased mold growth associated with higher temperature.

Portable dehumidifiers and fans waiting to be deployed.

Yet another way to dry the building is to call a fire and restoration company. They usually have dozens of portable dehumidifiers and fans, as well as staff who know how to use them. Some of these companies can connect the building via ducts to large dehumidifiers mounted on trucks, which might be the only option if a fire or flood has destroyed the building's heating and cooling systems.

In order to prevent mold growth, these methods of drying the air inside a building should be implemented as soon as possible after a flood, even if the lower part of a building is still flooded. Next, the water flooding the lower part of the building should be removed as soon as possible, as described below.

2. Remove Liquid Water from the Building

Liquid water is best removed by gravity. If a sewer is available, that is the best place for the water to go. During floods, building contents can easily clog a floor drain. Therefore, the lower floor of a building should be kept clear of clutter.

It is common for sewers to back up during heavy rainstorms. A backup, unlike a clogged sewer, is when the water level in the sewer rises, sometimes above the level of drain pipe connections. If sewers frequently back up into a building, it is possible to protect the building by eliminating all sewer connections (sinks, toilets, floor drains, etc.) below a chosen flood level. Ground level is usually a good level to choose, because if the sewers in the area back up higher than the ground around the building, water will get into the building through doorways. All drains below the chosen level can drain by gravity to a container in the floor with a pump that pumps into the sewer, preventing backflow from the sewer into the container with either a check valve (one-way valve) or running the pipe above the flood level and back down (vented to prevent the sewage from siphoning back), or both. This strategy requires a pump and some extra piping, but it can permanently eliminate

flooding caused by a sewer backing up. In areas with sewers that back up, this can make the difference between a basement that is useless and one that is valuable space.

After most of the water from a flood is drained into a sewer or pumped out, there will probably still be some water in low spots on the floor. This water should be removed as a liquid, because removing it as a gas requires too much energy and too much time. A significant amount of mold can start to grow one to three days after the humidity gets high, so time is precious.

A quick and easy way to scoop up the last remaining puddles of water is to use a dustpan that has a cover, or scoop. The dustpan can scoop up the water, which can be dumped into a garbage can, from which it can be dumped into a toilet or outdoors. A second person using a broom to sweep water into the dustpan can help remove water even faster. Finally, a mop can get the last of the water off the floor. A mop with a lever on the handle to squeeze the water out will speed up the process by avoiding the need to bend down repeatedly.

Every last drop of water that can be removed as a liquid should be, because evaporation takes much longer. Also, as long as there is some liquid water in the building, it will be adding water vapor to the air, which will slow the drying of the materials the building is made of.

A dustpan with a scoop to hold dust works well for scooping water up from a floor.

Vinyl baseboard molding is a barrier to water vapor, which prevents drying at the bottom of the wall. Removing it allows the wall to dry.

3. Remove Wet Contents

Wet cardboard boxes, furniture, and books will not only get eaten by mold; they will act as a water reservoir, keeping the air in the building humid. Draining liquid water from a building is not complete until the wet contents of a building are removed from the building.

Wet belongings should be put outdoors in two piles: contents to save and contents to throw away. (If in doubt, throw it out.) A sunny location will accelerate drying. A large sheet of plastic can offer protection from rain, but it should be removed as soon as the rain stops.

The belongings that will not be saved should be placed some distance from the building to protect people in the building from mold.

4. Remove Liquid Water Absorbed in the Building's Materials

The liquid water absorbed into the walls and floors and maybe even ceilings of a flooded building (or any building that has a problem with dampness or the resulting mold) will only leave as a gas: water vapor.

If the first step was done properly, this part of the process will already be under way: the air in the building is as dry as possible. The highest-capacity dehumidifier available is cold outdoor air, which moves water outdoors as shown at the bottom of Page 220. When circulated through a heated building, this air will be drier than any

air a mechanical dehumidifier can produce. Mechanical dehumidifiers and cooling systems both work by passing air over a coil (heat exchanger) cooled by a refrigerant (Freon® or a modern equivalent), and the lowest indoor air temperature at which such a system can operate has to be above the freezing point of water, or ice will form on the cold coil. Because cold outdoor air does not have this limitation, it can be, and often is, much drier than all but what a special dehumidifier can produce. The only limitations on how many windows should be open, and how far they should be open, is damage to the interior by rain or snow or frozen pipes. A thermometer will reveal whether the building is warm enough to protect pipes from freezing. As already mentioned, using outdoor air to keep the building cold will also reduce mold growth.

The second-highest-capacity dehumidifier immediately available is probably the building's cooling system, which sends water down a nearby drain. If necessary, add a

The **dehumidifier** condenses water vapor out of the air and pumps the liquid water into the **garbage can**. The **fan** circulates dry air along the floor, preventing areas of high humidity where latent cooling near wet floors creates a layer of cool air. Note that the baseboard molding has been removed (see close-up at top of page) to increase drying at the bottom of the wall.

source of heat to keep the building's cooling system from turning off in response to the low temperature. If neither cold air nor the building's cooling system are available, use portable dehumidifiers. Portable dehumidifiers used in combination with a building's cooling system can speed drying. And, because portable dehumidifiers add some heat to the air, they help keep the cooling system from turning off, too.

Regardless of what type of drying is available, fans need to be used to circulate dry air through the wettest areas, especially near the bottoms of walls. Walls get wetter at the bottom, because gravity moves liquid water down, and because capillary suction moves water from wet floors up into walls bottom first. Also, not much air moves around near the intersection of floors and walls, because air circulation tends to be poor in corners. In addition, when floors are wet, latent cooling creates a layer of cool air that convection holds near the floor, which prevents drying. Baseboard moldings, even wood moldings, slow drying at the bottoms of walls, too. This combination of more wetting and less drying means the bottoms of walls are very vulnerable to mold growth after a flood. Because of this, baseboard moldings should be removed as soon as possible after a flood and should not be reinstalled until the building is thoroughly dried.

The last part of a house to dry can be the wall behind the kitchen cabinets, because air can't get to it, and because kitchen cabinets typically have a gloss finish, which acts as a barrier to water vapor. This can cause the wall behind cabinets to grow mold while the rest of the house dries out quickly enough to prevent mold growth. Opening the cabinet drawers and doors encourages drying, but, in many cases, the cabinets need to be removed to allow the walls to fully dry. Removing them is a lot of work but not as much work as removing them and then replacing the wall behind them.

This file cabinet is made of steel, which is a barrier to water vapor. If the steel bottom is left flat on the floor, it will prevent water from evaporating out of the carpet underneath it. After the flood, the cabinet was raised off the floor on pieces of cardboard to allow air to circulate underneath. Cardboard is a good choice, because water in the carpet will move by capillary suction up through the cardboard to its surface, where it will evaporate. The cabinet has also been moved away from the wall to allow air to circulate behind it. The fan is moving air around, under, and behind the cabinet to speed up evaporation. Note that the baseboard molding has been removed.

To allow office floors to dry, file cabinets without legs, like the one in the photo at left, need to be lifted off the floor, and plastic chair mats need to be removed. Furniture that will be used in any flood-prone part of a building should be chosen to allow drying from underneath. In homes, kitchen cabinet doors should be opened. Unfortunately, the cabinets themselves often need to be removed, too. (See photo caption above).

The methods described here, which are based on building science principles, can minimize damage to a flooded building. The two most important are reducing humidity, and, if possible, also reducing temperature, both as quickly as possible. This can make the difference between a building so damaged that it needs to be completely replaced and a building so little damaged that it can be used again as soon as it dries out.

PREVENT FLOODING CAUSED BY FROZEN PIPES

It is good to know how to dry out a building after a flood but even better to prevent a flood in the first place. Any building located in a climate cold enough for water to freeze will probably someday be without heat, either because of an equipment breakdown or because of an electricity outage. It is worth looking at a building, or a building design, and figuring out where the "first freeze" location is: the water pipe most vulnerable to freezing. After finding it, prevent freezing by moving the pipe or adding additional airtightening, insulation, or heat.

During unusually cold weather, pipes can freeze in buildings even while the heating system is working. Unusually cold outdoor temperature can cause an extra strong stack effect to pull more air than usual in at the bottom of the building, which can cause pipes to freeze. The lower floors of buildings can be the most vulnerable when the heat is off, because solar gain and other sources of heat such as lights and people create a stack effect.

The drawings below show the same bathroom with the water pipes installed in different locations. The pipes in the drawing at bottom left are installed inside the wall on the right, which is an outdoor wall. The drawing at bottom right shows the pipes for the tub and shower in the interior wall on the left and the pipes for the toilet and sink in the floor. If the heat stops working during cold weather, the pipes in the bathroom on the left will freeze first, because its pipes are in an outside wall, where they will cool more quickly than pipes in a floor or an interior wall, regardless of how well the wall or the pipes are insulated. Gaps around pipes in an outside wall can create a pathway for air to leak through a wall, making it difficult to airtighten the building and prevent freezing. It is smarter and safer to locate water pipes in interior walls and floors.

Looking for the most likely first freeze locations and reducing the chances of those pipes freezing can prevent floods. An even better strategy is to protect the piping with an airtightened and insulated building enclosure, so solar gain in the windows will prevent freezing even if the building goes without heat or electricity during the winter.

Wall Quiz #3: Why is green moss growing on the wall in that strange curved pattern? Wetting, storage, or drying? Answer on Page 561.

Wall Quizzes
What is going on with these walls?

Wall Quiz #4: Why is moss growing on only one part of this wall, but not on the rest of the wall or the fence to the right? Wetting, storage, or drying? Clue: Photo was taken during the winter. Answer on Page 562.

Wall Quiz #5: Why is moss growing on only one part of the brick chimney? Wetting, storage, or drying? Answer on Page 564.

BUILDINGS START LIFE WET

Many new buildings have moisture problems that can be traced back to rain wetting the building materials on the delivery truck or before the roof and windows were installed. Paint, joint compound, caulk, adhesives, and new wood all add water vapor to air as they cure or dry out. And a large amount of water evaporates from new concrete in the first year or two, too.

During the winter, as soon as a new building is reasonably raintight, it should be dried with ventilation and heating. If people have not moved in yet, ventilation can be done with windows. Buildings under construction are actually more vulnerable to water damage during the summer, when they are surrounded by and filled with hot, humid air. During the summer, as soon as a new building is reasonably airtight, it should be dried with dehumidifiers.

SUMMARY

Some building designs depend on a perfect barrier to liquid water or water vapor as part of the assembly. This is a risky way to design an assembly, because it is hard to do anything perfectly or keep anything in perfect condition. A barrier to water vapor, in particular, is risky, because it reduces drying. The safest approach is to minimize wetting as much as possible, but assume that everything gets wet sooner or later, while paying attention to the three water questions:

1. How often will the building materials get wet, and how wet will each building material get?

2. How well can these building materials store water?

3. How soon will these building materials dry?

Mold Quiz: This bedroom is in a building that is heated by a steam heating system. A radiator in this room leaked steam, increasing the humidity and causing mold to grow. Why is mold growing on two walls but not on the ceiling or on the wall to the right? Wetting, storage, or drying? Answer on Page 562.

Chapter 7 **Light** Basic Science

WHAT IS LIGHT?

Light is energy in the form of a stream of photon particles or a series of electromagnetic waves—or both—a contradiction that can only be answered in the realm of quantum physics, which is not necessary for understanding building science.

Visible light behaves about the same as infrared radiation: it generally travels in a straight line and is so fast that its speed is difficult to measure. Some materials absorb it, some reflect it, and some materials, such as air, are completely or almost completely transparent to it. And just like infrared radiation (covered in Chapter 1: Heat - Basic Science), visible light varies in intensity from a small quantity to a large quantity. Unlike infrared radiation, however, visible light can be seen with the human eye.

Light travels until it hits an object, at which point it is usually partly reflected, partly absorbed, and—if the object has some transparency—partly transmitted. In theory, light does not lose any intensity as a result of traveling through air; it only loses intensity from spreading out in many directions from its source. In reality, air contains dust, which reflects light and which turns light into heat by absorbing it. Most other objects also turn light into heat when they absorb it, with the notable exception of solar electric panels, which turn some visible light (and some of the ultraviolet light in sunlight) into electricity. If a light is turned on in a room with no windows or other openings, and there is no solar-powered calculator in the room, all the light will be absorbed by objects in the room and will become heat as soon as it is absorbed. The light may be reflected back and forth many times before being absorbed, but eventually it will all be absorbed.

What Is Color?

People perceive different wavelengths of light as different colors.[1] Sunlight is a mixture of light of many different wavelengths, only some of which people can see.

Our brains perceive white light when a mix of all the colors of the rainbow reaches our eyes. Described another way, light looks white when in fact it is a mix of all the wavelengths of light between infrared radiation and ultraviolet light. The white light reaching our eyes could be reflected from an object such as a white piece of paper, or it could be emitted directly from a source, such as the sun or a white light bulb.

If the light reaching our eyes is not a mixture of all the colors of the rainbow, our eyes perceive the light as being colored. For example, **this text** looks red, because the ink it was printed with absorbs light of all colors except red, while reflecting red light. A car's red taillight has a white light bulb that gives off all the colors of the rainbow (white light) and a plastic lens that absorbs light of all colors except red, leaving only red light passing through the lens, which makes the light look red.

In theory, light can travel indefinitely through air, but, in reality, light is reflected and absorbed by dust in air. The light streaming through the windows is visible in this photo because it is reflecting off dust, without which the light would not produce a dramatic image like this.

1   Nobody has ever seen the images our eyes send to our brains, leaving open the question of whether it is our eyes or our brains that create the images we see as colors. Creating the images is a little like manufacturing an infrared camera: the designer gets to choose which wavelengths the camera shows as each visible light color. One can only imagine what images in the brains of other animals look like to them, especially animals that can see different wavelengths than we can, such as ticks who can see infrared radiation, or bats, who can "see" by reflecting sound waves off objects.

If a red object such as a tomato is lit with white light, it looks red because it absorbs all the colors in white light except red, which it reflects. If the tomato is lit only with red light from a car's taillight, and no other light, the tomato would still look red, because the red light is reflected off the red tomato to the viewer's eyes, making the tomato look red.

A green object looks black when lit up in the red light of a car's taillight (see next page), because a green object absorbs all colors of light except green, including red. It would not look exactly the same as a black piece of paper, because the human brain uses many other clues to determine what color something really is, including the texture of an object and the colors of surrounding objects. The situation is further confused because the taillight lens is not a perfect filter and therefore does allow some light that is not red to pass through, and the green object is not perfectly green either and therefore does reflect some light that is not green. But, a perfectly green colored object would look black if lit by a perfectly red light.

A black object would look black when lit with a red taillight, because it reflects little light of any color. A white object would look red when lit with a red taillight, because it would be reflecting only the red light hitting it, instead of the mixture of light that makes up white light.

The red taillight is an extreme example of a problem called "color rendering," which is the effect a light source has on the apparent color of an object.

A lettuce and tomato salad on a white plate on a black and white background, lit by the white lights of car taillights (the red and amber lights are off). The salad looks normal, because the white taillights are capable of good color rendering.

Color Rendering

Color rendering is considered as accurate as possible in sunlight and inaccurate when ambient light is not a mix of colors approximating white light.

Color rendering is one of the reasons people prefer sunlight to any other source of light: the colors are accurate. Incandescent bulbs—that is, the now-obsolete screw-in bulbs that were the standard household bulb for many years—have relatively good color rendering, while most other types of artificial light cause some inaccuracy. The worst are probably the sodium vapor lights that are sometimes used in parking lots because they are energy efficient. The color rendering with these lights is so inaccurate that everything looks yellow, which makes it hard to find your car at night. The photos on the next page, taken with different-colored car taillights, are an extreme example of color rendering.

As the taillight example illustrates, colors perceived by the eye and brain depend on two main factors: the mixture of colors of light coming from the source and the colors of light reflected by the subject.

In the photo at right, only the bulbs behind the amber (yellowish) part of each lens are lit. In the photo below, only the bulbs behind the red part of each lens are lit.

The lettuce in the photo at right still looks a little green, maybe because the amber lenses allow some green light to pass through. The lettuce below looks black, as it should when lit by a red light.

In both photos, the black parts of the background still look black, because black does not reflect much light of any color.

In both photos, the white parts of the background have taken on a color similar to the color of the lens that is lit up, because white surfaces reflect all colors of light, and mostly amber (above) and red (left) pass through the taillight lenses.

Color Rendering Index

In the mid-1900s, the lighting industry developed a way of rating the color rendering quality of a light source, which is called the "Color Rendering Index." Most incandescent bulbs have a CRI of 100, which is the highest rating possible. Light sources that do not do as good a job of rendering colors are rated at lower CRI numbers, sometimes as low as zero or even lower.

Unfortunately, CRI ratings are not as useful with newer lighting sources, such as fluorescent lights and LEDs. CRI ratings were created to rate how well a light source renders a selection of eight pastel colors. That was a good way to rate incandescent bulbs, which generally did a good job of rendering skin tones and other non-pastel colors but sometimes did a bad job of rendering pastel colors. But many new light sources might do well with pastel colors, earning a high CRI rating, while doing a bad job rendering other colors.

The lighting industry is working on better ways to describe a light source's rendering accuracy. But until a new system is widely adopted, CRI ratings should be seen as a helpful but incomplete indication of a light source's rendering accuracy. Fortunately, the human brain is good at adjusting for inaccurate color rendering, making inaccurate color rendering a minor annoyance with most everyday tasks.

Color Temperature

The mix of all the colors of the rainbow that adds up to white light can have more of some colors than others, which causes minor differences in color rendering. "Color temperature" is a way of describing the mix of colors in a white light source. The color temperature of a light source is rated by a number that roughly follows the mix of white light that can be expected to be emitted by a piece of iron heated to the temperature specified by the color temperature rating number. A mix with a lot of blue is assigned a high temperature number and is paradoxically described as a "cold" light, while lower temperature numbers are more "warm," or red. The color temperature of a candle is "warm," as is sunrise. Light from incandescent bulbs is slightly cooler (more blue). Fluorescent lights and LEDs are available in a wide range of color temperatures but generally produce light cooler than incandescent bulbs.

Sunlight has a lot of red in the mix near sunrise and sundown (is warmer) and has more blue in the mix at other times (is cooler).

Light that is more blue in color helps with contrast, which causes people to perceive it as brighter than equally bright light that is more red in color. This could be used as a strategy to save electricity by installing fewer lights of a bluer color. However, studies have shown that light that is more red in color, also known as light that is "warmer," can change people's perceptions of thermal comfort—they think the room is warmer, and stop complaining that they are cold, even with no change in actual room temperature.

The best choice is generally a light that looks as white as possible, which generally means a high CRI, or a high rating on whatever scale is used to rate color rendering in the future. All the bulbs in one room should be the same or a similar color temperature, to make the color look more uniform than in the photo below.

The bulb in **one of the light fixtures** is a different color temperature than the others. The difference can be seen by looking at either the light reflecting off the ceiling near the fixtures or the light reflecting off the wall. The bulb should be replaced with one that has the same color temperature as the others.

How Much Light?

How much light a person needs to see what she is doing depends on the person and the task she is performing. Old people need more light than young people, and tasks such as sports, personal grooming, cooking, and surgery need more light than eating, bathing, and walking down a hallway.

People's eyes are especially good at seeing differences in color, such as in the photo on the previous page, and differences in light levels. Consistent, even light levels help people pay attention to the task at hand, instead of paying attention to different light levels. People's eyes can adjust to dim lighting but cannot easily read a poorly lit book in a brightly lit surrounding. A person can read a brightly lit book in an otherwise dark room but would have a hard time seeing anything else in the room at the same time.

The human eye can see about twenty "stops" of light—that is, twenty doublings or halvings of light levels, from the smallest amount of light people's eyes can see to light so bright that more light would be painful. But people cannot see twenty stops of light at once. They can only see perhaps four or five stops of light at once and take time to adjust to larger differences in light levels.

For example, when walking through the woods at night with a flashlight, a person can see the area lit by the flashlight but not much outside the flashlight beam. If she turns the flashlight off and waits until her eyes adjust to the darkness, she might be able to see all around herself.

A similar situation is created by a brightly lit gas station on a dark road. A person's eyes adjust to the light level near the gas station but cannot easily see the surrounding road. Somebody hiding in the bushes near the gas station would be hard to see because the bright light would prevent anyone from seeing into the darker areas near the bushes. And as soon as a person drives past a brightly lit gas station, they have a hard time seeing the comparatively dim road just past the bright lights.

As the amount of light reaching a person's eyes changes, the eyes automatically adjust to the amount of light they receive. The iris opens and closes, quickly adjusting incoming light levels by about four stops. Chemical changes in the eye, which take more time, adjust the eye over a much wider range of light levels. These changes do not happen instantly, which is why turning on a bright light at night can be painful for a short time, while the eyes adapt to the new light level.

The protective plastic film is being removed from this new window. The window rating label indicates that the window has a visible light transmittance of 0.53, which means it transmits 53 percent of the visible light that reaches it. Comparing the view through the part of the glass without the protective film to the view through the opening above the glass demonstrates that cutting the light level by half is hardly noticeable to the camera. It is not obvious to the human eye either, which demonstrates the wide range of light levels the human eye can detect and adjust to.

Contrast

The traffic lights in the photo at right have dark-colored background plates mounted around them to create contrast between the lights and their surrounding.

Without the dark plate, there would not be enough contrast between a daytime sky and the light, which would make the light difficult to see, especially when the sun is in the background.

The automated toll-collecting station in the photo at left is equipped with **video cameras** aimed at the driver's face. The cameras cannot see much when the sun is in the background. The tent was erected to shade the cameras from the sun.

Note that the tent is low on only one side, which protects the cameras from the sun when it is low in the sky in the direction the cameras face.

Reflection and Glare

Some surfaces, such as polished marble and gloss paint, reflect light directly back the way a mirror reflects light, which can be distracting or annoying. These surfaces usually reflect light of any color.

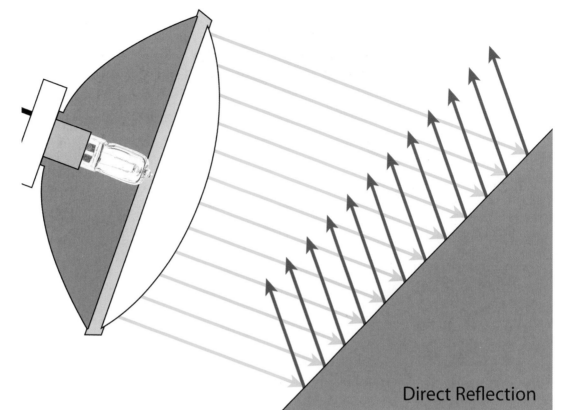

Direct Reflection

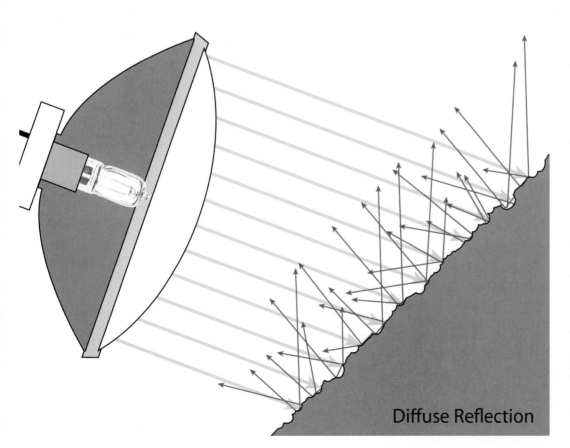

Diffuse Reflection

Other surfaces, such as the rough concrete wall in the drawing at left, scatter light in many directions as they reflect it, which is called diffuse reflection. This is less distracting than direct reflection.

Most rough surfaces also absorb more light than smooth surfaces.

Examples of surfaces that scatter light are acoustic ceiling tiles, limestone, concrete, and paint with a flat finish.

Reflectiveness of Paint

The mix of ingredients in paint—colored pigments, binders (materials that hold the pigment in place), and other chemicals—helps determine the texture of the painted surface and therefore how much light will be reflected directly and how much will be scattered.

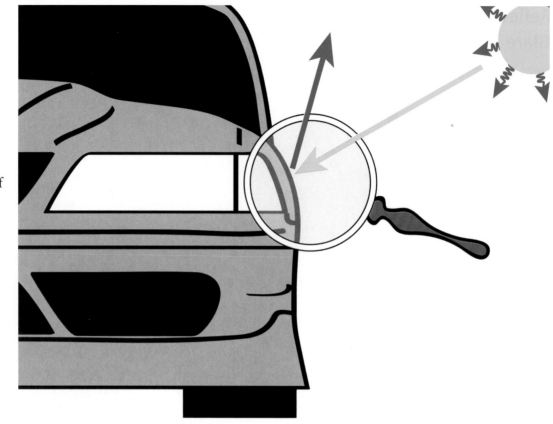

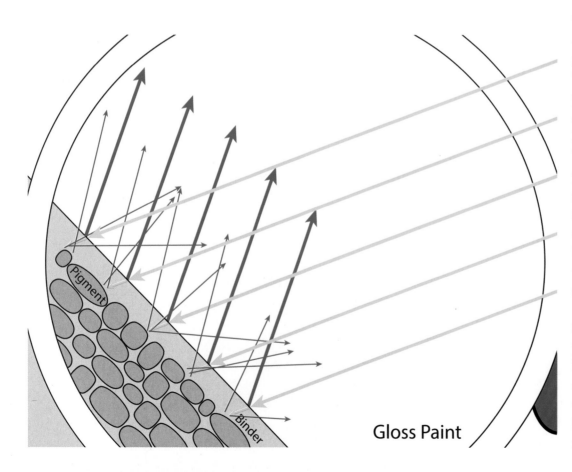

Gloss Paint

The gloss paint on the car on this page was made with a lot of binder and not much pigment. The paint dried with a smooth layer of transparent binder on top of the pigments, which generates a direct reflection. Some light of all colors reflects off the binder layer, causing a white reflection known as glare.

Some light also penetrates the binder layer, and whatever color is not absorbed by the pigment is reflected back, giving the paint its color.

The house in the drawing at right is covered with a non-gloss paint. This type of paint has what is called a "flat" finish, also sometimes called a "matte" finish.

Flat paint scatters light in all directions and does not create much glare. But flat paint can look darker, because it does not reflect as much light back in any one direction and because the rough surface tends to collect more dirt than gloss paint. It is also harder to clean than gloss paint.

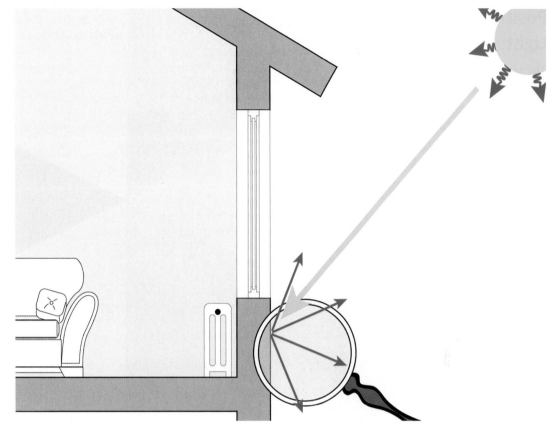

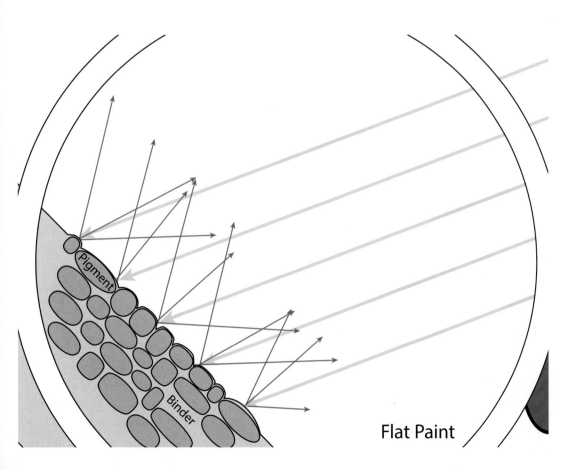

Flat Paint

The drawing at left shows a close-up of the flat paint used to paint the house in the drawing above. The factory made the paint flat by including less binder in the mix than was in the gloss paint shown on Page 238.

There is not enough binder in this formula to create a smooth layer of binder on top of the pigment. Therefore the paint dries with a rougher surface than the gloss paint. The rough surface causes a diffuse reflection.

Position of the Light

The photo at right shows an ordinary piece of gypsum board painted with primer, then painted black and white. Some of the paint is flat, some is semi-gloss, and some is gloss.

The gloss and semi-gloss paint create glare, the flat does not.

Note that each paint is from the same manufacturer, and each of the whites is the manufacturer's same exact shade of white, yet the whites look different from each other

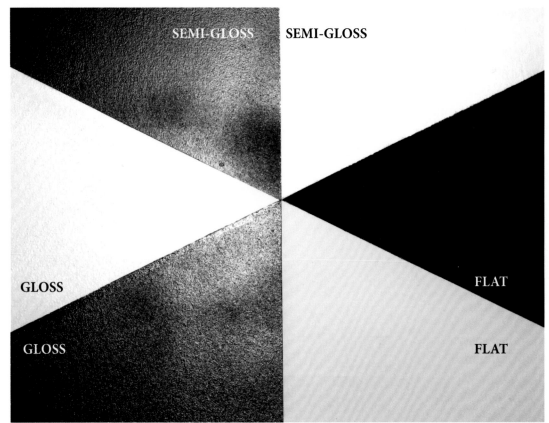

The drawing at left shows how the light was positioned for the photo above. A single, small light was pointed at the center of the piece of gypsum board, and the camera was positioned so the light reflected straight into the camera.

The high gloss and semi-gloss paints reflected the light directly into the camera, causing a potentially annoying glare. The flat paint caused a diffuse reflection, which did not create any glare. Note that even the white parts look different.

The same panel is shown in the photo at right, with the camera in the same position.

The only difference is the lighting. As shown in the drawing below, two lights were used, and they were bounced off the walls and ceiling, sending light to the panel from many different directions. Neither one of the lights was positioned where its light would reflect directly into the camera.

Note that the whites all look the same as each other when lit this way.

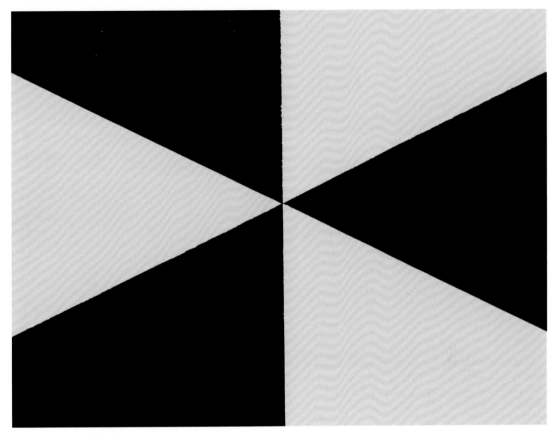

This indirect lighting arrangement makes the panel much easier to see, regardless of the type of paint used, which makes it much more comfortable on the eyes.

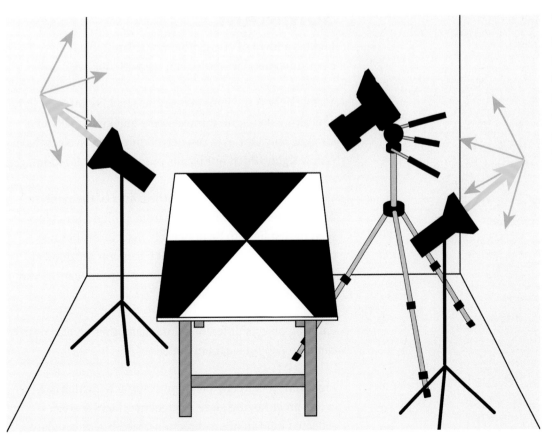

The dome-shaped roof is covered with gold leaf (a thin layer of gold). Gold is very resistant to any chemical reaction. The lack of chemical reaction helps keep the surface of the roof very smooth, too smooth to collect a lot of dirt or trap water. The lack of dirt and water on the surface limits biological activity the way a smooth surface on a spoon helps limit biological activity. Lack of chemical reactivity also prevents the formation of oxides (chemical compounds made of oxygen and another element), which are usually dark in color. The lack of chemical reactivity and biological activity keeps the gold smooth and shiny for many years, shiny enough for its reflection to be visible from far away.

SUMMARY

Light is a form of energy that is transmitted as electromagnetic waves we can see with our eyes.

Visible light is the light people can see. Like infrared light and ultraviolet light, it travels very quickly, usually in a straight line. Our eyes can detect different wavelengths of visible light, which our brains process into colored images.

White light is a mixture of all the colors of the rainbow. The mixture has to be very far from sunlight for colors seen in that light to be noticeably inaccurate, because both our eyes and modern digital cameras are good at compensating in a way that makes colors appear the way we are used to seeing them.

Painting objects different colors than other objects nearby can help people see them better.

Light reflects directly off smooth surfaces, which can create an annoying glare. Rougher surfaces scatter reflected light in many directions, which reduces glare.

Chapter 8 **LIGHT** Applied Science

THE MOVEMENT OF LIGHT THROUGH BUILDINGS

Lighting has a significant impact on the quality of a person's experience in a building. An appropriate amount of light at the right time in the right place makes a building easier to see and work in, as well as safer: light helps reduce trip and fall hazards. Using the right amount of light can also save energy.

Until artificial lighting was developed, people couldn't do much indoors after the sun went down because it was too dark. Castles were lit by brightly burning torches, which must have cost a fortune while covering everything with a layer of soot. In the late 1800s, people were still lighting buildings by burning oil from whales caught by ships that had to sail halfway around the world to catch them, which no doubt cost more than torches. Thanks to the many people who helped develop better lighting technologies and systems to supply electricity, lighting is far more convenient and efficient today, but electricity costs are rising.

Good lighting design today does not simply mean a lot of sunlight. Nor does it mean a lot of artificial light.

Good lighting design includes choosing light levels appropriate to the task (more light on stairways than in hallways), the right type of light fixtures, the right number of light fixtures, appropriate locations for their installation, and appropriate controls. Good lighting design also considers windows: how many, how large, what shape, facing which way, and on which side of the room. Room colors and finishes are also part of good lighting design. Neither artificial lighting and daylighting nor colors and finishes should be chosen in isolation—all these factors should be taken into consideration as part of good lighting design.

Comfortable lighting means even lighting. A strong light from behind a person is generally comfortable, but not many rooms can be designed around the assumption that all people will always be facing one direction. An example of a room with bad lighting design is one with three walls with no windows and one side that is all glass. If the room were used as a lecture hall, having the audience face the window would make it hard for the audience to see the speaker on a sunny day. Having the speaker face the window would make most of the audience invisible to the speaker. Glass on one side would make the light uneven.

Light that is even in all directions makes a room easy to be in and work in at any time of day or night, regardless of which direction a person is facing. This is difficult to achieve in a room with windows on one side. Examining the sun's position in relation to the windows and to the likely position of people in the room plays a role in good lighting design.

Even lighting is easy to be around, but it can look boring. Uneven or contrasting lighting can be used to highlight decorative features or to make a room more stimulating.

It is okay to break some rules of good lighting in places where people do not spend much time. For example, harsh or noticeable lights are acceptable for transitory areas, such as lobbies. The exception in lobbies is a sign-in or security desk, where the people behind the desk need to see the whole lobby at any time of night or day, and visitors need to be able to see the people behind the desk, as well as the papers on the desk that they might be asked to sign. Stimulating light should be avoided in rooms where people are already stimulated, such as a classroom. An office is easier to work in for long periods of time if the light levels are even, while parts of a home where people tend to move around can be more pleasant with some contrasting lighting. The exception is the kitchen, which should have bright and even lighting, because people are working with fire, sharp knives, and boiling water—not a good place for shadows.

The next sections show examples of bad and good daylighting design and then bad and good artificial lighting design.

CONTRAST

People's eyes can adjust to dim lighting but cannot easily see a poorly lit object in a brightly lit surrounding.

The dark-colored walls and ceiling in the room at right do not reflect much light onto the book, which is why the boy needs to use a flashlight.

The light-colored walls and ceiling in the room at left are an improvement, because they reflect much more light onto the book. But the boy is wearing sunglasses to protect his eyes from the light reflecting from the bright spot on the floor. The bright spot behind the book makes the book harder to see.

A matte (flat) floor finish would produce less glare but be harder to keep clean than a gloss finish.

The arrangement in the room at right is an improvement, because the bright spot on the floor is now behind the reader, where it does not create a sharp contrast with the amount of light reflected from the book.

However, it is not always possible to face away from the sun, especially as the sun's direction changes throughout the day.

The see-through curtain over the window in the drawing at left reduces the amount of light coming in the window and scatters what does get in. This allows a person to read comfortably in a variety of positions.

In the drawings on this page and the next page, the sunlight is no longer coming directly through the window.

The walls and ceiling in the drawing at right do not reflect much light onto the book. This makes the book hard to read, especially if the floor has a gloss finish, which reflects a lot of glare into the reader's eyes. Dark wall surfaces are best limited to small areas, such as molding, to make a room look interesting.

The paint on the walls in the room at left makes the book even harder to read. Light is coming from the window in front of the reader and from the wall and ceiling in front of him, causing his eyes to adjust to the bright light.

Little light is reflected from the dark wall behind him onto the book, which makes the book even harder to read.

The book in the room at right is easy to see, because the white wall and ceiling behind the reader are reflecting light onto the book. But this will only happen if the window does not receive direct sunlight and if the reader is facing the dark wall. This arrangement is acceptable in rooms where the seating direction is known, such as a classroom where the students face a dark chalkboard, but it is not acceptable in most rooms.

The room at left works well. A highly reflective ceiling makes it feel more open and evenly lit. It also saves energy by allowing a lower level of artificial light.

Walls should be a little less reflective than ceilings but reflective enough to make the room feel large and the light even.

Floors should have low reflectivity (relatively dark color) to hide dirt and to make the light more comfortable.

DAYLIGHTING

Direct sunlight is extremely bright compared to artificial light. People close shades in an attempt to balance out lighting levels, often turning lights on at the same time. There are several things wrong with this scenario: using lights on a sunny day wastes electricity, glass is more expensive to build with than opaque walls, and glass also reduces thermal comfort and adds to heating and cooling bills.

Too much sunlight, even indirect sunlight, can make a room much brighter than nearby rooms that are not lit by sunlight. When people leave a sunlit room, their eyes cannot adjust to the relative darkness quickly enough to see well, leaving little option but to increase the level of artificial lighting in nearby rooms. And walking from an artificially lit room into a very brightly sunlit room will be painful unless the artificially lit room is also brightly lit.

The problem is reversed at night, when the room that had a lot of sunlight also requires a high level of artificial light to match the brightly lit nearby rooms. The solution is to limit the amount of daylight into a room to a comfortable amount that can easily be matched with artificial light or sunlight in nearby rooms.

Window Location

It is hard to know ahead of time which way a person will face in every room, but a smart designer can make reasonable assumptions.

Offices and many other rooms will likely contain computers. A complete design anticipates where people might locate the screens and avoids having the bright light from a window reflected on the screen. Orienting the screen perpendicular to a window is often best.

As noted above, lecture halls generally do not benefit from windows, because windows

behind the speaker make the speaker hard to see silhouetted against the bright light, while windows behind the audience make it hard for the speaker to see the audience. Because lecture halls do not benefit from sunlight as much as other rooms, they can be located in basements or other windowless areas of a building, leaving rooms with windows for other purposes. If a lecture hall has windows at all, they are best located high up on a side wall and protected with light shelves (described later in this chapter) or awnings, plus shades a teacher can close when a movie is shown.

Bathroom windows are best not located in a shower, because windows are more vulnerable to water damage than walls. The best location for a bathroom window is near the toilet, preferably high up to increase privacy.

Kitchens benefit from a window above the sink or the counter, lighting the work area and giving the cook or dishwasher a view.

Good daylighting design starts with thinking about how well the building will work with sunlight alone and then proceeds by adding artificial lights as appropriate.

The whole wall of windows makes it hard to see the computer screen, so the shades on the left are closed completely. The rest of them are closed most of the way to avoid glare and to balance out the light levels in the room. All the electric lights are on. Though it is too late to change now, smaller windows better protected from direct sunlight, perhaps on a different wall, could offer a nice view while adding a pleasant amount of daylight to the office. A better office plan would consider the position of the desk and the computer screen with respect to the position of the windows.

Many window shades are closed in the glass office building at right. In a typical glass building they stay closed much of the time, regardless of the sun's position or which direction the windows face.

The building would be more comfortable and energy efficient if it were to have windows sized, shaped, and positioned to provide a good view and a comfortable level of daylight.

The living room window in the photo at left has a fabulous view of a bridge over a river, but the bright sunlight reflecting off the water makes it uncomfortable to look in that direction during the afternoon.

If the owner of this apartment could have chosen which rooms to have face which direction, it would have been better to locate a bedroom here, since people rarely spend time in bedrooms during the afternoon. The kitchen, living room, and dining room should be located where windows have no glare during the afternoon.

The glass windows and ceiling in the hotel lobby at right are completely covered with shades, because otherwise the sunlight would be too bright. The shades stay closed all day and night, while the artificial lights stay on.

Better window design would include smaller windows, which would make the space more pleasant and thermally comfortable, while saving on the cost of construction, energy, heating and cooling equipment, and window shades and their maintenance.

The shades covering the wall of windows at left also stay closed permanently, while the artificial lights stay on all day.

The gap between the shades and the windows acts like a chimney, pulling room temperature air down along the cold glass during the winter and up along the hot glass during the summer. This increases energy-wasting heat conduction through the glass while making people near the windows uncomfortable.

The school at right was built before electric lighting was developed, so designers had to optimize daylighting.

The glass in the roof faces away from the earth's equator, protecting it from direct sunlight. The side of the building facing the equator (not shown) contains the entrance lobby, (which gets direct sunlight), stairs, and an elevator shaft instead of classrooms. This smart design has served the students and professors well for over 150 years.

The second floor of this house used to have a large window, which someone has covered up, possibly because it faced the midday sun.

It is hard to imagine that a better solution was not possible.

Instead of replacing the window with a wall, they could have hung curtains or installed one or more small windows.

Protection outside of Windows

Light shelves, which are mounted outside of windows, inside of windows, or both, are an ingenious invention: they reflect light up onto the ceiling of a room and at the same time protect the room from direct sunlight.

The light shelves in the photos at right and below right are mounted outdoors only. They will reflect light onto the ceiling, while partly shading the room from direct sunlight. The light shelves below right are not saving any electricity though, because the light on the ceiling is not switched off. Because people forget, automatic lighting controls are the most reliable way of turning lights off when they are not needed.

The light shelf in the drawing below is mounted both indoors and outdoors, where it can reflect more light and provide shade for a larger portion of the room.

Light shelves reflect sunlight onto the ceiling some distance into the building from the windows (see arrow below), from where much of the light reflects back down into the room. This balances the bright sunlight at the windows with the less bright artificial light in the room. If the artificial lights become unnecessary and are turned off, the light shelves also save electricity.

The building in the photo above has light shelves on only one side, because not all sides of the building get sunlight from an angle that would make light shelves advantageous. Light shelves can be very effective at blocking and reflecting midday sunlight but are less effective at controlling sunlight from low in the sky.

The wall in the photo above is cut away on the right side of the windows to let light through the windows when the sun is low and to the right in the photo. The white marble mounted on the left side reflects light into the windows. Marble also protrudes above the windows like a hat brim, shading the windows from midday sun high in the sky.

The building at left has different daylighting designs for each part of the building. At the left side of the first floor is an all-glass lobby, which might be an uncomfortable place to work, but few people spend their whole day there. The second floor offices above the lobby have windows high up, shaded by a roof overhang. This allows some natural light but shields the offices from direct sunlight. The two-story warehouse at the right side of the photo has unshaded windows, but they are too small to throw direct sunlight on anyone's workplace for long.

Hotel Meeting Rooms

A person standing at the podium at right will be lit by light from the windows and silhouetted against the curtains in the background, which will make the person reasonably easy to see from this perspective.

If the ceiling lights are on while sunlight is coming in the windows, there will be less contrast between the person and the brightly lit windows, which will make the person even easier to see.

Viewing the same person at the same podium head on (see left) would be difficult, because the window in the background is too bright. Closing the opaque curtains would solve the problem but would also eliminate all natural light.

Small windows high on a wall not behind the podium would be an effective solution. Or, the podium could be moved to a wall that does not have windows.

The photo at right shows part of the same room with all the curtains closed.

The large number of ceiling light fixtures produce an even light, making it easy to see something on the tables or people sitting across a table, but the lack of daylight makes the room dull.

The addition of strategically placed windows, perhaps high up, might make the room feel more open or welcoming, while also saving some electricity.

Windows behind the tables can make food or merchandise on the tables easier to see but would make people who stand behind the tables harder to see.

Small windows high up with light shelves would solve the problem. This would give the people behind the tables or someone speaking at a podium a wall to stand in front of, which would make them easier to see. Smaller windows would also allow the use of smaller heating and cooling equipment.

ARTIFICIAL LIGHTING (ELECTRIC LIGHTING)

A comfortable and energy-efficient lighting arrangement has some direct ambient light, which comes directly from light fixtures into the room; some indirect ambient light, which fixtures aim toward room surfaces that reflect it around the room; and maybe some task light, which is directed at specific areas that need higher light levels. A room can also have some light that is mostly for decorative purposes, called accent lighting, which highlights artwork or architectural details.

For example, in an office, fixtures that hang from the ceiling shine some direct light down while usually also directing light up that is reflected off a wide area of the ceiling—the reflected light is less harsh than direct light. The hanging lights should produce enough light for people to walk around and see each other, and ideally should be positioned to avoid reflecting off computer screens. Desks can be equipped with task lights that people can turn on and off as needed and position wherever they like. Supplying enough ambient light to avoid the need for task lighting is expensive, uses a lot of energy, and often provokes complaints that the lighting is harsh.

Areas where people will not be working can be lit with a combination of ambient light and accent light. The ambient lights should produce a more diffuse (spread-out) light than the accent lights. People's eyes are especially good at noticing contrast, so while a small number of very bright accent lights narrowly focused on specific features of a room can be attractive, too much contrast can be distracting and should be reserved for rooms where people don't spend much time, such as lobbies. Accent lights should be on separate switches, so they can be turned off to save energy when few people are using the space or to create a more subdued mood when desired.

Ambient light can come from indirect light bounced off walls or ceilings. A good example of indirect light is wall sconces, which direct most of their light

onto the wall they are mounted on or onto the ceiling. Hallways in apartment buildings can be lit entirely by wall sconces, an arrangement that will generally use less electricity than recessed ceiling lights while having the additional advantage of freeing up space above the ceiling for pipes, ducts, wires, and other equipment. If additional hallway lighting is desired, such as in hotels, small ceiling lights can be carefully positioned above doors, so guests can see to unlock doors.

Accent lights should be positioned carefully. While windows can't always be positioned where they will produce the optimal lighting conditions, lights usually can be. They should be located and aimed where they will not produce reflections off computer screens or artwork. Lights directed toward artwork hung on a wall and covered by glass should generally be close enough to the wall so the reflection is directed to the floor in front of the artwork. This way, the reflection cannot be seen by a person standing in front of the artwork, even when stepping in for a close look.

The office kitchen in the photo above has a large fixture on the ceiling that provides direct light above the table and some indirect light bounced off the ceiling around it. It is large enough to create a soft light that will not generate noticeable shadows. On the ceiling above the walkway between the table and the coffee area are ambient lights that are less bright, which is suitable for a walkway. The task light above the coffee station is close to the wall where it can bounce some indirect light off the wall. Neither the direct nor the indirect light from the task light will throw shadows on the workspace, even when people are there pouring coffee. This helps people see what they are doing with hot coffee.

The cafeteria at right is attractively lit with a combination of direct ambient light from lights above the decorative strips on the ceiling and from the fixtures hanging above the tables; indirect ambient light reflected off the ceiling from the upper side of the hanging light fixtures, and task lights above the counter. The decorative strips on the ceiling reflect a lot of light. The lighting is brightest at the counter and tables, and less bright on the walkway. The daylighting is pleasant but not overwhelming.

The office building lobby at left is invitingly lit with an unusual combination of cove lighting on the ceiling (that reflects light off the ceiling), a hanging light fixture, the brightly lit "38" address sign, small spotlights recessed into the wooden soffit, and even some accent lights recessed into the exposed brick wall. The light-colored finishes for the wall, the floor, and the wood soffit, combined with the mirror-like surface on the reception desk, all reflect enough light to keep the space bright with a reasonable amount of artificial light.

Direct and Indirect Ambient Light

The drawing at right shows lights hanging from an office ceiling. The fixtures emit some direct light down and to the sides but send most of their light up to the ceiling, where it is reflected back as indirect light.

The lights are mounted close to the ceiling, creating small areas of very bright reflected light above each fixture, which can be distracting and uncomfortably bright.

The drawing at left shows the same office with the same lights, but now the lights are mounted lower. This spreads out the light reflected off the ceiling, creating larger, less brightly lit areas of the ceiling. (Or, the lights could have lenses that spread the upward light out at a wider angle.)

This is easier on the eyes and less distracting because it reduces the contrast between the brighter and darker areas of the ceiling.

Task Lighting

The drawing at right shows task lights on each desk: small lamps that people can move around as they like and turn on and off as needed without bothering other people.

The overhead lights provide enough ambient light to see other people, while the task lights provide higher light levels directly on each workspace.

Task Light Locations at Home

It is common to see a single light above a bathroom mirror, but this throws a harsh light down onto a person's face. A better choice is to hang two lights, high above either side of the mirror, preferably on adjacent walls (not the wall where the mirror hangs). This reduces shadows on a person's face as they look in the mirror, while keeping uncomfortably direct light out of the person's eyes.

Kitchen counters should be more brightly lit than other parts of the kitchen. If kitchen lighting is mounted on the ceiling behind a person working at the counter, multiple lights should be spread out over a wide area to avoid casting a shadow from the person onto the counter. A good addition would be to mount task lights on the underside of the kitchen cabinets, carefully positioned where they will not cause glare on the counter. (This usually means mounting them close to the front of the cabinets.)

Lighting Quiz:
The photo at right shows the view when stepping out of the shower in an expensive custom-built home. What is wrong here? Answer on Page 263.

Avoid Glare

The photo at right shows the same black and white panel from Pages 240 and 241, with a page from a magazine on it (top left) and a page from a newspaper (top right).

The light is positioned to create glare, which makes the magazine impossible to read but has no effect on the newspaper. This is because the magazine's surface is glossy, creating direct reflections, while the newspaper is printed on rough, non-glossy paper, creating diffuse reflections.

The photo at left shows the same magazine and newspaper pages but with the lights positioned so they reflect off the walls and ceiling, as in the drawing on the bottom of Page 241. This time there is no glare on either page.

Because it is impossible to predict when someone might want to read a magazine, it is best to plan lighting to avoid glare on any work surface.

The photo at right shows poorly lit artwork.

The position of the light just above the painting of flowers is causing glare as the light reflects directly off the painting and the wall. Its position close to the wall at right concentrates the glare in one area, making the glare appear brighter. The light is also shining directly in the viewer's eyes.

If moving the lights is not practical, the light on the right could be aimed toward the painting on the back wall, which is getting even less light. Nobody would see glare from that light reflecting off the painting on the back wall unless they put their head on the floor under the painting. The light in the upper left corner is aimed at the painting at right—perhaps it alone could light the painting well enough. If not, it could be replaced with a brighter one. Either light that still causes glare could be replaced with a fixture that has a larger diameter reflector (the part of the fixture that directs the light) to spread the light.

The artwork on the wall in the photo below apparently used to be lit with those spotlights on the ceiling. What probably happened is that glare was reflecting off the artwork, or the glass covering it, directly into people's eyes. Now they are aimed at the wall above the art, which only serves to create annoying bright spots on the wall above the art. Better solutions for lighting the art include bulbs that are not as bright, larger reflectors, lenses on the front of the lights to spread the light, or lights in a different location.

Bad Lighting or Bad Sign Choice?

The sign in the photo at right is difficult to see because the lighting is dim and most of the sign is the same color as the door.

The sign in the photo below is easier to see and would be easy to see even if the lighting were dim.

Clear signs with carefully chosen colors are cheaper than adding lights and also don't require electricity.

Answer to Lighting Quiz

The photo at right shows what's wrong in the photo on the bottom of Page 259: the bathroom has a step that is hard for a person stepping out of the shower to see. This is hazardous.

The hazard could be reduced by carefully positioning a light where it would cause the step to cast a shadow and by making sure that light was wired to go on whenever the main light in the bathroom is switched on.

Another option is to run the wood floorboards a different direction on each level of the floor. Or, the last board at the edge of the step could be a different color wood.

Another approach is shown in the photo below. A step in a restaurant is lit up to help make it visible. Lights like this might not be welcome in most homes but are appropriate in a public place or any building occupied by people who can't see well, such as a nursing home.

Shadow Design

Good lighting design includes anticipating what shadows will be caused by the lighting.

Where is the top row of keys on the keypad in the photo at right? Hidden in a shadow. The photo below shows a close-up of the keypad.

The solution is to move the light source to a position where it will send about the same amount of light to all parts of the keyboard.

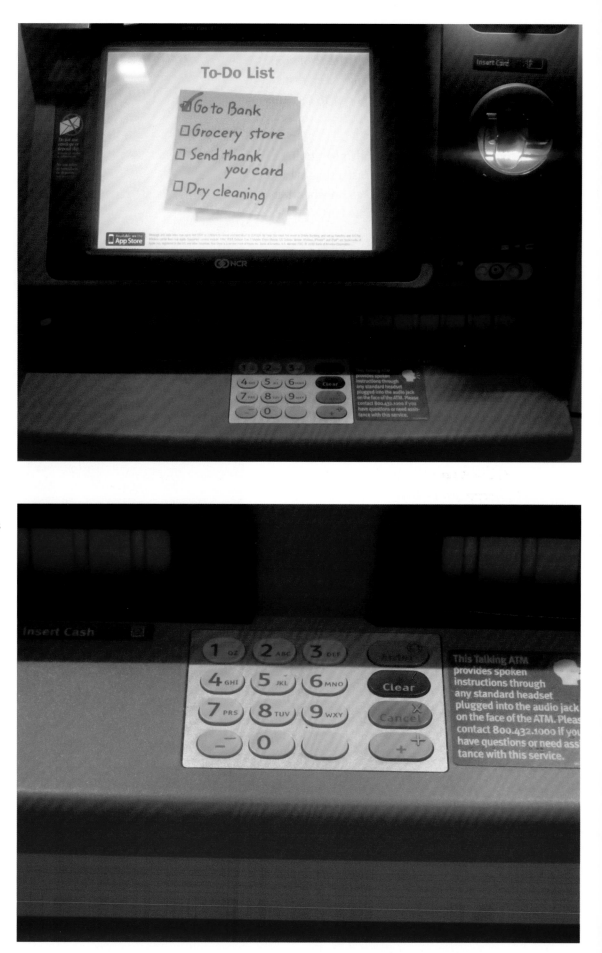

Adding light can make some areas harder to see. The brighter a bright area is, the harder it will be for someone's eyes to adjust to see something in a nearby shadow.

The man in the photo at right is signing in at the front desk of an apartment building. Because all the lights are mounted on the ceiling, his head is positioned where it will cast a shadow onto the counter in front of him. This makes it hard for him to see what he is signing, especially after walking into the lobby on a sunny day. If some lights were mounted on the wall behind the desk, the person standing behind the desk would cast a shadow onto the desk, which would also be a problem. One solution is a row of small lights on the ceiling directly over the desk, so nobody's head would block the light from more than one of the lights. Another possible solution is task lighting on the counter.

In the photos below, the door of apartment 314 is lit by a single overhead light. The door of apartment 315 is lit by an identical overhead light, as well as by another light to the right of the door. The additional light casts a shadow on the keyhole, making it much harder to see than the keyhole of apartment 314. Paying attention to shadows when choosing and positioning lights would prevent this problem.

Types of Artificial Lighting

In the early 1900s, incandescent bulbs were the mainstream lighting technology. In the mid-1900s, fluorescent lights became popular. Early fluorescent lights took several seconds to light up, flickered, and often made vibrating or humming noises. But they were popular because they required much less electricity than incandescent lights, which helped keep buildings cool. (This was especially important in the days before air conditioning.) By the end of the 1900s, the start-up delay, flicker, and hum of fluorescent lights were gone, and electronic ballasts and smaller-diameter bulbs reduced their electricity requirements. Bulbs were also available in a choice of at least four color temperatures.

More recently, LEDs (light emitting diodes) became more popular. Early versions were expensive, it was difficult to find different types of fixtures with matching color temperatures, and dimming was difficult or impractical. However, by 2015, prices were competitive with fluorescent lights, and quality had improved enough that some new buildings were being built with only LED lighting. In 2016, LEDs achieved a market share of seven percent worldwide, and over 25 percent in the U.S.

Lighting Efficiency

The decrease in electricity required to light a building with more energy-efficient lighting fixtures is very significant. A halogen light requires about 90 percent of the electricity that an incandescent light requires, a fluorescent light requires about 17 percent, and a good LED light requires only 12 percent. Note that these numbers are rough approximations as of 2017, and improving technology will change these percentages in the future. The above percentages are for bulbs used in fixtures designed specifically for them. (The lighting industry calls a bulb a "lamp" and a fixture a "luminaire.")

It is generally best to use the type of bulb a light fixture is designed to be used with. A bulb used in a fixture not designed specifically for that type of bulb will not perform as well. For example, a screw-in compact fluorescent bulb used in a fixture designed for an incandescent bulb will not position the light source where the fixture designer expected it to be, which will cause the light to be reflected out of the fixture in an unpredictable pattern.

Lighting efficiency and lifespan choices should be based on expected hours of use. An apartment building hallway light is lit 24 hours per day (unless it is controlled by a motion sensor), an outdoor light maybe 12 hours per day, and a boiler room light perhaps one hour per month. The least efficient light should be installed in the boiler room.

Areas where the finish will be bare concrete, such as parking garages, can be made from light-colored concrete, which reflects more light. Not only will lighter colors save energy, but the building won't need as many light fixtures.

Because one watt of electricity going to an indoor light becomes one watt of heat in the space (minus any light that escapes out a window), more efficient lighting reduces the amount of air conditioning required. Money saved by buying smaller cooling equipment can more than pay for better lights, which makes the building less expensive to build and less expensive to buy energy for.

Someone put bulbs of different wattages in some of these fixtures, causing the uneven lighting pattern on the floor. Light levels in different parts of a building can be varied by using different bulbs with varying levels of brightness or by spacing identical fixtures with identical bulbs closer to each other or further from each other. Installing fixtures that use the same bulbs greatly simplifies maintenance.

Light Lifespan

Generally speaking, halogen bulbs have the shortest lifespan, incandescent bulbs have a longer lifespan, fluorescents last much longer, and LEDs last longest of all. But rated lifespan does not tell the whole story.

A bulb's light output typically declines with age. Incandescent bulbs fail before their light output declines noticeably. Fluorescent bulb light output declines about ten to twenty percent before the bulb fails. This is a significant decline but generally not enough for the bulb to require replacement. Output from LEDs declines also and becomes significant long before the end of the rated life, which for many LEDs is 100,000 hours (24 hours per day for 11 years). Because of the reduced output, it might be reasonable to think of 50,000 hours as a realistic life for an LED. Or, extra LED lights could be installed and dimmed when new, so that later, when output is reduced, the lights could be turned up and continue to do their job at the same light level. At least one manufacturer sells fixtures that automatically dim themselves when new and maintain the same output as they age.

Design with Maintenance in Mind

Lights require maintenance. Bulbs and electronics burn out; electric connections fail; screws rust in place; plastic lenses crack; glass lenses break; reflectors and lenses get dirty. Lighting should be designed with future maintenance in mind.

When possible, use popular fixtures, bulbs, and electronic components to increase the odds of replacements being available in the future.

Difficult-to-access locations such as the ceiling above a swimming pool and any location high above the ground should be avoided when possible. If lights are installed in these locations, they should be the longest-lasting types available. Sometimes a small change in the location of a fixture can make it much easier to access later; for example, a light on a high ceiling can be located where a ladder can be placed against a nearby wall. Both of the lobbies in the photos below could have been lit with lights mounted at a reasonable height on the walls, aimed at an angle that would bounce light off the ceiling.

The lights in this office building lobby are positioned where they cannot be maintained without using a portable lift.

A scaffold is necessary for changing bulbs in this movie theatre lobby. This is hazardous, expensive, and disruptive to business.

LIGHTING CONTROLS

Photocells

Timers do not do a good job of controlling outdoor lights because they need to be adjusted as nights get longer or shorter, and because people mistakenly adjust them for daylight savings time (which is not necessary). A better way to control outdoor lights, which does not require adjustment, is with a daylight sensing control, also called a photocell control.

The lights on the front of the school at right should have an automatic control to switch them off during the day.

Photocell controls last a very long time if they are set up to send electricity to a relay (a magnetic switch), which switches the electricity to the lights. For large buildings with many lights, it is common to wire every second light on a different circuit breaker. That way, if there is a problem, every second light will stay lit. Two photocells and two relays can be set up this way to improve reliability.

There is no excuse for these lights to be on during the day.
Photo: Neal Gifford.

Airport terminals are probably the worst offenders when it comes to leaving lights on while sufficient sunlight is streaming in the windows. But they are far from the only offenders. Many lights, both outdoors and indoors, in many types of buildings all over the world, are needlessly left on every day.

Switches

It is best not to put all the lights in one room on one switch. Different switches for different areas of the room, or for partially lighting or fully lighting parts of a room, allow people to keep some lights off to save electricity or improve comfort.

Daylight Harvesting

People rarely turn off lights in response to sunlight coming in windows. Automatic "daylight harvesting" dimmers work much better. Daylight harvesting dimmers automatically turn indoor lights lower or off in response to sunlight coming in through windows. Some types are sophisticated systems complete with computerized digital controls that can communicate only with specially adapted light fixtures. Other types are built into each fixture to simplify the controls and avoid the possibility of a control failure causing all the lights to go out when they should be on. For rooms with many fixtures, such as classrooms and gymnasiums, it is practical to use a daylighting control to turn some fixtures off entirely, which is simpler, less expensive, and more energy efficient than dimming some or all of the lights.

Motion Sensors

Motion sensors can keep lights off many hours per year and are available in many varieties. One type, called an "occupancy sensor," turns the lights on when someone enters the area and turns them off if no motion is sensed for a set (or adjustable) period of time. This type is good for a room with no windows.

Another type—a good choice for a room with a window—is called a "vacancy sensor," which does not turn the light on automatically. The light only gets turned on with a control (mounted on the wall in the place of a normal switch), so it might be left off on a sunny day. The light turns off when someone pushes the button to turn it off. But if someone forgets to turn the light off, and no motion is sensed for a set period of time, the control will switch the light off automatically.

It is a good idea to use motion sensors to control hallway and stairway lights in office buildings, apartment buildings, and schools—when allowed by codes. Some people say that for security reasons some lights should always remain on; others argue that it is safer to use motion sensors, because if a criminal is lurking in an area, the lights will turn on, announcing that someone is there.

A motion sensor in a classroom should be mounted on the ceiling where it can "see" the whole room. A wall-mounted sensor generally doesn't work in a classroom, because the sensor cannot sense motion throughout the room.

This classroom is wired with four light switches. One controls the light over the teacher's desk, which can be turned off when the teacher shows a movie. The lights over the students' desks are wired in three zones: close to the window, far from the window, and in between. Each zone can be turned off manually or controlled by daylight harvesting dimmers. Motion sensors can keep the lights off when nobody is in the room.

This hallway is partially lit by the least expensive and most reliable lighting available: light-colored walls, floor, and ceiling. (It also happens to be the most energy-efficient option.) The dark-colored doorways and the patterns on the floor and ceiling help with depth perception in a space such as this that is otherwise almost all one color. This is a hallway that never gets any daylight. If it had windows, or if it were a room people spent a lot of time in, a less reflective floor would be more appropriate.

Sadly, signs on light switches don't work any better than signs on thermostats. Automatic controls are more dependable than people because they have nothing else to do but control the lights.

SUMMARY

Good lighting is even. More light does not necessarily mean better lighting, especially if it creates glare or shadows.

Plan carefully to avoid glare, uneven lighting, and undesirable shadows.

Light shelves can greatly improve daylighting.

Ceilings should be very reflective, walls less reflective, and floors—especially in daylit areas—even less reflective.

Use the highest-efficiency lighting systems, with the longest life and the whitest color temperature, in nearly all cases.

Control outdoor lights with a photocell wired to a relay to switch electricity to the lights. Control indoor lights with daylight harvesting controls and motion sensors when appropriate. Do not put all the lights in a room on one switch.

Chapter 9 **SOUND** Basic Science

WHAT IS SOUND?

Sound is energy in the form of vibrations or pressure waves traveling through any material that can vibrate, including air, water, or solid objects. Sound cannot travel through a vacuum like outer space. Air and other substances can vibrate on many different wavelengths (frequencies), but human ears can hear only certain wavelengths. Dogs and some other animals can hear wavelengths that people cannot hear. The distance between the orange lines in the two drawings below represents the approximate range of wavelengths of sound people can hear.

The drum in the drawing below left is making a sound that has one of the longest wavelengths (distance between waves) people can hear: about the height of five floors of a building. The flute below right is making a sound that

has the shortest wavelength people can hear: about half as long as a person's nose. Human speech, a dog's bark, and music are all sounds made up of different combinations and patterns of various wavelengths that people can hear.

The speed of sound in air varies with temperature and other factors, but does not vary by much. The short-wavelength sound waves from the flute will reach a listener more frequently than the long-wavelength sound waves from the drum, which is why short-wavelength sound is called high-frequency sound. Described another way, the sound waves from the drummer will travel through the air at the same speed as the sound waves from the flute, but because they are farther apart from each other (longer wavelength) they will reach a listener's ear less frequently. Therefore, the sound from the drum is called low-frequency sound. High-frequency sound is also called high pitch, and low-frequency is called low pitch.

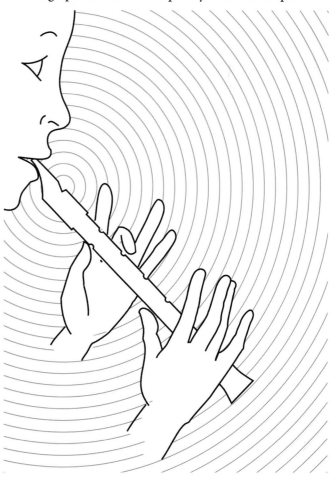

Drum Generating Sound Waves ①The drummer hits the drumskin with the drumstick, pushing it into the drum, away from the air surrounding the drum, creating a low-air-pressure zone along the surface of the drumskin, shown by a dashed orange line. ②The low-pressure zone moves away from the drum while the drumskin rebounds outward, creating a high-air-pressure zone that spreads outward, shown by a solid orange line. ③Without

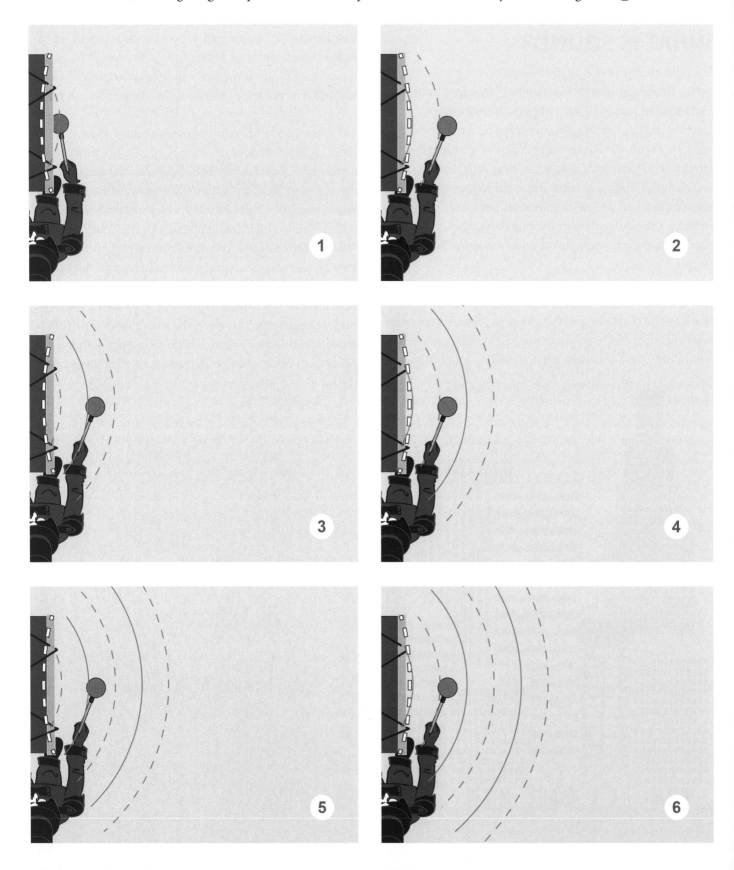

being hit again, the drumskin flexes back into the drum, creating another low-pressure zone, which follows the other pressure waves outward. ④ - ⑫ The drumskin flexes out and in at a frequency determined by how the drum is built and adjusted, creating high-pressure waves each time it flexes outward and low-pressure waves each time it flexes inward. The waves move outward from the drum at the speed of sound (about three seconds to travel one kilometer through air), each wave following the previous wave at a distance determined by the frequency of the drumskin flexing in and out.

Sound Waves and Pressure Gauges

The pressure gauges in the drawing at right show the fluctuations in air pressure as the sound waves from one single drumbeat pass.

The gauge at the extreme right, where the first sound wave has not yet reached, shows neutral pressure. The air pressure there has not changed yet. The second gauge from the right is pointing to the left, indicating low air pressure as the first low-pressure wave passes that gauge. The needle on the next gauge to the left, between waves, is neutral, and the needle on the next one is to the right, indicating high pressure as the first high-pressure wave passes that gauge.

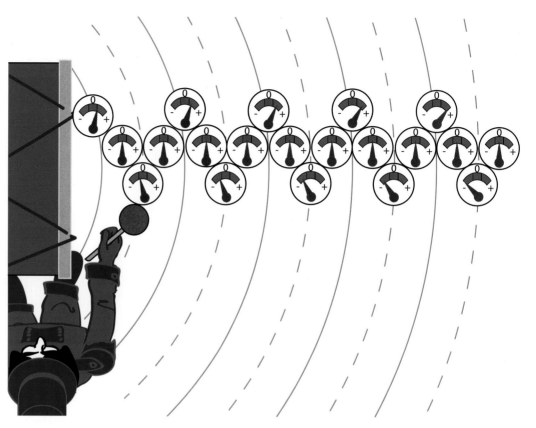

Sound Waves as a Pressure Graph

The drawing below shows the same sound waves and the same pressure gauges with the same pressure readings as in the drawing above. But here, the sound wave is shown as a pressure graph, with the brown line drawn high to indicate high pressure and low to indicate low pressure. The waves at right are taller, indicating louder sound (higher volume) just after the drummer hit the drum. The smaller waves at left indicate lower volume as the drum gradually stops vibrating. Both drawings on this page use common ways of showing sound waves.

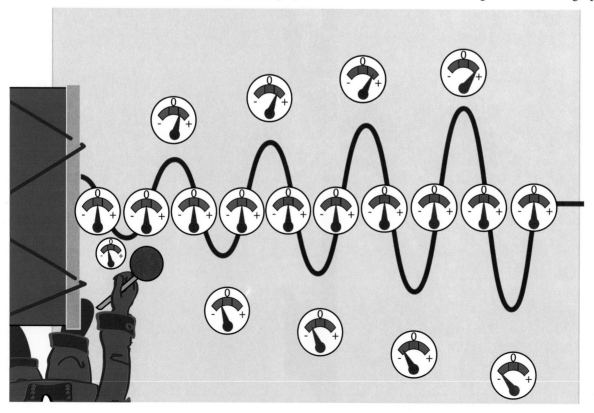

Waves in Water Waves behave differently in water than they do in air, because air is compressible, while water is almost not. The rock thrown into the pond below generates waves that spread out in all directions from where the rock lands. Viewed from the side, the waves are seen as an up-and-down motion of the water. The water moves in small circles as the waves pass but does not follow the waves outward. All the water stays close to where it started. Friction generated by the moving water adds a little heat, eventually turning all the wave energy into heat.

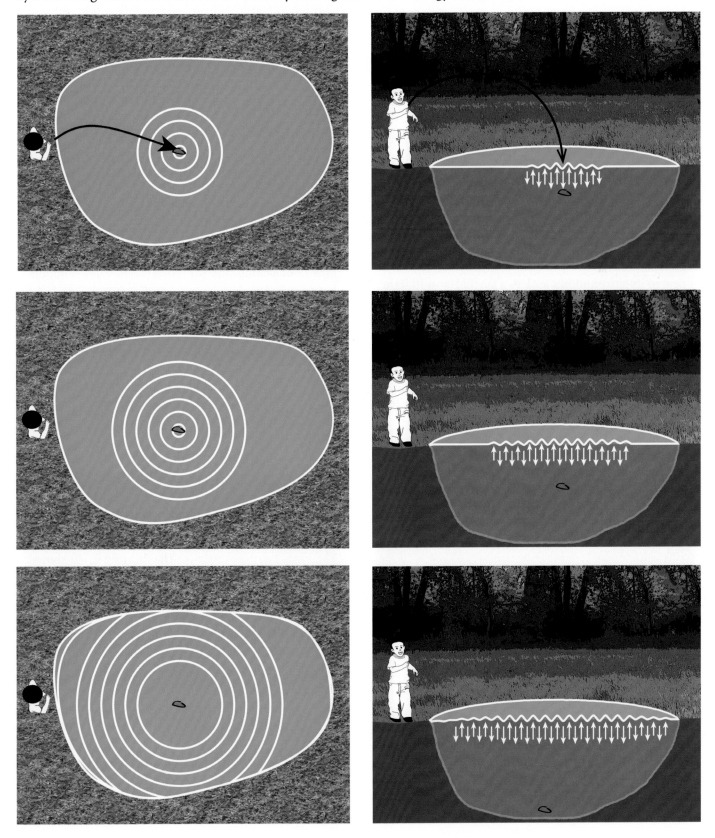

Sound and Energy

Energy is required to make anything move or vibrate. Sound is a form of kinetic energy, similar to the kinetic energy in a football flying through the air after someone kicks it. In obedience with the first law of thermodynamics, just as all the kinetic energy in the football will soon become heat, sound will soon become heat. Sound adds heat to the air it travels through as a result of friction between moving air molecules. If sound hits a solid object such as a rock, wall, or tree, it will cause the object to vibrate, which will heat up the object as a result of friction between moving molecules in that object.

Sound does not contain much energy. The power[1] required to produce the very loud noise made by a smoke alarm or a radio can come from a small battery. The power in the sound coming from a piano is about 0.5 watts, and the power from an orchestra is about 100 watts, which means the sound from an orchestra adds the same amount of heat to its surroundings as does a single 100-watt light bulb.

1   The difference between energy and power is subtle. Energy is a quantity, while power is a rate. The price to buy a hat is a quantity; the weekly or monthly price to rent an apartment is a rate. The amount of energy stored in a flashlight battery is a quantity; the amount of power it can put out at one point in time is a rate, usually described in watts. For more on watts, see Footnote 2 on Page 367.

The reason such small amounts of energy sound so loud is that people's ears are very sensitive. People's ears can hear sound that changes the pressure of air one billionth of normal atmospheric pressure. When people spend time in a quiet room their ears become even more sensitive. In a specially built room that allows almost no sound in, and reflects almost no sound, a person can hear her own heartbeat within about an hour. When people live in houses or apartments with good soundproofing, they start to complain that the refrigerator is too noisy.

Sound cannot keep traveling forever, because it heats air or anything else it travels through. This is one reason why sound is less loud at a distance. Another reason sound is less loud at a distance is that sound spreads out from its source in all directions, the same way light does.

The perceived volume of sound at a distance from its source is different indoors than outdoors. Sound bounces off the floor, ceiling, and walls of a room, while outdoors it has far fewer surfaces to reflect off of. This is why indoor noise sounds almost equally loud anywhere in a room, whereas outdoor sound gets quieter at a distance.

Keeping annoying sounds out of a room requires turning all the sound approaching the room into heat, which of course nobody can hear. The drawings on this page and the next two pages show some of the ways sound behaves and some of the ways it gets turned into heat.

The drawing at left shows sound waves reflecting off a smooth surface.

The reflections are relatively neat and orderly, maintaining patterns that would be recognizable as speech or music.

Only the high pressure waves are shown; the low pressure waves are not.

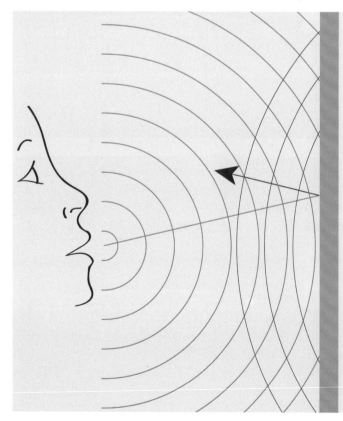

The drawing at right shows sound waves causing a wall to vibrate like a drumskin, which generates new sound waves on the other side of the wall.

Some of the energy that makes the wall vibrate heats the wall, while some of it becomes sound on both sides of the wall.

However, because some of the energy in the sound heats the air and the wall, and some is reflected back, the sound on the other side of the wall will be much less loud.

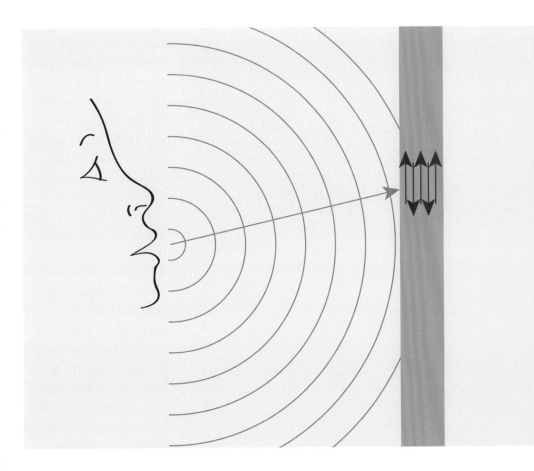

The drawing at left shows sound waves hitting a wall and causing transverse waves, also called shear waves. Shear waves are generated more in soft, flexible materials such as rubber, cork, or caulk than in hard or stiff objects (which tend to vibrate as a whole). Almost all the energy required to generate transverse waves heats the wall through friction between moving molecules, and almost none of it generates new sound waves.

When two high- or low-pressure points in the sound waves reach the same place at the same time (shown by solid circles) the sound waves reinforce each other. When high- and low-pressure points reach the same place at the same time, shown by dotted line circles, they cancel each other out. The same is true for any part of a wave, not just the peaks and valleys shown here.

These interference patterns—reinforcing some sounds and canceling others—are one reason why it is difficult to understand one person's voice when other people are speaking.

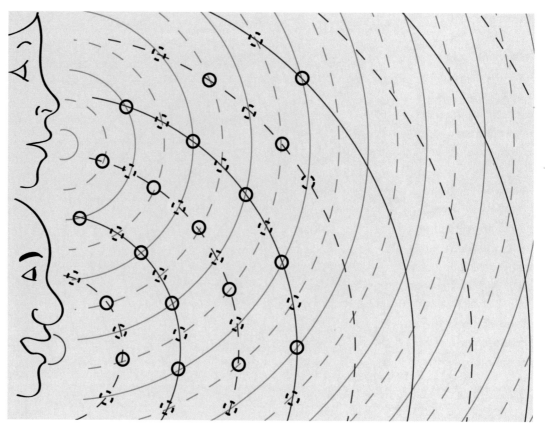

The drawing at left shows sound waves reflecting off a rough surface, such as an acoustic ceiling tile. Instead of reflecting whole waves neatly back toward the source as a smooth surface would do, the rough surface breaks the sound waves up into many smaller waves reflected in many directions.

The small waves travel in many directions, interfering with each other, making any sound reflected back to a person's ears sound like white noise. This is why it is easier to carry on a conversation in a room with a rough ceiling: the listener does not hear the words a second time.

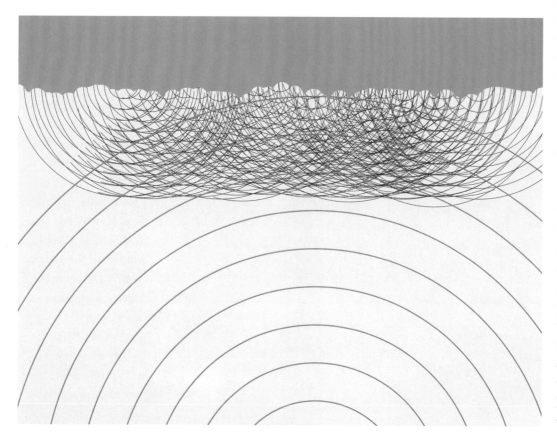

Waves Reflecting off Smooth and Rough Surfaces, and Interfering

①This is a bathtub with a little water in it. At one end of the tub is a piece of aluminum foil folded accordion-style and stapled to some wood. ② A table tennis ball dropped into the water sends a wave out in all directions.

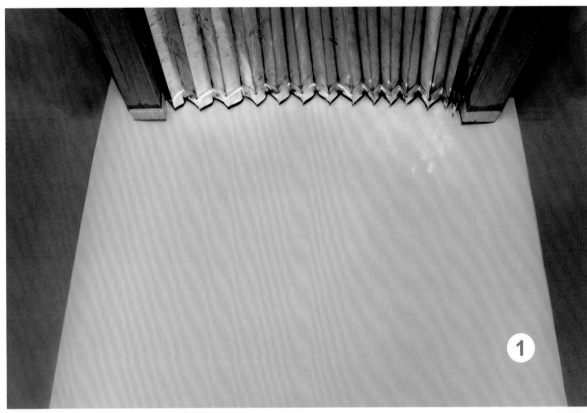

Photos in this series by Giorgio Guidi.

③ The ball is no longer in the exact center of the wave, because it was not dropped perfectly straight down into the water, but the wave continues spreading out at the same speed in all directions. ④ The wave reaches the aluminum back wall.

⑤ The wave is reflecting off the aluminum foil wall and the two side walls. The reflections off the smooth side walls are about as neat as the reflections shown in the drawing on the bottom of Page 276, while the reflections off the aluminum foil wall are starting to show interference. ⑥ The reflections off the aluminum foil wall are generating a classic interference pattern much like the one shown in the drawing on the top of Page 278.

Between the times when photos ⑦ and ⑧ were taken, the reflections from the side walls keep advancing further from the walls, while the waves reflected off the back wall do not advance much further. This is because each of the many small waves reflecting off the rough surface of the back wall is weaker than the large, single waves, and they are spreading in different directions, interfering with each other, sometimes reinforcing each other, but mostly canceling each other out.

⑨ The waves that reflected off the back wall are all gone: all their energy has been turned into heat, while the waves reflecting off the smooth sides of the bathtub are still neat and coherent and continue to advance toward each other (as their energy has not yet turned into heat). ⑩ The waves reflecting off the side walls meet each other and cancel each other out, finally turning their energy into heat.

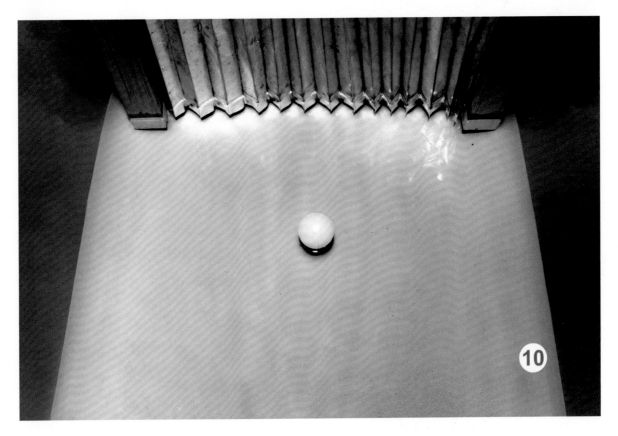

(11) The water is now almost completely still. The potential energy of the ball held above the water turned into kinetic energy as it fell, then turned into kinetic energy in the form of waves in the water and a little turbulence in the air. Finally, the waves heated the water through friction, turning the energy into heat. A little of the potential energy in the ball became heat in the air from friction, a little became heat in the ball, and most of it became heat in the water.

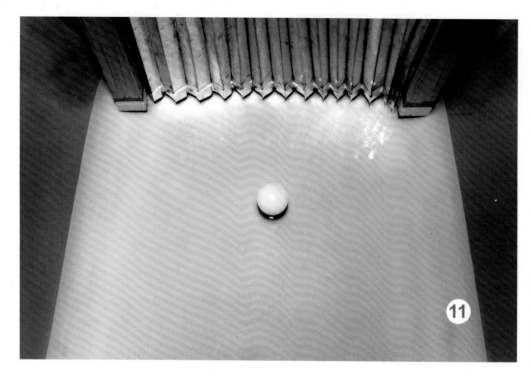

SUMMARY

Sound is energy in the form of vibrations that people's ears can sense. It is always on its way to becoming heat added to the substance that vibrates.

Our ears are sensitive to different frequencies (or wavelengths) of sound.

Flat and hard surfaces are good reflectors of sound waves. Soft surfaces absorb the energy in sound, and rough surfaces reflect sound in different directions, causing interference.

The wave created by the boat is reflecting off the smooth wall on the right side of the photo but not reflecting off the rough, rocky riverbank on the left side of the photo. Sound waves behave in a similar way.

Chapter 10 **SOUND** Applied Science

WHY IS IT IMPORTANT TO UNDERSTAND SOUND MOVEMENT THROUGH BUILDINGS?

A good building isolates people from sounds coming from outdoors and from elsewhere in the building. Sound annoys people because it distracts them from what they are trying to do or think about. Voice sounds—including TV and radio noise—are the worst because they convey ideas that compete with what people are trying to think. "White noise," sound patterns with no language or rhythm, is not as distracting because it does not convey information. The round, light blue objects hanging from the ceiling in the photo on the bottom of Page 313 are speakers that play white noise to make the office seem quieter by drowning out conversation.

A building can be made quieter by turning as much sound as possible into heat before it reaches a person's ears. Or, if sound patterns are broken up into white noise, a building will seem quieter than it really is.

Understanding how to make a building quiet requires first understanding how sound travels through a building.

TWO MAIN WAYS SOUND IS TRANSMITTED THROUGH WALLS AND FLOOR/CEILING ASSEMBLIES

1. Sound causes an assembly or parts of an assembly to vibrate like a drumskin, generating new sound waves on the other side of the assembly.

2. Sound waves travel through the air inside holes that go all the way through assemblies. Examples include a gap between gypsum board and the floor, or between a window and a wall (if it is not properly installed).

Sound can also be transmitted through an assembly by a combination of these mechanisms.

Reducing Sound Transmitted by an Assembly Vibrating Like a Drumskin

When sound waves reach a wall or ceiling or chair or any other object, some of the sound is reflected off the surface, and some is absorbed by the object and causes it to vibrate. As the surface of the object vibrates, it sends new sound waves out into the room the same way a vibrating drumskin sends sound waves out into the room. When walls and ceilings vibrate they can send sound out to the other side of the wall or ceiling.

This wall is being built with extra mass in the form of a layer of plywood behind the gypsum board. This increases the amount of energy required to cause the wall to vibrate. The fiberglass insulation between the studs will also control sound by breaking up sound into smaller, weaker waves, causing some waves to cancel each other and helping to make white noise out of the remaining sound.

Different types of material absorb sound very differently. Objects made of hard, stiff materials such as steel or glass vibrate as a whole, causing nearby air to vibrate and sending new sound waves out through the surrounding air. Objects made of soft, flexible materials such as rubber or caulk do not vibrate as a whole. Instead, the surface that absorbs the sound vibrates a lot while other parts do not vibrate as much, creating internal shear waves. Internal friction in the flexible material transforms most of the energy of the vibrations into heat.

Because flexible materials do not transmit sound very well, they can be used to control sound within a building by isolating one part of an assembly from another. Not only does a flexible material turn sound into heat, but as different parts of an assembly connected to each other with flexible materials vibrate independently of each other, they vibrate at different frequencies, creating both interference and white noise.

Another fundamental sound control technique is adding mass (weight) to something, which increases the amount of energy required to make it vibrate. Solid doors transmit less sound than hollow doors because they are heavier. Adding extra layers of gypsum board to walls adds mass, but there are better (and less expensive) ways of reducing sound transmission through walls, as will be explained later in this chapter.

As sound waves traveling through air hit a wall, the wall will move back and forth slightly, generating new sound waves on both sides of the wall.

Adding mass to a wall reduces wall movement, which reduces sound transmission. Another way of reducing sound transmission is mounting gypsum boards with flexible connections that let them vibrate independently. For sound to get through it has to vibrate the gypsum board on one side of the wall, which vibrates the air inside the wall, which vibrates the gypsum board on the other side, which vibrates the air on the other side of the wall. This creates interference and white noise patterns in the air inside the wall. Interference turns some of the sound into heat, shear waves in the flexible connections turn more sound into heat, and most of the noise that gets through is white noise, with no discernible pattern.

If the space inside the wall is filled with fiberglass or mineral wool insulation (the same type as used for thermal insulation), the sound patterns inside the wall will be disrupted, further reducing sound transmission.

Reducing Sound Transmission through Air

One of the most effective ways of reducing sound transmission through building assemblies is also the most overlooked: adding an air barrier. Sound will bypass a wall built with the best isolation and massing techniques as long as it can get through a small air gap. The air barrier methods described in Chapter 4: Air - Applied Science should be applied to any building assembly that is intended to control sound. Pages 288-293 show how to build walls that transmit very little sound.

Mass: Noisy pumps are mounted on a heavy concrete base, which is too heavy to easily vibrate.

Isolation: The heavy concrete base is supported by springs, which allow the concrete base to vibrate independently of the floor.

Sound Causing a Wall to Vibrate Like a Drumskin

① - ② The first low-pressure wave reaches the wall, causing a small difference in air pressure between one side of the wall and the other, which moves the wall toward the drummer. ③ The first high-pressure wave reaches the wall and moves it in the other direction. ④ - ⑥ the wall moves back and forth repeatedly, generating new sound waves on both sides. New waves are shown here on only one side.

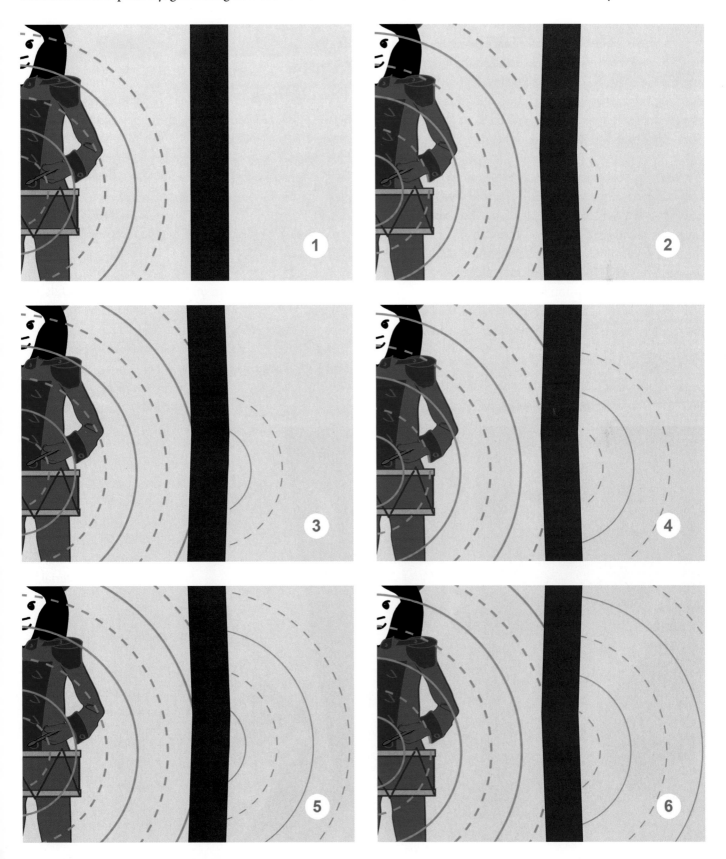

BUILDING A (VIRTUALLY) SOUNDPROOF WALL

The wall construction described on these two pages will pass a "boom box test," where a radio is played very loudly in an apartment—far too loudly for people to carry on a conversation—and someone in the next apartment cannot hear it. This assumes the floor/ceiling assemblies are made of concrete and the doors between the apartments and the hallway are weatherstripped well. If not, noise passing over and under the wall through the floor/ceiling assembly, or out to the hallway and back, might transmit noise from one side of the wall to the other.

The first step, as shown in the photo below, is to stagger the studs when framing the wall. The **wall studs** are one size narrower than the **floor track** (and the ceiling track, not shown) and are positioned alternately on one side of the track or the other. This creates a pattern of **alternating gaps** between the studs and the track. Because each stud will only touch the gypsum board on one side of the wall, the studs are spaced more closely than they would normally be spaced. This requires more studs than are usually used to build a wall.

Next, electric boxes and wires get installed in the normal manner, except that all electric boxes on opposite sides

of the wall are separated by at least one stud. No electric boxes should be mounted on the same stud (as they are in the photo on the bottom of the next page) or back to back in the same stud bay (the empty space between studs). Then all the electric boxes get airtightened as shown on Pages 120-122.

Next, fiberglass or mineral wool insulation gets woven between the studs as shown in the photo on the top of the next page. Mineral wool is a little more effective than fiberglass because it is slightly heavier. The insulation will fill the gap between the gypsum boards, as well as the gaps between the studs and the gypsum board.

Finally, gypsum boards get installed on each side of the wall with a three-way caulk joint between the track or end stud, the floor or ceiling or intersecting wall, and the gypsum board, as shown on Pages 117-119. Caulk fills the gap between the gypsum board and the electric boxes as shown on Page 122. Acoustic caulk, which is specially formulated to remain flexible so it can absorb vibrations, is a good choice because it won't transmit vibrations between adjoining materials. A second piece of gypsum board on one or both sides of the wall will reduce sound transmission further. (Two pieces of gypsum board are usually required on each side of fire-rated walls between apartments anyway.)

Because there is no continuous path for sound to take through solid material, this wall will not transmit sound the way the wall shown on Page 287 will.

Also, because of the air barrier built into the wall, there will be no continuous air pathway to transmit sound through the wall.

If more walls were built like this, many people would sleep better.

The photo at right shows unfaced fiberglass insulation batts being woven between staggered studs. The insulation is only partly installed in the photo. When the installation is complete, the insulation will be installed in the whole wall from floor to ceiling.

The fiberglass insulation blocks many audible sound waves because the gaps between fibers are smaller than sound waves that people can hear.

The electric boxes at left will allow sound to travel from one side of the wall to the other through the stud and through the air between the boxes. Much less sound passes through a wall if electric boxes are staggered, with a stud or two between boxes on opposite sides of the wall.

Light fixtures recessed into ceilings also transmit sound. Airtight fixtures (unlike the one shown on the bottom of Page 95) reduce sound transmission (and air leakage).

Resilient Channel Allows Gypsum Board to Vibrate Independently

While the wall described on the previous two pages will pass a boom box test, adding resilient channel will reduce sound transmission even further. The photo at right shows a piece of resilient channel, which is a strip of thin steel used as a flexible mounting for gypsum board.

One leg of the channel gets screwed to the wall studs or the ceiling structure, and the gypsum board is screwed to the **other leg**. Only **a small amount of metal** connects one leg to another. (Caution: some inferior products have more metal connecting the two legs.) Because very little solid material connects the gypsum board to whatever the channel is mounted on, the gypsum board will vibrate independently, keeping sound transmission to a minimum.

The photo below shows a wall being built with resilient channel. **One leg of the resilient channel** is **screwed** to every second stud (the studs are staggered, with only every second stud connected to each side of the wall), and the gypsum board is **screwed** to the other leg. The **green material** between the resilient channel and the gypsum board is a soundproofing compound (a flexible material similar to acoustic caulk) that helps absorb vibration.

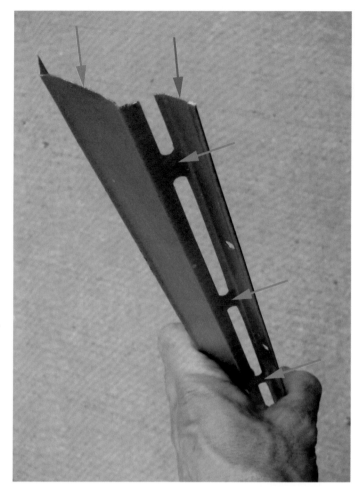

Don't Make a Solid Connection through the Resilient Channel

The drawing at right shows gypsum board mounted with screws that go through the leg of the resilient channel, intended for connection to the gypsum board only, and then into the studs. This renders the resilient channel useless because the screws will hold the gypsum board securely to the studs, preventing the gypsum board from vibrating independently of the rest of the wall.

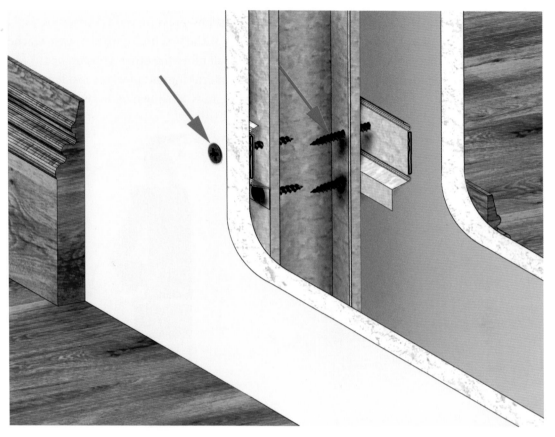

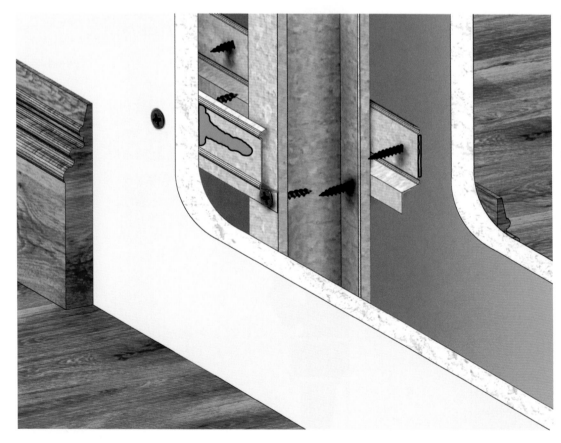

The drawing at left shows the proper way to mount the gypsum board: with screws that go through the resilient channel only but not through the studs. Separate screws connect the resilient channel to the studs.

This allows the gypsum board to vibrate independently of the studs.

The green material between the resilient channel and the gypsum board is soundproofing compound that helps absorb vibrations.

Wall with Resilient Channel

① - ② The first low-pressure wave reaches the wall and moves the gypsum board on only one side of the wall toward the drummer. ③ The first high-pressure wave reaches the gypsum board, moving it in the other direction while waves inside the wall move the other gypsum board. ④ - ⑥ The two gypsum boards move independently and chaotically, generating interfering sound waves inside the wall cavity and much weaker sound waves on the other side of the wall. Staggering the studs, as shown on Pages 288 and 289, also helps the gypsum board on each side of the wall to vibrate independently.

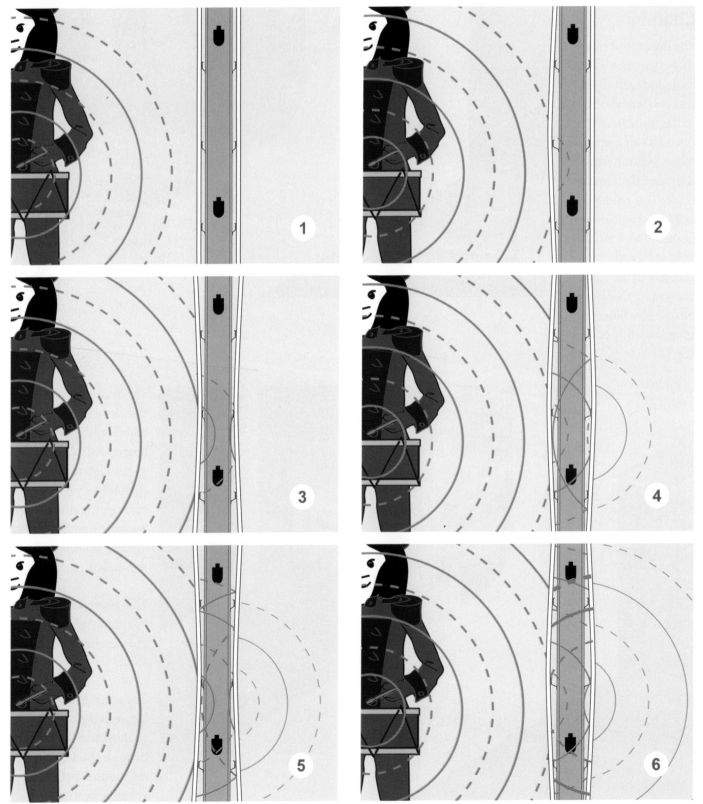

The resilient channel being installed in the photo at near right is oriented correctly: the leg attached to the studs is at the bottom, so the weight of the gypsum board pulls the channel away from the wall.

In the photo at far right, the resilient channel will reduce sound transmission vertically through the floor/ceiling assembly.

Model: Sumeyye Sarac.

The photo at left shows the room above with foam insulation sprayed between the floor/ceiling joists, which will also reduce sound transmission.

Foam has also been sprayed between the wall studs along the wall with windows—an outside wall. This insulation will reduce heat movement, air leaks, and sound transmission from the street.

SOUND REFLECTION WITHIN A ROOM

How sound behaves within a room helps determine how a person perceives the room.

Smooth surfaces reflect sound waves with minimal change to the wave patterns, as shown in the drawing on Page 276. This creates an echo, which can enhance the enjoyment of music but tends to be distracting to someone listening to a person speaking.

Rough surfaces reflect sound in many directions, much as rough surfaces reflect light in many directions. This creates chaotic wave patterns that interfere with each other, turning voice or music into white noise.

Sound reaching soft surfaces at certain angles cannot be reflected, only absorbed. The softer the material, the more angles this is true for, and therefore the more sound the material absorbs. Hard surfaces of any texture reflect more sound than soft surfaces.

Different rooms with different surfaces absorb sound at different rates. An empty room with flat and hard surfaces for the floor, walls, and ceiling will not absorb much sound. Any sound generated in the room or entering the room from elsewhere will echo back and forth in the room for a relatively long time, perhaps several seconds.

A room with many soft surfaces, such as carpet on the floor and an acoustic tile ceiling, that also contains many soft objects such as people and upholstered chairs, will absorb sound before it has a chance to echo back and forth many times. Music might sound dead because of so little echo, but it will be relatively easy to hear and understand what a person is saying.

Experts have studied how much sound is absorbed by different surfaces or objects, comparing them to an open window, which reflects zero sound. A person absorbs as much sound as an open window measuring about 0.5 square meters. An upholstered chair will absorb about half that, which is ten times as much as an unupholstered chair will absorb. Chairs in concert halls are sometimes luxuriously upholstered to

minimize the change in acoustics between practice time and when people fill the seats.

An acoustic ceiling—made of rough-surfaced, cardboard-like tiles hung in a suspended grid—absorbs ten or twenty times as much sound as a painted gypsum board ceiling. This is why acoustic tile ceilings are commonly used in offices. Unpainted concrete absorbs about four times as much sound as painted concrete because the painted surface is smoother. Large, flat ceiling light fixtures can also reflect sound, which can be a problem in offices.

Sound is hard to judge in an empty room because there is no furniture to absorb and break up sound waves. But if a room sounds quiet enough when it is empty, it will almost surely be acceptable later, when it is filled with furniture.

A stairway under construction filled with spray foam absorbs sound generated by someone walking on the stairs, making life quieter for other people in the house.

The office in the drawing at right has a smooth, hard ceiling, which reflects a lot of sound.

Office partitions that are tall enough to provide good sound isolation (about two meters, or six feet) tend to create isolated temperature zones, causing some people to feel cold, while others are hot. Larger distances between people help reduce distraction from people talking nearby, but space for this is not always available.

One solution is partitions low enough to avoid creating microclimates, with enough rough and absorptive surfaces to reduce echo, such as the acoustic tile ceiling at left. The ceiling makes up a large percentage of the room's exposed surface, which is why an acoustic tile ceiling is so important.

Acoustic ceilings are not usually included on lists of inventions that make modern office buildings possible, but perhaps they should be.

Noise-Control Devices

The photo at right shows a restaurant with acoustic ceiling tiles. Hanging below the acoustic ceiling tiles is a wooden device that controls sound.

When someone sitting at a table talks, sound that would otherwise reflect off the ceiling and head toward another table is broken up into smaller waves as it hits the device. The smaller waves are partly absorbed by the ceiling, and then broken up again after being partly reflected by the ceiling and passing back through the device, which of course also absorbs some sound. The device is simple, inexpensive, and effective. However, making it look attractive is a challenge.

The photo below shows a restaurant with a sheet metal ceiling, which like any hard, relatively smooth surface is a very good reflector of sound. **Sound-absorbing panels** mounted on the wall near the ceiling help control sound reflection.

The ceiling decoration in the cafeteria on the top of Page 257 looks like it also functions as a sound control device.

REDUCING SOUND TRANSMISSION THROUGH WINDOWS

Vibrating a pane of glass requires energy. The thicker the pane, the better it is at reducing sound transmission. Two panes of glass can reduce sound transmission better than a single pane. However, when a triple-pane window is compared to a double-pane window, three panes only reduce noise significantly better than two panes if the air gaps between the panes are at least 20 mm or wider, which is wider than found in most windows.

What works better is varying the thicknesses of the panes of glass in a window because different thicknesses of glass vibrate at different frequencies. Different thicknesses work best if the thickness of one pane is at least double the thickness of another. Different pane thicknesses show up as different distances between adjacent laser pointer reflections, as shown on the top of Page 48.

Two separate windows work better than the same number of panes built into a single window because they create a large air gap and because they prevent sound transmission through a single frame. The photos at right each show two complete windows installed in one window opening. Both are intended to reduce indoor noise near airports. Some building codes require two windows when buildings are built near airports and railroads.

Laminating two panes of glass together with a piece of plastic between them can reduce noise better than one single-pane that is as thick as the two pieces of glass. Casement windows reduce sound transmission, especially high-frequency sound, better than sliding windows. Inoperable windows reduce sound transmission better than casement windows. Curtains and drapes also help a little—the more tightly woven the better.

REDUCING SOUND TRANSMISSION THROUGH DOORS

When walls between apartments are built as described on Pages 288 and 289, and no significant sound is getting from one apartment to another through the floor/ceiling assemblies, the only remaining path for audible sound to get from one apartment to another is usually out through one apartment's doorway, through the public hall, and into the other apartment's doorway. Sound can pass through thin but long gaps between the doors and the frames, or through the doors themselves, or both.

The heavier a door the less sound gets through because more energy is required to vibrate a heavy door. This is why solid doors generally transmit less sound than hollow doors. Locating doors so they are not directly across from each other, as shown on Page 532, also helps. Sliding doors are usually an air leak and sound transmission nightmare. Sound transmission through gaps between doors and frames can be reduced or stopped with any of the airtightening technologies on Pages 125-127.

DON'T LET SOUND ESCAPE FROM AN EQUIPMENT ROOM

The photo at right shows a new boiler room built on an apartment building roof to prevent damage to the boiler when the basement floods (again). The boiler is equipped with a burner that has a fan that pushes combustion air through the boiler. Because of the proximity to apartment windows, steps were taken to minimize fan noise coming out of the boiler room's fresh air intake.

The diagram below is from the blueprints for this boiler room and boiler installation. The **burner** and its noisy fan are strategically located at the end of the boiler room furthest from the fresh air intake. The amount of sound reaching the fresh air intake is minimized both by maximizing the distance between the fan and the fresh air intake and by placing the big, heavy boiler and most of the pipes (and the soft fiberglass insulation covering them) between the fan and the fresh air intake.

Some sound inevitably travels through the boiler room to the fresh air intake. The next page shows how the amount of sound that escapes from the room through the fresh air intake is minimized.

The photo above shows two pieces of tile backer board hanging from the ceiling on the indoor (boiler room) side of the fresh air intake. Tile backer board is normally used as wallboard behind bathroom tiles. Tile backer board is made of a mixture of cement (similar to what is used to make sidewalks) and fiberglass mesh. Its surface is rougher than the boiler room walls, and it is heavy enough that it won't vibrate easily. A softer material would probably absorb more sound, but tile backer board was chosen because it is water resistant, fireproof, and durable. If more sound reduction was desired, one or more boards could be covered with mineral wool insulation (fluffy fibers that are also water resistant and fireproof). The two boards are hung close enough to the fresh air intakes to block large sound waves, but not close enough to reduce the supply of air to the burner. The mounting chains are flexible enough to isolate the boards from the ceiling structure.

The photo at right shows the special sound-resistant louver (with its screen removed for clarity). Each of the louver's blades is made of a thick layer of soft, flexible fibers.

The combination of all these sound-reducing techniques works so well that more sound escapes out of the gap under the boiler room door than through the fresh air louver.

These apartment buildings are located on a busy street. Replacing the windows with modern windows, and installing them with a good airtight connection to the walls, would greatly reduce traffic noise in the apartments. When calculating the economics of replacing windows, better occupant satisfaction should be considered in addition to reduced maintenance costs and reduced energy costs.

EVEN QUIETER

Holes for wires to circuit breaker panels, sound systems, burglar alarms, thermostats, and similar devices can increase sound transmission through a wall. Additional holes are made when wires are added later. Devices with many wires are best located where sound transmission through the wall will not be objectionable, such as a wall backed up by a closet with a door to the same room. Not only will the clothing in the closet absorb some sound, but also sound will not be transmitted to another room.

Many dedicated sound-control products are available, including heavy sheets of vinyl to add mass and flexibility to a wall, gypsum board with a flexible layer sandwiched in the middle, and springy connectors to isolate parts of a building. But the basics described here can be expected to produce satisfactory results for most situations, if the airtightening is done well.

Bushes and trees planted near a building absorb a little noise, especially when they have leaves on them. Evergreens provide the best year-round sound reduction.

Water falling through a drain pipe creates noise. Cast iron pipes are quieter than plastic. Pipe insulation also helps.

SUMMARY

By far the most important factor in reducing sound transmission between rooms in a building or between indoors and outdoors is a continuous air barrier. Adding mass and isolating building materials from each other with flexible connections are the next most important factors. Adding mass is usually more expensive but easier than isolation.

Sound reflection within a room is reduced by rough surfaces that scatter sound and by soft or porous materials that absorb sound.

Chapter 11 **FIRE** Basic Science

WHAT IS FIRE?

It may seem surprising, but the fire that burns on a stove or burns a house down is the same chemical reaction that our bodies use to produce energy from food or that takes place when an iron fence rusts: oxidation.

In each case, oxygen from air reacts chemically with another material. When we digest food, our bodies combine oxygen molecules from the air we breathe with the molecules in our food, producing the energy we use to live. In conformance with the first law of thermodynamics, digestion produces new chemicals that contain less chemical energy than the chemicals that make up our food. The new chemicals are carbon dioxide (CO_2) and water (H_2O). We exhale the carbon dioxide from our lungs. The water leaves our bodies[1] as water vapor exhaled from our lungs, sweat from our skin, or urine. The carbon dioxide is invisible, but the water is sometimes visible as fog coming out of our lungs on a cold day, as explained on Page 142. Some of the energy we produce by digesting food is stored as special chemicals our muscles use later. Most of the energy we produce leaves our bodies as heat.[2]

In the case of a rusting fence, oxygen combines with iron, producing heat and a chemical containing less chemical energy: iron oxide, also known as rust. The heat is produced so slowly that it is difficult to detect.

A fire does the same thing as digestion or rusting but faster. Whatever is burning—bread left in the toaster too long, wood, plastic, gasoline—combines chemically with oxygen from the air, producing heat and new chemicals, mostly water and carbon dioxide.

The main difference between fire and similar processes such as rusting and digestion is the speed of the reaction. Fire is such a fast reaction that it produces heat quickly enough to raise the temperature enough to pyrolyze fuel.

Pyrolysis is the conversion of solids and liquids, such as kitchen cabinets or grease in a frying pan, into gases. "Pyrolyze" is a combination of the Greek words "pyr" (fire) and "lysis" (separation). The process is simple: heat something until it turns into a gas. When heated, solids such as wood or liquids such as oil are converted into a mix of gases that includes methane, butane, propane, and others, similar to the mix that makes up natural gas.

Strictly speaking, solids and liquids do not burn. Pyrolysis first turns "burning" solids and liquids into gases. Flames are burning gases, not burning solids or liquids. The gases in a flame either started out as gases, such as natural gas or propane piped to a kitchen stove, or were produced by pyrolyzing solid or liquid fuel. The same basic processes take place in every fire, but there are particular ways fires inside of buildings behave.

THE THREE STAGES OF FIRE IN A BUILDING

A fire burning in a building goes through three stages. During each stage, the rate of burn is limited by a different factor:

Stage One: Burn rate limited by availability of heat.

Stage Two: Burn rate limited by availability of oxygen.

Stage Three: Burn rate limited by availability of fuel.

The chemical process is the same in each stage: oxygen combines with fuel, producing heat and new chemicals.

---

1   More water leaves our bodies than enters our bodies, because digesting food produces new water that did not exist before. Photosynthesis in plants breaks water down into oxygen that gets released and hydrogen that gets combined with carbon to produce hydrocarbons (branches, leaves, vegetables). This "hydrogen cycle" of animals creating and plants destroying water is parallel to the "carbon cycle" of animals creating and plants destroying carbon dioxide. Burning fossil fuel creates both carbon dioxide and water. Yes, burning fossil fuel is not only continuously increasing the amount of carbon dioxide on the earth but also adding new water.
2   Modern-day calculations have shown that some of the early polar explorers who died of "exposure" did not bring enough food to survive. Without enough food, their bodies could not produce enough heat to stay warm. In an extremely cold environment, starving to death and dying of exposure are sort of the same thing.

Stage One: Heat Limited

If grease is burning in a frying pan on a stove, the wood table on the other side of the room is not burning because it is not hot enough. The only fuels that are hot enough are the grease and food in the frying pan. But if there are cabinets above the stove, the fire will heat them, which is how many house and apartment fires spread.

Because the cabinets are porous, and have been exposed to air since the day they were manufactured, they have absorbed water vapor from the air. As the cabinets absorb heat from the fire, they dry out. Whatever water was previously absorbed in the wood changes from a liquid to a gas, absorbing latent heat in the process.[3] As long as there is still some absorbed water in the cabinets, latent cooling will limit the temperature of the cabinets. Described another way, as fire adds heat to the cabinets, the portion of the heat that changes the liquid water to a gas (water vapor) does not increase the temperature of the cabinets, because it is used to change liquid water into water vapor.

The fire is still a Stage One fire because there is not enough heat to ignite fuel throughout the room (such as the wood table). A firefighter might call a Stage One fire a "developing" fire. As a Stage One (heat-limited) fire progresses, smoke fills the room. Because the smoke is much hotter than the air in the room, strong convective currents move it to the ceiling and spread it out as a layer tightly hugging the ceiling. The smoke heats the ceiling by conduction, and by radiation from the soot particles in the smoke, while the ceiling radiates infrared radiation back down throughout the room. This process heats the room fairly evenly, except for objects closer to the fire, such as the cabinets, which are getting hotter faster because they are also being heated by more intense infrared radiation from the fire and by conduction from the smoke where the smoke is hottest.

As the fire heats the room, absorbed water in materials throughout the room turns to water vapor, absorbing latent heat of vaporization. As the fire keeps producing

The heat from a candle flame turns the wax and the wick into gases, which then burn. The wax and wick do not burn as solids or liquids but as gases.

heat, the rise in the temperature of the room is limited by latent cooling, just as latent cooling limits the rise in the temperature of the cabinets. Usually the store of absorbed water runs out long before the fuel does. At the end of the first stage, the supply of absorbed water is exhausted, which stops latent cooling, allowing the temperature of the room to suddenly increase and fuel throughout the room to pyrolyze.

Stage Two: Oxygen Limited

The start of a Stage Two fire is marked by a transition called "flashover." Gas from pyrolyzed fuel throughout the room ignites, sometimes quite suddenly, and the temperature in the room increases sharply. According to the National Fire Protection Association® (US), flashover is a "transition phase in the development of a compartment fire in which surfaces exposed to thermal radiation reach ignition temperature more or

3   Water absorbed into materials can be thought of as a liquid with a slightly different energy state than liquid water because it is magnetically bound to the surfaces of the material.

Notice how the fire is more intense at the edge of the rear window where pyrolyzed fuel is mixing with air and less intense inside the cab.

less simultaneously and fire spreads rapidly throughout the space, resulting in full room involvement or total involvement of the compartment or enclosed space."[4] Now the fire is a Stage Two fire, which a firefighter might call a "ventilation-controlled" or "fully involved" fire.

Test fires in old buildings with old furniture can take thirty minutes or longer to flash over, or might not flash over at all, instead exhausting all the fuel without flashing over. A fire in a modern building furnished with modern plastic and synthetic furniture can flash over in five minutes or less. This is because newer building materials and new furniture do not absorb as much water as older materials such as wood and cotton. Also, the humidity in newer buildings is more likely to be low due to fans, ducts, and air leaks during the winter or air conditioning during the summer, thereby reducing the amount of absorbed water, which reduces the available latent cooling.

At flashover, combustible gases produced by pyrolysis burn in all parts of the room, quickly consuming oxygen. After flashover, the supply of pyrolyzed fuel exceeds the supply of oxygen, so the rate of burn is limited by the supply of oxygen to the fire. Because the oxygen is coming from air, the rate of burn is limited by availability of air reaching the fire.

A Stage Two fire in a building is characterized by flames coming out of windows. The sight of flames shooting out of windows might lead a person to think a fire is even more intense inside the building. In reality, it is most intense (highest burn rate) where the pyrolyzed fuel meets air, which is often just outside or inside the windows, near elevator shafts, or near stairways.

4   National Fire Protection Association, <u>NFPA 921: Guide for Fire & Explosion Investigations</u> (Quincy, MA: NFPA, 2011), Page 14.

Stage Three: Fuel Limited

If a Stage Two fire continues burning, it will reach the third and final stage, where the supply of fuel starts to be exhausted, and there is more oxygen available than fuel. A firefighter might call this stage a "decaying" fire or a "fuel-controlled" fire. If nothing else puts the fire out, the third stage continues until all the fuel is burned.

Not all building fires go through all three of these stages. Some fires are put out by water from an automatic sprinkler system or a firefighter's hose before they reach Stage Two or Stage Three. And some fires start so suddenly they effectively skip Stage One. For example, when the planes hit the World Trade Center towers on September 11, 2001, the fires started as Stage Two almost immediately.

HOW DOES A FIRE KILL PEOPLE?

In the vast majority of cases, people trapped in a burning building are not killed by heat but by breathing carbon monoxide (CO). Carbon monoxide is so poisonous that at concentrations of two or three percent, as is often found in smoke, two breaths can kill someone.[5] In cleaner combustion, such as a properly tuned boiler or car, almost every one of the carbon molecules in the fuel combines with two oxygen molecules, producing carbon dioxide (CO_2). A fire produces carbon monoxide when some of the carbon in the pyrolyzed fuel does not get exposed to enough air or heat to combine each carbon molecule with two oxygen molecules, instead combining some carbon molecules with only one oxygen molecule. Unlike a car engine or a boiler, a fire in a building has no mechanism to control the mixing of fuel and air, which causes it to produce large amounts of deadly carbon monoxide.

5   Carbon monoxide interferes with the ability of blood to transport oxygen. A protein in red blood cells called hemoglobin normally absorbs oxygen in the lungs and releases it wherever it is needed in the body, but hemoglobin absorbs carbon monoxide about 250 times as readily as oxygen, forming a chemical called carboxyhemoglobin, rendering hemoglobin unable to transport oxygen. The half life of carboxyhemoglobin in the human body is about five hours, so if the person survives, the blood will regain its ability to transport oxygen. Repeated or long-term exposure to low concentrations of carbon monoxide is damaging to the human body, especially the brain, but is easily overlooked because the symptoms mimic the flu. Inexpensive and reliable carbon monoxide detectors are now available, and should be used in any building that contains any oil-, gas-, or wood-burning appliance, including a cooking stove.

People might survive for a short time in a Stage One fire, but unlike fires in movies, which somehow produce lots of flames but almost no smoke, even a Stage One fire produces lethal concentrations of carbon monoxide. A Stage Two fire produces carbon monoxide and heat at a rate that will kill a person almost instantly.

HOW DOES WATER EXTINGUISH A FIRE?

At any stage of a fire, firefighters or an automatic sprinkler system might extinguish a fire with water. This brings up a question that was reportedly asked on a firefighter's exam: What are the four ways water puts out a fire?

The Four Ways Water Puts Out a Fire

- As the water droplets approach the fire, they absorb infrared radiation and visible light, and reflect visible light, which interferes with movement of heat to nearby fuel.

- When the water wets the fuel, it cools the fuel, slowing or stopping pyrolysis.

- Heat from the fire turns some of the water into steam (a gas which is 100 percent water vapor), which suffocates the fire by displacing air, starving the fire of oxygen.

- The steam mixes with and cools the hot smoke, reducing heat movement to nearby fuel.

SUMMARY

Fire is the chemical reaction that rapidly combines fuel with oxygen, producing heat, water vapor, carbon dioxide, and other chemicals. It is the same chemical process as digestion or rusting but takes place at a much faster rate.

A fire in a building has three stages: first it is limited by heat, then it is limited by the supply of air, and finally it is limited by the availability of fuel.

Chapter 12 **FIRE** Applied Science

WHY IS IT IMPORTANT TO UNDERSTAND FIRE MOVEMENT IN BUILDINGS?

A fire in any type of building—from a log cabin to a castle to a modern house—can kill people. Fire can also destroy valuable contents and, of course, the building itself. Understanding the unique ways fire behaves inside a building and how to stop fire from spreading in a building can guide decisions that make buildings safer for people and resistant to being destroyed by fire.

PREVENTING FIRE

As described in Chapter 11: Fire - Basic Science, fire needs oxygen and fuel. Oxygen usually comes mainly from air, except in cases of hospitals or industrial facilities that have pipes, tanks, or chemicals that supply oxygen. Obviously, it is not practical to eliminate air from a building, because without it people could not survive.

Eliminating all the fuel in a building is unrealistic, too, except perhaps in an unusual room such as one that is built completely out of fireproof materials and that contains a swimming pool and nothing else. But even if nobody brings any chairs or towels into that room, paint on the wall can burn.

Because virtually all rooms in all buildings contain enough air and fuel to sustain a fire, the most realistic way to prevent fire is to prevent fuel from getting hot enough to pyrolyze.

Faulty electric wiring used to start many fires, but improved equipment and continuously updated electric codes keep reducing the number of fires started this way. For example, codes generally prohibit locating a circuit breaker panel in a closet, because if the lights go out and someone lights a match to see the circuit breaker panel, he might accidently set the clothes on fire.

Extension cords still cause a significant number of fires, however. Sometimes people put them under rugs, where they get damaged by people walking on the rug, leaving them unable to conduct electricity without overheating. As soon as they overheat, the rug catches on fire. Undamaged extension cords sometimes overheat, because the wires in them are usually too small to conduct a large amount of electricity, such as what is needed to power an electric heater. Electric codes discourage the use of extension cords by limiting the distance between electric outlets, making it possible to locate an electric appliance anywhere along a wall and plug it into an outlet without the use of an extension cord.

A fire was caused by not following electric codes. The burned paper on the floor is what remains of an instruction book that caught fire, because someone stored it inside the **electric wiring box**. The infrared photo on the next page offers evidence that the fire was probably started by wires that overheated, because they were thinner than required by code. Fortunately, the box was made of metal and was closed when the fire started, which prevented the fire from spreading.

After an electrician cut away the parts of the wires where the insulation had been burned off and reconnected the wires, the power was turned on, and the infrared photo at right was taken. Some of the wires are white, which means they are overheated. It turns out they were feeding a large electric motor, but they are too small for the amount of electric current the motor requires. Codes clearly prohibit use of this size wire for such a large current. The electrician replaced them with thicker wires.

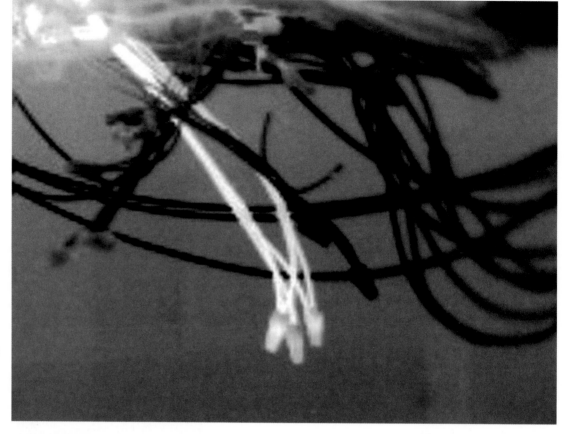

The photo at right is of the same wires shown in the infrared photo at top.

The short piece of white wire taped on the offending wires identifies them as the ones the electrician needs to replace.

The other wires do not need to be replaced, because they are carrying much smaller amounts of electric current, which they are rated for.

In recent years, safer electric appliances, heating systems, and cooking equipment have also reduced the incidence of fires. Induction stoves work by creating a magnetic field that heats iron cooking pots. An induction stove does not get as hot as an ordinary electric stove (which reduces summer cooling load) and doesn't have the open flame of a gas stove. Both of these features are thought to reduce the incidence of fires. Today, far fewer people smoke—and this has prevented many fires, too.

Unfortunately, fires still start. The rest of this chapter discusses reducing damage from fires that do start.

REDUCING DAMAGE FROM FIRE

Smoke Detectors Save Lives

The widespread use of reliable and inexpensive smoke detectors has saved many lives and buildings. Smoke detectors can "smell" smoke long before people can, and they alert people—even when they are sleeping—before the smoke becomes deadly.

Newer smoke detectors are powered by both batteries and "line voltage"—the electricity that powers the rest of the building. Having two sources of power greatly increases a smoke detector's reliability, but the batteries still need to be changed periodically in case the electricity to the building is disabled by a fire or turned off. Fortunately, most smoke detectors will make an annoying noise when the batteries get weak.

Many millions of smoke detectors are still powered by batteries only, though, and those batteries definitely need to be changed regularly. A smoke detector with a dead battery is more dangerous than no smoke detector, because it gives a sense of protection when none exists.

Many smoke detectors, including the one shown in the photo below, also detect carbon monoxide. This feature has saved many lives, because carbon monoxide is odorless and colorless, and without a detector announcing its presence, unsuspecting people inhale it.

Despite all the advances in safeguards, and the trend toward fewer fires, buildings still need to be designed and built to resist the spread of smoke and fire and to resist damage from fire. For the fires that will inevitably start, it is best if the building itself can resist the spread of smoke and fire—and even better if the building is equipped with a system to automatically extinguish the fire.

The best type of smoke detector is powered both by a battery and by wires connected to the building's electricity supply, as shown at left.

Automatic Fire Sprinkler Systems

More and more buildings, including single-family houses, are being built with automatic sprinkler systems that spray water on a fire, usually before it flashes over. A water piping network is connected to spray heads ("sprinkler heads") throughout the building. Each sprinkler head has a water opening that is plugged by a heat-sensing element that gets destroyed when there is a fire, as shown on the next page. This allows water to flow from the sprinkler head, extinguishing the fire. Sprinkler heads are generally located at or near the ceiling, so their heat-sensing element can detect hot gases rising by convection and the water spray can cover a large area of the room.

In unheated buildings such as warehouses and parking garages, special "dry" sprinkler systems are filled with compressed air to keep water from freezing in the pipes. When heat destroys the heat-sensing element, the compressed air quickly flows out of the sprinkler head and is soon followed by water, which flows into the piping in response to the drop in air pressure.

Unlike in some movies, most sprinkler systems spray water from only the sprinkler head or heads that have been heated by the fire. This insures that all the available water will go where it needs to go—directly on the fire—while also limiting water damage. According to the National Fire Protection Association, an automatic sprinkler system sprays about one-tenth the amount of water that firefighters spray in buildings without sprinklers. Automatic sprinkler systems usually put the fire out before firefighters arrive.[1]

Many sprinkler systems also perform another important function: they automatically notify the fire department when there is a fire in the building. As soon as heat from a fire causes a sprinkler head to start spraying water, an automatic flow detector senses water flow in the piping, which sets off alarm bells inside and maybe outside the building and also triggers an alarm that notifies the fire department that there is a fire.

It is impossible to overstate the importance of a properly designed, installed, and maintained sprinkler system. If a sprinkler system does not put the fire completely out without help from firefighters, it will usually prevent flashover while limiting smoke generation to a level that greatly reduces the risk of people dying in the fire. Fire sprinklers have saved the lives of countless people, including firefighters, and will continue to do so in the future.

In 2013, a fire started in a condominium building in Massachusetts. Someone was smoking and accidently set fire to a couch. Next to the couch was a Christmas tree. Fortunately, the building had a sprinkler system. When firefighters arrived, they found that a single sprinkler head had extinguished the fire. The local fire chief was quoted as saying, "As fast as we were able to get there, the fire sprinkler was faster and had the fire under control, frankly, before we even left the station. It is absolutely amazing that the Christmas tree was never involved in this fire and that everyone got out safely. What is even more amazing is that everyone can sleep here tonight."[2] Not only was nobody injured, but damage to the building and its contents from fire, smoke, and water was minimal. The outcome could have been tragic if the building had not had a sprinkler system.

Not all buildings have fire sprinkler systems, and, like any mechanical system, they can fail. As buildings get larger and taller, sprinkler systems get more complicated, and therefore more vulnerable to failure. They can fail because someone closed a water valve to repair a leak and forgot to re-open it, or because fires start while a system is shut down for construction in the building, or because pumps required for providing pressure in larger systems or in taller buildings might not work. They can also fail because ever more sophisticated electronic controls might fail, or because electricity needed to operate pumps might not be available, or because the water supply might be shut off in the street or destroyed by an earthquake—or for any number of other reasons. But regular maintenance and testing can improve reliability, helping to give a building and the people in it the level of protection that only a sprinkler system can provide.

The next few pages show automatic sprinkler systems, and then Pages 316 and 317 show standpipe systems, which supply water to hand-held hoses.

---

1 National Fire Protection Association, "The Truth about Home Fire Sprinklers," Fire Sprinkler Initiative.

2 Kenneth J. Tremblay, "Firewatch," <u>NFPA Journal</u>, March/April 2013, Pages 19-20.

The black pipe at right is connected to a source of water under pressure, ready to supply water to the sprinkler head. The candle is heating the sprinkler head, including **the part that is heat sensitive,** which secures a plug that holds the water back.

Below, the heat-sensitive part of the sprinkler head has been destroyed by the candle flame. It released the plug, allowing water to spray from the pipe.

The heat-sensing element in sprinkler heads used to be a piece of metal alloy with a low melting temperature, but now it is a glass vial filled with a liquid that expands and breaks the glass. Colored dye is added to the liquid to make it easy to see if it has leaked out (and can no longer expand and break the glass in a fire). Different colors indicate different temperatures for different applications. For example, high-temperature heads are used in boiler rooms.

Concealed Sprinkler Heads

① The round white disk hides a sprinkler head above a ceiling. The propane torch is heating the disk.

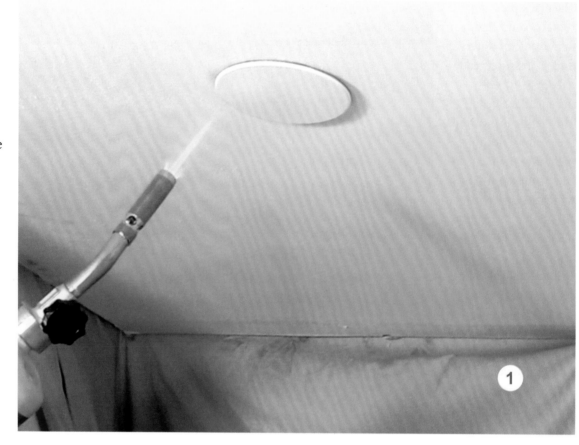

② After about ten seconds, the heat has melted the solder holding the disk in place. The disk falls down away from the sprinkler head, exposing it to heat from the torch.

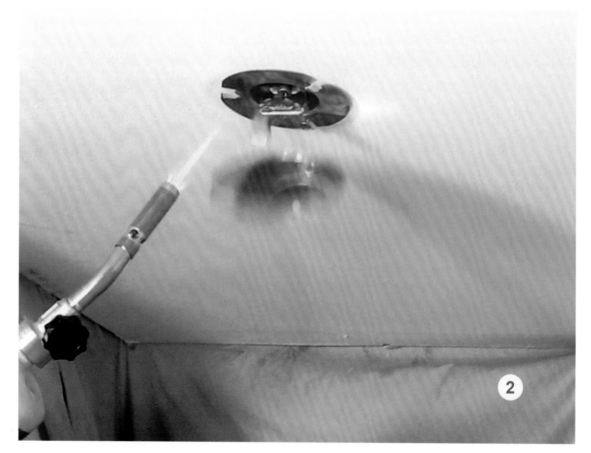

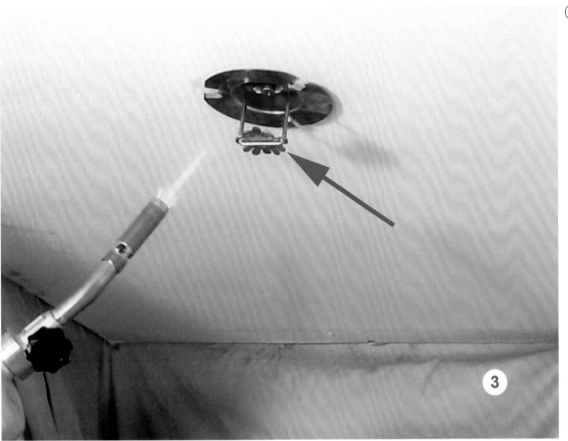

③ The **spray diffuser**, which shapes the spray of water from the sprinkler head, has slid down and is held in place by its wire bracket.

④ The heat-sensitive part of the sprinkler head has released the water, which instantly extinguishes the torch flame.

Sidewall Heads

The photo at right shows a close-up of a sidewall sprinkler head, which sprays water out far enough to provide protection for a small hotel room. The advantage of sidewall sprinkler heads is that the pipes can be run in the walls, which can avoid the need to lower the ceiling to make space for sprinkler pipes. Sidewall sprinklers also free up space above the ceiling for ducts, wires, and other types of pipes.

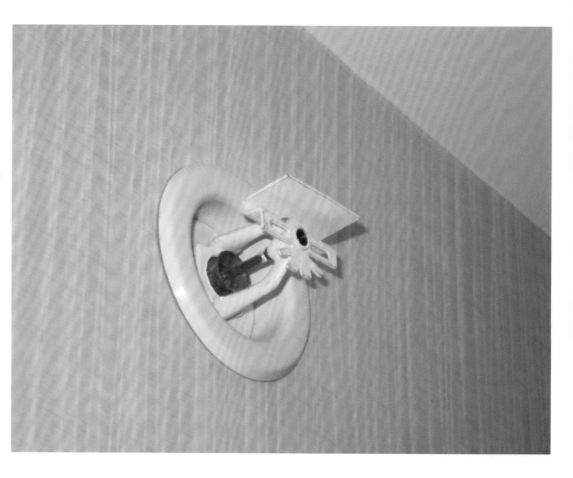

The photo at left shows two sidewall sprinkler heads connected to a water pipe that will be above a closet ceiling. Each sprinkler head has an orange plastic shield that protects it from someone accidently bumping it and setting it off during construction. When the building is finished, the orange plastic shields will be removed.

Sprinkler Pipes

The red pipes in the photo at right are the water pipes for an automatic sprinkler system in the stairway of an apartment building. The sprinkler heads are visible along the pipe and at the ends of the branches. The system only protects the stairway, which is how people escape from the building in a fire.

The pipes are painted red, because code in that area requires that all fire sprinkler pipes be painted red.

The red pipes in the photo at left are part of a sprinkler system in an office.

Sprinkler systems are usually installed in new buildings when they are built. However, with some difficulty, they can also be added to existing buildings.

The red pipes in the photo at right are part of the water supply for an automatic sprinkler system in an apartment building. The large red pump on the right turns on any time the system senses flow from one or more sprinkler heads. The pump and piping are sized to supply many heads if necessary and to provide enough pressure to supply sprinklers on all floors of the six-floor building. The small black pump on the left is controlled by a pressure sensor, which turns the pump on periodically to maintain pressure in the sprinkler piping, making up for pressure lost due to any small leaks in the pipes.

The plumbers in the photo below are in a ditch in the street that has been shored up with wood to keep the dirt from collapsing in on them. The white concrete near the top of the photo is the sidewalk. The old brown pipe running across the bottom of the photo is the water main that feeds all the buildings on that street. The plumbers have clamped two branch pipes onto the water main, each closed off with a red valve. One branch will feed water to the sinks, tubs, and toilets in an apartment building, and the other will feed water to the same building's sprinkler system.

The reason for a separate connection to the water main is simple: there is no excuse for the sprinkler water to be turned off, except for repairs. This system is equipped with alarms that notify the fire department if the valves controlling the flow of water to the sprinklers are turned off.

Codes in other areas allow sprinkler systems to be connected to the faucet water pipes (the same piping system that supplies the kitchens and bathrooms in the building). This encourages installation of more fire sprinkler systems by reducing the cost. And, this way, if the water to the sprinklers is turned off, everyone will know about it. But one disadvantage is that the sprinkler water will probably be turned off more frequently.

Is the Water Valve Open?

Some fire protection systems are required to have a valve with an "open stem and yoke." This means the stem is visible, so people can see if the valve is open or closed. The stem is the brass rod that connects the handle to the internal operating parts that open and close the valve. Another name for it is the "rising stem" valve, because the stem rises out of the valve as the valve opens.

In the photo above, the brass stem is not protruding, indicating that the valve is closed. This means that a gate inside the valve has been pushed into the water pathway, closing off the flow of water.

In the photo at left, the valve is open, which is apparent because the brass stem is protruding from the valve handle. This indicates that the gate has been withdrawn from the water pathway, allowing water to flow through the valve and to the sprinkler heads.

Standpipe Systems

A standpipe is a piping system that supplies water to a handheld firefighting hose. The photo at right shows a standpipe valve with a red handle and a hose in a hose rack. The pipe is hidden in the wall. Assuming everything is in working order, when the valve is opened, a lot of water will come rushing out of the nozzle. The photo at bottom right shows a standpipe in a hotel hallway.

Standpipes can be used by anyone to fight a fire before firefighters arrive, and firefighters can put them into service faster than assembling their own hoses.

The photo below shows three pipes in the stairway of an apartment building. The one on the right is a standpipe, with a valve for a hose. The one on the left feeds the sprinkler system. The small pipe in the middle is a drain used for maintenance, which allows the piping on one floor to be drained without draining other floors. This pipe is also used for testing. An inspector can open a valve that allows a little water flow through the sprinkler system and down the drain pipe to make sure that the water flow activates the pump and alarms.

Each of the buildings on this page is protected by an old-fashioned technology: outdoor standpipes. Each of these standpipes is accessible from a fire escape. Firefighters can stand on the fire escape, hopefully breathing clean air while they connect a hose to the standpipe, then attack the fire through the windows. The standpipes get water from a hose connected to a **fire department connection** at the bottom of the standpipe. The firefighters use powerful pumps in their trucks to pump water from a fire hydrant into the hose that feeds the standpipe.

Carrying a hose up and connecting it to the standpipe takes valuable time, but is much faster than assembling a hoseline up the stairs.

Outdoor standpipes are normally not filled with water, and have largely been replaced with standpipes located indoors, where the building's heating system protects them from freezing.

The outdoor standpipe in the photo below right is being tested for leaks. The fire truck is being used to pump water into it for the test.

Fire Department Connection

Many modern sprinkler and standpipe systems include hose connections outside the building, which firefighters can use to supply water to the system.

Firefighters use these connections if the building's own water supply is not connected or if a pump in the building is not supplying sufficient pressure. Firetrucks have powerful pumps that can be supplied with water from a fire hydrant and feed the water to the building's outdoor connection at high pressure.

The outdoor connection at right has a sign listing which floors of this office building are protected by sprinklers. The building was built without a sprinkler system at a time before codes in that area required them. Later, codes in that area required that office buildings be fully sprinklered by a future date. As tenants moved out and in, sprinklers were installed when each floor was vacated. The whole building will presumably be protected by sprinklers by the required date. For some insight into what might happen when only part of a building is sprinklered, see the next page.

The outdoor connection below is made of brass, which is kept polished out of pride.

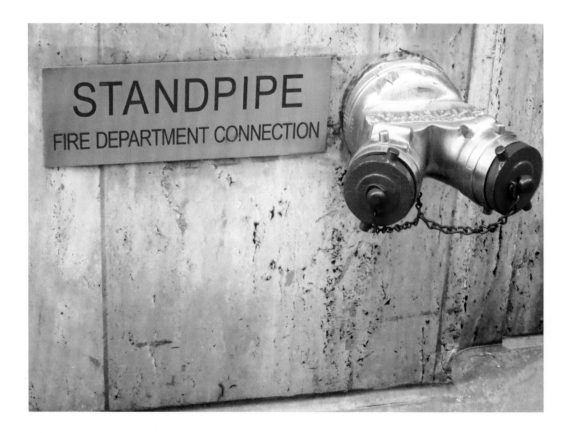

Firefighting Systems that Fail

At about 8:30 PM on the 23rd of February, 1991, a fire started on the 22nd floor of One Meridian Plaza, a 38-floor office building in Philadelphia, Pennsylvania. The building had been built in 1973, with no sprinklers in any floors above street level. Over the years, sprinklers had been installed in some of the upper floors, but the 22nd floor was not one of them. Firefighters responding to calls hooked up a hose to the standpipe system in the stairway, opened the valve, and were surprised to see almost no water come out—there was barely enough to spray the water out of their hose nozzles. They tried another standpipe system in the building with the same result. By the time firefighters rigged up enough hose sections to extend from fire trucks via the stairway to the 22nd floor, the fire had been burning for a long time.

The firefighters made sure they had good water pressure in two hoses and opened the door from the stairway to the 22nd floor. One team of firefighters sprayed all the water from one large hose directly onto the fire, while another team used the other hose to spray water on the team that was spraying water onto the fire, to cool them. They sprayed and sprayed, but the water had no noticeable effect on the fire.

Meanwhile, three firefighters on a floor above the fire were trapped by heavy smoke and became disoriented. While trying to find their way out, their portable breathing supplies all ran out, and all three of them died. An eight-member team searching for them also became disoriented and ran out of air but were rescued by another team.

The fire continued to spread upward from floor to floor. It spread outside the building from one floor of the glass facade to another. It also spread inside the building through penetrations in the floor/ceiling assembly that were not properly firestopped, as well as through HVAC ducts that were not protected with fire dampers (such as those shown on Page 325). By 7:00 the next morning, the fire had spread to the 26th floor and was still spreading upward.

The firefighters became concerned that the building might collapse. The building had a steel frame protected by spray-on fireproofing, but the fire had been burning for eleven hours, and there was structural damage on fire floors. After consultation with a structural engineer, the order was given to abandon the building. Firefighters continued to spray water on the fire from nearby buildings, but the fire continued to spread upward.

Early in the afternoon, the fire reached the 30th floor, which was sprinklered. A total of 10 sprinkler heads activated and put the fire out. The fire was declared under control at 3:01 that afternoon. The 30th floor had so little damage that most of the contents could be saved.

Investigation after the fire revealed that pressure-regulating valves in the standpipe systems were not set properly—they had been set improperly since 1973. Investigators checked standpipes elsewhere in the city and found that many of them were also set improperly. If it were not for this investigation, many other standpipe systems in Philadelphia would be useless in a fire.

This expensive lesson that cost three firefighters their lives is a reminder that any mechanical system can fail. Periodic inspections and testing help, but, without a real fire, there is no 100 percent reliable way to test a firefighting system. Standpipe systems, sprinkler systems, and the pumps and piping systems that supply water to them have failed in the past and will fail again in the future.

This is why buildings should be designed and built in a way that discourages the spread of smoke and fire as much as is practical, which also reduces the chances of a building collapsing due to fire.

COMPARTMENTALIZE TO FIGHT THE SPREAD OF SMOKE AND FIRE

Aside from making sure sprinkler and standpipe systems work, the basic strategy for stopping the spread of smoke and fire is to use fire boundaries to compartmentalize a building into rooms, or groups of rooms. Fire at any stage spreads by heating nearby fuel and igniting the resulting gases. Stopping the flow of hot gases, either smoke or pyrolyzed fuel, is critical to stopping the spread of fire. Everything in Chapter 4: Air - Applied Science about slowing or stopping the movement of air through buildings also applies to slowing or stopping the movement of smoke and fire through buildings.

Fires generate a tremendous volume of smoke, which needs to go somewhere. If a room is perfectly airtight, a fire could theoretically be smothered once it uses up all the oxygen in the room, but most rooms leak some air from outdoors or other rooms. Keeping doors and windows closed can greatly slow the spread of smoke and fire but will not usually smother it completely. People who close doors in a building that is on fire, or who avoid opening doors that don't need to be opened, have saved many lives over the years by slowing the spread of smoke and fire.

Codes and common sense require large buildings to be subdivided by floor/ceiling assemblies and walls that are not only completely smoketight but also made of fire-resistant materials. These fire-resistant separations, which are rated to resist the passage of fire for one to four hours, are sometimes called "demising" partitions or assemblies. For example, in an apartment building, codes generally require that each apartment be separated from other apartments and from the common areas (hallways, stairways, etc.) by demising assemblies. Walls within apartments are not generally required to be demising partitions because doors within the apartment are expected to be left open much of the time.

a certain amount of time, too, usually anywhere from twenty minutes (basically to stop smoke) to three hours. They also have springs or other mechanisms that make them close automatically. But as those mechanisms get old and the doors get coated with layers of paint, they might not close as well. And, at any time, people can prop them open.

Large amounts of smoke can spread through doors, stairways, and elevator shafts. Stairways and elevator shafts act as chimneys, quickly filling with rising smoke—which is a deadly hazard to anyone in the stairway or elevator above the level of the fire. Many stairways are protected by doors, but in buildings with many people using the stairways, such as movie theatres, shopping malls, and airport terminals, the stairways are usually open. In those buildings, stairways are sometimes protected by a piece of glass or other material that extends down below the ceiling, as shown on the next page. This simple solution is not as effective as a door, but it can trap some smoke before it rises up the stairway.

The following pages show ways buildings are designed and built to resist the spread of smoke and fire.

Even though demising assemblies are usually built out of the required fireproof materials, they are often not as smoketight (airtight) as required by codes. Often, assemblies are smoketight when built but damaged later by people cutting holes in them for pipes or wires and not repairing the assembly afterward. (See photo on the bottom of Page 94.) Fire can spread through a building unless the holes— even small holes—in the demising assemblies are carefully smoketightened and fireproofed.

Doors in demising partitions are rated to resist fire for

Labels on a fire-rated door and doorframe show that the door and frame are rated to resist the passage of fire for a specified length of time. The glass in the door is wire glass: wire mesh inside the glass holds it together well enough to stop the spread of smoke and fire even if it cracks.

Stop Deadly Smoke from Spreading

The glass on the ceiling around the stairway at right will keep smoke from a fire on the lower floor from rising up the stairway. Extra sprinkler heads near the glass will protect it from cracking or melting in a fire.

In the open atrium at left, the glass at the top of the opening on the left side of the photo will prevent smoke from a fire in the gym from rising up into the atrium. Hopefully smoke would hug the gym's ceiling until it sets off the sprinkler system, extinguishing the fire. Without the glass, the smoke would spread out into the atrium and might not set off the sprinkler system as quickly.

The wire glass window at right is in the hallway of an apartment building. The chain leading to the counterweight (hidden inside the window frame) is connected with a fusible link (a piece of metal with a low melting temperature—see inset photo). If the window is left open, and fire starts to spread through it, the fire will melt the fusible link, letting gravity close the window.

The door at left divides a public hallway in an apartment building from a stairway. It is held open by a steel chain incorporating a fusible link (see inset). In a fire, the metal will melt, and spring hinges will (hopefully) close the door, preventing smoke and fire from spreading.

Instead of using old-fashioned technologies such as gravity and melting metal, the fire doors at right use sophisticated electronic equipment to sense fire and close the doors.

Smoke alarms similar to household smoke alarms, located throughout the building, sense smoke. The alarm system sends a signal to release **electromagnetic latches** holding the doors open, allowing springs to close the doors.

The fire doors in the photo above separate a hotel hallway from the elevator lobby, which would prevent the spread of smoke and fire from the elevator shaft to the hallway, or from the hallway to the elevator shaft.

The fire doors at left automatically close off part of a long hallway in a hotel, but they have grills in them, which is a flaw that will allow the spread of smoke and fire.

Fire Stairs

The apartment building at right protects the people in it with fire stairs that are separated from the building with an air gap. In the event of a fire, the air gap prevents the stack effect (a temperature-driven upward flow, like smoke in a chimney; see Page 80) from filling the stairway with smoke, which would kill anyone above the fire trying to escape down the stairs.

Any stack effect in this stairway would pull on outdoor air instead of smoky air from the building, minimizing the amount of smoke that could enter the stairs, even if wind is blowing smoke toward the stairs.

Many buildings, including the Empire State Building in New York City, have fire stairs that are vented to outdoors without being as separated from the building as the stairway shown at right. Even though the vents are much less visible, these stairs achieve the same goal: preventing the stack effect from filling the stairway with smoke. Instead, the stack effect in the stairway will pull only relatively smoke-free air from outdoors into the stairway. Another example is the outdoor fire stairway tucked into the wall of the building on the right side of Page 82.

The **balconies** in the photo at left are escape routes between the building's hallways and fire stairways. The fire stairway is inside the building, with doors leading only to the outdoor balconies and the street. The balconies allow people to escape from a smoke-filled hallway to the fire stairs without letting smoke into the fire stairs.

The **exterior stairway** on the building at right is an old-fashioned, reliable outdoor fire escape.

Fire Dampers

The photo below shows fire dampers of various sizes stored on a shelf in a contractor's shop. A fire damper is a door-like mechanism that stops the spread of smoke and fire through heating and ventilating ducts. (Ducts are tubes that air flows through, typically for heating, ventilating, and cooling a building.)

The photos at right show a fire damper installed in a duct inside a wall.

If a fire occurs, a fusible link will melt and allow a spring to close the damper. Dampers are generally installed in ducts that pass through a demising assembly. The damper helps maintain the integrity of the fireproof separation. If fire dampers don't work, or are not installed, fire can spread through ducts, as happened during the fire described on Page 319.

(1) This fire damper is connected to a duct. It is positioned flush with the gypsum board in a demising wall, so it can prevent fire from spreading through the duct to the other side of the demising wall.

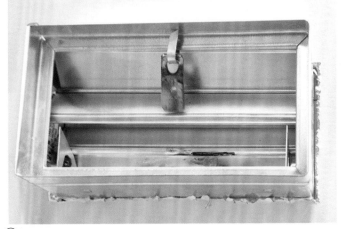

(2) A propane torch is heating the fusible link that holds the damper open.

(3) The fusible link has melted, allowing a spring to quickly close the damper.

Fire Walls

The photos on this page show attached houses with **firewalls** extending up past the roofs. Connected roof cavities are notorious for acting as superhighways for fire, spreading it from one building to another. In theory, a firewall can be contained within a common roof and still protect against the spread of fire, but, in practice, firewalls built that way have a bad record. It is more effective to extend the firewall up past the roof, as shown here.

The photo at right shows plaster walls with one side removed. The wall on the left is made of plaster troweled onto strips called wood lath (rhymes with "bath"), which are nailed to the studs. The wall on the right was built with a wire mesh called metal lath. In both cases, the wet plaster oozes partway through the lath, locking itself onto the lath and making a good barrier to fire. The plaster connects to many other materials and assemblies, forming a decent smoke and air barrier.

The photo at left shows a demising wall made of plaster on metal lath. Above the wall, the gaps between the floor/ceiling joists are firestopped with **terracotta blocks**, without which a fire could bypass the wall by going up into the ceiling and through the wall. A modern version of extending a firewall to the floor above, using gypsum board, is shown on the top of Page 124. Gypsum board, a good fireproofing material, can be part of a fire-resistant assembly if it is properly connected to other materials.

Fire Walls Save Lives

The fire that started in the apartment building shown on these two pages would not have spread as far if the building had had better fire barriers between apartments.

Both **the apartment where the fire started (3A)** and **the apartment next door (3B)** still had the original plaster-on-lath walls the building was built with in the 1920s. The original walls formed a good fire barrier.

Apartment 4A, which is directly above **3A**, had been renovated and had new gypsum board walls. Gypsum board can be a good fireproofing material, but as installed it was not connected well to other materials and thus did not form part of a good fire barrier assembly. Despite the plaster ceiling in **apartment 3A** (which likely was not in good condition), the fire spread upward within the building, completely destroying **4A** and badly damaging the apartment above 4A.

The only damage in **3B** was a small **smoke stain**, shown in the photo at bottom right, where smoke came in through the door from the public hallway. The photo at top right shows the clean-up crew sent by the insurance company to clean smoke damage in the public hallway.

In buildings with good fire barriers between apartments, there have been cases of a fire completely destroying the apartment where the fire started, yet leaving all the other apartments in the building undamaged and habitable as soon as the firefighters put out the fire (and as soon as the apartments below dried out).

Safe Fire Wall Intersections

All of the wall intersections in the drawings on these two pages look the same after they are built, but only two of them are built correctly.

In the drawing at right, all the walls are supposed to be fire rated. One is made of concrete blocks covered with gypsum board. The other has two layers of gypsum board on each side but is not fireproof, because it does not extend all the way to the concrete block wall. Fire could get through the gap and spread to the next room.

The drawing at left shows the same types of walls as in the drawing above, with one small but crucial difference: the double gypsum board wall extends all the way to the concrete block wall. This is the same technique used in the wall in the drawing on Page 119.

This prevents fire from spreading by passing around the end of the double gypsum board wall.

One of the walls in the drawing at right is covered with two layers of gypsum board on each side.

Walls with two pieces of gypsum board on each side are generally rated as being fireproof enough for use as demising partitions. But because the double layers of gypsum board do not run continuously through the intersection with the other wall, the wall is vulnerable to fire.

In the drawing at left, the wall that is covered with two layers of gypsum board runs continuously through the intersection with the other wall, leaving the fire no gap through which to travel.

This is the correct way to build the intersection between a fire-rated demising partition and a non-fire-rated partition (wall).

Leave Space for the Gypsum Board

Fire-resistant wall intersections require walls framed with space for the correct number of gypsum boards arranged in the correct ways.

The photos on this page show **ceiling tracks** and **floor tracks** for a fire-rated gypsum board wall that will intersect with a **masonry wall**. Spaces have been left for the gypsum boards to extend to the masonry wall.

Extending the gypsum boards all the way to the next demising partition and avoiding interruptions in the boards where they pass through non-fireproof partitions is vitally important. Otherwise a fire could get through. If a fire gets through a demising assembly, it can cost people their lives.

The photos on this page show a **gap** left for the gypsum boards on a **fire-rated wall** to continue uninterrupted past an intersection with a **non-fire-rated gypsum board wall**.

If the framing does not have the gap, either the gap will be made when the gypsum board is being installed (unlikely because this is difficult and time consuming to do), or the gypsum board won't continue past the non-rated wall, which would allow fire to spread.

STRUCTURAL COLLAPSE FROM FIRE

A fire produces the most heat, and represents the greatest danger to a building's structure, during Stage Two.

Structural collapse is not usually what kills people: by the time a fire progresses to this point, carbon monoxide inhalation has probably already killed them. But firefighters who are in the building with special breathing equipment can die as a result of structural collapse, as can anyone who is in another part of the building or in a nearby building damaged in the collapse. Structural collapse can also kill firefighters who are on the roof of the building or outside near the building.

Structural collapse renders the whole building worthless, requiring complete replacement. Even collapse of part of the structure usually renders the building worthless, as the cost of structural repair often exceeds the cost of tearing the building down and building a new one.

For these reasons, buildings should be designed and built to resist collapse in a fire. This section describes how fire causes different types of buildings to collapse.

How Does Fire Cause a Building to Collapse?

The mechanism of collapse for a wood-frame building is simple: the wood burns until there is not enough wood to support the building, and the building falls down.

The mechanism of collapse for a steel-frame building is also simple. The heat weakens the steel (which usually takes less time than required for wood to burn enough to collapse), and the building falls down. Significant weakening happens long before the steel melts into a completely liquid state, because steel gradually weakens as it heats up and eventually cannot support the building.

Concrete is much more resistant to fire than either wood or steel and is often used to protect structural steel. But even a concrete building can be destroyed by fire.

The concrete that buildings, bridges, and sidewalks are made of is structurally similar to stone: strong in compression (squeezing) but weak in tension (stretching), or lacking what is called "tensile strength." Compressive strength is why the stones at the bottom of a mountain rarely break: they are strong in compression. Stone's lack of tensile strength is why the vertical columns supporting the roofs of ancient buildings are close together: when gravity pulls down on a piece of horizontal stone bridging between two columns, it applies compression to the top of the stone and tension to the bottom of the stone. If the columns were not close together, the stone would crack under tension and fall down.

Wood and steel are both strong in both compression and tension. When they form a floor/ceiling assembly bridging between two walls, they resist the compressive force at the top and the stretching force at the bottom if they are sized properly for the length of the span between supporting walls.

This wood-frame house collapsed when a fire destroyed enough of the wood supporting it, as well as the connections between the parts of the wood structure.

Ancient people had no steel beams and wanted buildings to last longer than wood structures could be expected to last with their limited waterproofing, fireproofing, and pestproofing technologies. So they built curved stone arches, which load stone in compression only, not in tension. But arches are an inconvenient shape for a ceiling of a room unless the ceiling is very high, as in a cathedral. Today people work around this limitation by grinding limestone into fine dust, baking it in an airtight oven that drives off the oxygen, mixing in a little dried clay, and calling it "Portland Cement." At a construction site, the Portland Cement is mixed with water, sand, and stones (gravel) and is poured around steel bars. The water sets off chemical reactions that cause the mixture to harden into concrete, which is strong in compression. And since it is, in effect, stone with steel bars inside of it, it also has strength in tension. The steel-reinforced concrete hardens in the size and shape required, exactly where it is needed. But predicting exactly how steel-reinforced concrete will behave in a fire is not simple.

How well the concrete resists fire varies with the thickness of the concrete covering the steel, the quality of the concrete, and the concrete's durability over time. Regardless of these factors, all concrete can be damaged by fire.

Fire generally does not damage the stones in concrete. A stone fireplace, for example, can withstand fires for years. But fire damages concrete by reversing the chemical reactions that took place when water was mixed with Portland Cement to make the concrete, turning it into water vapor and white powder.

Concrete can harden in a closed container. It does not need air to "dry," because it does not harden by evaporating water. Concrete (like plaster) hardens because

the water starts a chemical reaction. This reaction gives off heat, which anyone who has had a plaster cast put on a broken arm or leg has felt as the plaster hardened.

Other materials harden the same way, including the core of gypsum board that covers modern walls and ceilings. Spray-on fireproofing (described later in this chapter) that is used to protect steel from fire works the same way. When "dry," these materials still contain the water that was mixed with the dry powder to create the finished product. After these materials cure, they act like other porous materials, absorbing water vapor from the air.

In a fire, heat turns the absorbed water in the concrete into water vapor. After all the absorbed water is gone, the concrete heats up faster. As the temperature increases, the chemical reaction that cured the material is reversed, absorbing heat without an increase in temperature, which protects the building for a while. The water released as the hardening reaction is reversed becomes steam, which helps smother the fire. But reversal of the chemical reaction ultimately destroys the concrete. If the fire continues long enough, all that will be left of the once-strong cement will be a crumbling white powder. But the process of damaging the concrete is so slow that concrete or concrete-like materials are still used to protect structural steel, as shown on the following pages.

This steel-frame warehouse collapsed when heat from a fire weakened the structural steel so much that it could no longer support the weight of the roof, or its own weight.

PROTECTING STRUCTURAL STEEL FROM FIRE

The structural columns on this page are made of cast iron, which is similar to steel and, like steel, needs to be protected from fire. Cast iron was used for structural columns until the early 1900s, when steel became more popular. The cast iron columns on this page are protected by curved terracotta tiles, similar to the material used for clay flowerpots. Terracotta fireproofing was popular in the 1800s and early 1900s.

The terracotta protects the cast iron by acting as insulation, slowing down heat movement to the iron, and by absorbing latent heat of vaporization of absorbed water. Ideally, this protects the iron until the fire is put out by firefighters or reaches Stage Three and stops burning for lack of fuel.

Some of the fireproofing has been removed from the column at right, revealing the layers of materials making up the assembly. The **column** is covered by curved pieces of **terracotta**. Pieces of **steel wire** hold the terracotta in place, and a layer of **plaster** provides additional fire protection while also protecting the steel wire.

In the photo at left, the plaster has been removed, but the terracotta has not been removed, probably to create an interesting look. This compromises the fireproofing, because plaster is an effective fireproofing material. The way it behaves in a fire is similar to how concrete behaves, which was explained on Page 335.

The sprinkler heads on either side of this cast iron column (right) will protect it from weakening in a fire.

The photo below shows a floor/ceiling assembly supported by a mixture of wood beams (joists) and steel beams. The **wood beams** are visible in the photo, but the steel beams are not, because the steel beams are covered by gypsum board to protect them from fire.

Even though wood is an excellent fuel for a fire, fire codes do not require that the wood joists in this photo be protected from fire with a layer of gypsum board. The wood joists will be protected only by the gypsum board ceiling that will be hung on the lightweight steel strips visible in the photo. The steel beams, however, are required to be protected by both the ceiling and the gypsum board wrapped around them. There is some good logic to this: it will take the wood a long time to burn to the point where it causes a structural collapse, while steel will weaken from heat much faster.

Protecting structural steel by, in effect, building a "fireproof" (actually, fire resistant) box around it is a popular and effective way of protecting steel from fire.

The photos at right and below left show structural steel columns in a 55-story building being built in New York City about a year after the attacks of September 11th, 2001. The building was designed before the attacks, but, as a result of the attacks, the design was modified: some of the structural columns were encased with concrete to make them more resistant to explosion and fire.

In the photo at right, **steel studs** are welded onto the steel, which will help hold the concrete in place.

The photo below shows the process. **Steel reinforcing bars** are arranged around the steel column, and then **wood forms** are built to hold the wet concrete. After the concrete hardens, the wood forms are removed, leaving the **concrete** protecting the steel reinforcing bars and the structural steel column inside. The steel reinforcing bars and the concrete hold each other in place, while the steel studs keep the concrete and reinforcing bars connected to the columns.

Stove Quiz
What is wrong in this photo? Answer on Page 561.

The structural steel column at right is protected by concrete which was cast in place around it. However, the concrete ends below the top of the column, because the top of the column used to be above a fireproof ceiling. The ceiling was removed, leaving the top of the column vulnerable to fire. New fire protection should be applied to the exposed steel.

The structural steel columns in the photo at left are surrounded by concrete blocks. While concrete blocks can be an effective form of fire protection, they occupy too much space to be a popular form of fire protection.

Fireproofing steel by casting concrete around it is also not very popular, because the process is very labor intensive.

Spray-On Fireproofing

The photos at right and below right show a popular method of protecting steel: spray-on fireproofing. It does not occupy much space and takes little time to apply.

The material is mostly gypsum, the same mineral used to make gypsum board. It protects steel from fire by acting as insulation, by releasing water absorbed from the air, and by releasing water bound up in the mix when it was applied.

The challenge of keeping spray-on fireproofing adhered to steel is a significant risk in buildings. It needs to stay tightly adhered for the life of the building, including when the steel expands from heat in a fire. It adheres best when sprayed onto steel that is clean, unpainted, dry, oil-free, and rust-free. This is an unrealistic expectation for steel exposed to the elements on a construction site, such as in the photo below.

One inexpensive solution is wrapping wire mesh around steel to help keep the fireproofing in place both before and during a fire, as will be discussed on the next two pages.

Keeping Fireproofing in Place with Wire Mesh

The photos on this page show a steel beam being fireproofed.

The photo at right shows concrete blocks and bricks inside the hollow of the beam covered with wire mesh. Below, cement (Portland Cement, sand, water, but no gravel) has been troweled onto the wire mesh. The cement will harden into an effective fireproof covering for the steel, which the wire mesh will hold in place for many years. The same wire mesh could help keep spray-on fireproofing in place.

This steel beam was fireproofed by applying cement instead of spray-on fireproofing because only a small piece of steel needed to be fireproofed. If more steel in the building needed to be fireproofed, it would have been worth setting up equipment to spray gypsum fireproofing onto the steel. If spray-on fireproofing were to be applied, it should also be held on with wire mesh.

The photos on this page, of the same building on Page 335, show how affixing fireproofing to steel with wire mesh can make it very effective. The photo at right shows a structural steel column that survived the fire. The wire mesh that held the fireproofing in place is visible in the close-up view. The fireproofing cracked, but the mesh held it in place, and the column survived. The column was maybe also protected by being inside a wall, and the top may have survived because it was protected by a ceiling. The photo below highlights the **fireproofed columns** on Page 335 that survived the fire intact enough to support melted beams.

In the photo below, some of the **heavy structural steel** that was weakened by the fire hardened in the shape of licorice candy, while the **columns that were protected by fireproofing affixed by wire mesh** survived fairly intact.

Fire Testing a Steel-Reinforced Concrete Floor/Ceiling Assembly

The photos on this page show a fire test of a prefabricated steel-reinforced concrete floor/ceiling assembly. The flames are coming from gas burners, similar to those used on a kitchen stove, except many times larger.

In the photo at right, the windows on the far wall are used for watching the test, and the vertical rods are there to prevent parts of assemblies that fail the test from falling and damaging the burners.

The test facility is a special room built within a large warehouse.

In the photo at left, the concrete ceiling has started to fall apart in one corner but is otherwise intact. The assembly lasted long enough to get a fire rating. Now a new one like it can be used as an approved floor/ceiling assembly in an apartment building.

Don't Trust the Truss

The photo at right shows a floor/ceiling assembly supported partly by lightweight **steel trusses** and partly by heavy **steel I beams**.

Because trusses are such an efficient use of material—they are strong but use little material (steel in this truss, wood in others)—their low thermal mass heats up quickly in a fire. This makes them more vulnerable to collapse in a fire than a heavy steel I-beam.

Trusses need to be well-protected from fire by a ceiling or other means.

The photo at left shows a building under construction where steel I beams are being used for the lower floor/ceiling assembly, and steel trusses are being used for the roof assembly. I beams were probably chosen to avoid bouncing when someone walks on the floors and to support the additional weight of the contents of the building. Building the roof structure from trusses saves money, and few people will walk on the roof. But the roof will be more vulnerable to collapse in a fire.

The trusses in the photo at right are made of wood connected with sheet metal plates, as shown in a close-up below. The plates are attached to the wood by a series of small metal spikes formed by cutting notches in the metal.

This is dangerous because in a fire, heat causes the metal spikes to loosen their grip on the wood, suddenly converting a strong truss into a collection of loose pieces of metal plates and wood.

All trusses, regardless of what they are made of, are lightweight construction and therefore have low thermal mass. This allows them to heat up quickly in a fire, making them more vulnerable to collapse than heavier construction like steel I beams or thick wood joists.

Fire Door Quizzes
What is wrong in the photos above?
Answers on Page 562.

The sign in the photo below, mounted next to the front door of a one-story retail building, alerts firefighters to a hazard they will face if there is a fire in the building.

SUMMARY

Preventing fire from starting in the first place is better than figuring out how to control and extinguish it. But fires are inevitable. Smoke detectors and sprinkler systems provide good protection for people, but buildings should still be built to resist the spread of smoke and fire. They should also be built to resist collapse from fire. They should also be maintained in a way that does not compromise the building's resistance to the spread of smoke or fire, or compromise the fire protection of the building's structure.

Chapter 13 **PESTS** Basic Science

COMMON HOUSEHOLD PESTS

Pests want the same comfortable living conditions people want. But people don't like to live with them. Not only are pests a nuisance, but they also transmit diseases. Also, the poisons we use to kill them are often toxic to people, too. Cockroaches have been strongly linked to asthma and are thought to be one reason for the prevalence of the disease among poor people. Cockroaches also transport bacteria.

Bedbugs are not known to transmit diseases, but their bites cause unsightly bumps that itch for weeks. Bedbugs are also hard to get rid of.

Mice and rats can transmit diseases, sometimes through ticks, fleas, or mites that live on them but also when people inadvertently touch the rodents' saliva, urine, or feces. They can also transmit disease by biting people. Rodents also destroy people's food, both by eating it and by contaminating it. The need to protect food from rodents is probably why cats were domesticated. Rodents can also start fires by chewing on wires, which is partly why codes require some wires to be covered with metal.

Termites do not make people sick, but the poisons used to kill them—like those used to kill other pests—are toxic to people. Termites are also very destructive. Because they like to eat wood, they can destroy a house.

Mosquitoes, which transmit many diseases, are the world's deadliest animal. Diseases transmitted by mosquitoes, including malaria and dengue fever, reportedly kill over 700,000 people each year. Getting bitten by a mosquito outside of the tropics used to be more of a nuisance than a health hazard. With the spread of West Nile virus and other diseases that were once confined to the tropics, it presents more of a risk.

Pigeons leave behind droppings, which can contain fungi that can make people sick. People who work on roofs are at the highest risk of exposure, but people with compromised immune systems are the most vulnerable.

Pests Want Your Water, Food, & House

Like people, pests just want a drink, a decent meal, and a cozy home. Buildings make good homes for pests because they contain food for people—and people as food, which some pests also enjoy eating. Cockroaches, rats, and pigeons (sometimes called "skyrats") need water. (Mice do not. They get it from their food and make it as a product of digestion.) Because living trees produce chemical defenses against insects, termites much prefer eating the dead wood used in buildings. Bedbugs, on the other hand, nourish themselves only with blood from mammals. Mosquitoes can eat flowers and other parts of plants but need the protein in blood to lay eggs.

A mattress and chair that someone was nice enough to mark as contaminated with bedbugs before leaving for trash pickup. Perhaps the frowny face symbol or the "XX" could become a universally recognized symbol of bedbug infestation.

Signs of Life

The photo at right and the close-up inset both show a filthy kitchen wall after the cabinets were removed.

The brown spots are not just dirt. They are cockroach feces. Roaches must have been nesting behind the cabinets.) Cockroaches love the small gap between the cabinet and the wall because it is a great hiding place, and it is also close to food and water. Other cockroaches are attracted by the smell of the feces, which communicates that this is a good place to live.

The photo at right shows a man's arm covered with bedbug bites.

The bites appear within a few days of contact and take a few weeks to go away.

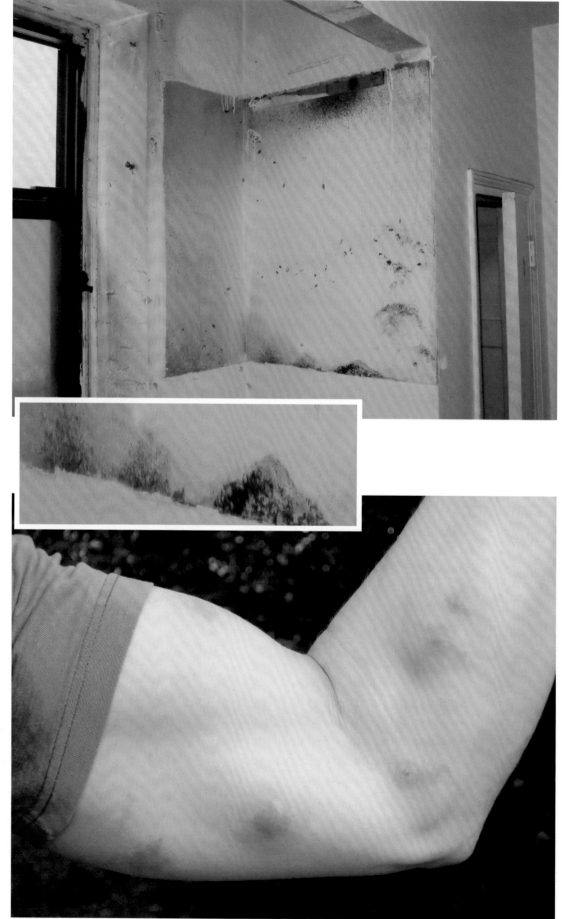

The photo above left shows the fabric of a box spring mattress peeled back with a pen to reveal bedbugs living between the fabric and the wood frame.

In the photo above right, some of the bedbugs have started crawling to a better hiding place.

In the photo at left the **black spots** are bedbug fecal matter, which is basically dried human blood minus the nutrients the bedbugs have removed. The light-colored, almost transparent forms are either shells discarded by bedbugs as they go through their five different stages of development or lighter-colored bedbugs that have not had a meal recently. Bedbugs need a meal before they can advance to the next stage in their development. They prefer blood from humans to blood from any other animal. The reddish-colored bugs are red because they recently ate. The white specks stuck to the pen are bedbug eggs, which are coated with just enough adhesive to get them a free ride via clothing or luggage to a new home.

The wood post in the photo at right is in a crawl space under a house. The post is supporting the house but not for much longer. It is being eaten away by termites. Slivers of wood around the post have fallen off as termites have chewed through the post.

Because the end of the post is buried underground, termites tunneling through the soil have direct access to the post without going above ground. This is advantageous to the termites because they avoid being seen by predators such as ants and spiders. Also, they avoid the problem of drying out, which tends to happen when they go above ground. A piece of concrete between the post and the soil would provide some protection for the wood. Special metal brackets made for the purpose of protecting wood posts from soil provide even more protection.

The photo below shows a piece of wood that has fallen off the post. The holes running the length of the wood are classic "termite tunnels." Not only is the wood tasty and nutritious, but the tunnels also protect the termites from predators and from dry air as they crawl to and from new wood. This particular piece of wood is hollowed out by so many termite tunnels that there is hardly any wood left, which is why it fell off the post.

The wood joists in the photo at right have been feasted on by termites, as evidenced by the classic termite tunnels on the underside of both joists. If the termites are not stopped, the floor will eventually collapse.

But termites don't just eat wood. They can chew through sheets of plastic or lead on their way to finding more wood.

Termites build termite tubes—a mixture of feces and sawdust that they can travel through without drying out or being exposed to predators.

The **termite tube** in the photo at left shelters termites while they travel between the soil and the wood behind the siding.

The photo at right shows a mouse eating cheese in a kitchen sink, with some **mouse feces** nearby.

The photo below shows **mouse feces** in a light fixture. Mice and rats can collapse their bodies nearly flat, which allows them to squeeze through holes much narrower and flatter than their bodies appear to be. Mice living in the ceiling crawled into the light fixture from above, perhaps attracted by the heat from the fixture.

One advantage of having rats is that they do eat mice, so mice and rats usually are not found together in the same building.

SUMMARY

Nobody wants to live with pests. Worse than a bad roommate, they will steal food and water, spread disease, and, in the case of termites, even eat the house.

Looking at life from their perspective helps explain why they move in with people. The next step is encouraging them to live someplace else and discouraging them from starting a family.

Chapter 14 **PESTS** Applied Science

WHY IS IT IMPORTANT TO UNDERSTAND PEST MOVEMENT THROUGH BUILDINGS?

It is no surprise that pest-resistant buildings are more pleasant for people. They are also healthier for people because pests both spread disease and encourage the use of toxic chemicals. In order to create pest-resistant buildings, it is important to first understand how pests move through buildings and what they are attracted to.

HOW TO WIN THE FIGHT

Killing insects and rodents is a numbers game, so think long term. If the number of pests in a building is zero, keeping all pests out forever will keep the number at zero. But expecting to forever prevent all pests from entering a building is unrealistic. They will probably get in eventually. Therefore a winning strategy should include making life hard for pests once they enter a building.

Make pests an endangered species. Endangered species become endangered or extinct because of predators, habitat loss, or lack of food or water. When their habitat is lost, the land is still there, but it has been changed in a way that makes it uninhabitable. Jungles and forests are cleared, and fences, highways, or other barriers separate food supplies from drinking water and from nesting areas. Effective pest control works in a similar way, using as many methods as possible to make the environment (the building) hard to live in.

Making a building very hot or cold would eliminate some pests, but it would also make an inhospitable environment for people. There are exceptions, such as running a very large heater in a room for a few hours to fight bedbugs, but this is a lot of trouble. Therefore, the best strategy is to create conditions that are comfortable and healthy for people but uncomfortable or deadly for pests.

Kill Them with Thirst

Eliminating water sources can solve many pest problems, which is another reason to follow the advice in Chapter 6: Water - Applied Science. (Mice are the exception. They can live on the water in their food and the water they create by digesting their food.) Insulate every cold pipe as shown on Pages 200-202. Ventilate when showering and when cooking, especially when cooking with gas (because combustion produces water vapor). Even drying dishes before putting them away can discourage pests. Fix even the smallest roof or plumbing leak. Mosquitoes lay eggs in stagnant water, so discard any outdoor containers rainwater can collect in, and clean clogged roof gutters that could trap standing water.

The dark coloring on the bottom half of this water tank is mold, which is evidence that water has been condensing on the tank (and attracting dust that mold eats). Pests will drink this water. Condensation is caused by the water in the tank sometimes being colder than the dewpoint temperature of the air. (The water is cold because it just came from a well.) Lowering the humidity in the air around the tank or insulating the tank will eliminate the condensation—and the pests.

Even a small leak that is not a threat to building durability can be enough to support pests in a luxurious lifestyle. In other words, anything that can be done to keep a building dry will make life harder and shorter for pests.

Termites need water, too, so it is wise to leave a space between bushes and a building to let the sun dry the soil. A space around the building also makes it easier to inspect for termite tubes like the one in the photo on the bottom of Page 351. All plants near a building should be types that do not need much water—not only to discourage termites but also to keep the building dry and to save water. Condensate drains (pipes that drain cold water from cooling and dehumidification systems) should be insulated to prevent water from condensing on them. They also should not drain to outdoors, both because that adds a hole to the building enclosure and creates a mud patch that will attract termites and other pests. Instead, condensate drains should be routed to a sink drain upstream of the P trap (the U-shaped part of the drain that stays filled with water to keep sewer gases from escaping). Connecting a condensate drain with its own P trap directly to a drain pipe is not a safe option because, during the time of year when no condensation is draining, the water seal in the P trap will dry out, allowing sewer gases to escape into indoor air.

These two drain pipes carry water condensed out of the air by indoor air conditioning systems and dump it outdoors. These pipes also allow air, water vapor, noise, smoke, and pests to pass through the wall. The water on the ground encourages infestations by pests, especially termites.

Mosquitoes, like many insects, spend part of their lives underwater. Adults lay eggs in water, and the eggs hatch into larvae that mature into pupae, which eventually mature into adults that fly and bite people. If a mosquito lays eggs in a lake or river, small animals living in the water can eat the eggs, the larvae, or the pupae. This is why mosquitoes prefer small pools of water that are relatively free of aquatic predators, such as the water lying in discarded bottles or spare tires. Not only are these good places to hide, but they also occasionally dry out, killing all aquatic species. Then after the next rain, another puddle of fresh water accumulates, ready for mosquitoes to lay eggs. Clogged or backpitched roof gutters are another favorite mosquito breeding ground because they are usually filled with leaves and other plant matter that provide bacteria and algae to nourish young mosquitoes. Mosquito populations can be greatly reduced by eliminating all standing water.

Starve Them to Death

Don't leave food lying out, including pet food. Wash dishes right away, wipe up crumbs, and put food in secure containers. Clean grease from the stove, including on the sides, as well as below and behind it, which means pulling the stove away from the wall periodically. Take the garbage out right away, especially if it contains food scraps. Get a garbage disposal for the kitchen sink, so food scraps get sent down the drain instead of sitting around generating smells that telegraph their presence to hungry pests. Or, best of all, compost food scraps in a secure container and empty it frequently. When building a building, consider using less wood, especially near the ground where it will be most accessible to termites, and consider using steel or concrete instead.

Clean Up after Pests

Cockroaches, rats, and other pests use the smell of their droppings to advertise good living places to their friends and family.

Clean up after them to discourage a family reunion.

Terminate Roof Drain Pipes away from Buildings

Pests go where the water is. The farther away from the building the water goes, the better.

The roof drain pipe in the photo below directs water away from the building, which makes it a great improvement over the broken pipe in the photo at right. A longer pipe that moves the water further away would be even better.

Another consequence of the missing piece of drain pipe in the photo above is that the siding just below the end of the pipe is rotting where it has been getting wet.

A building also stays drier when porches, sidewalks, and the adjacent ground are pitched away from the building. (See Pages 198 and 199.)

Block Transportation Routes

All pests travel between the places where they eat, drink, and nest, and most also like to travel between indoors and outdoors. Bedbugs travel from one bedroom to another hunting for new victims. Termites travel between soil and wood in a building.

Cockroaches can hitch a ride on food brought home from the store, but in apartment buildings roaches also crawl through walls from nearby apartments or stores. A complete air barrier around an apartment is enough to stop cockroaches from traveling from one apartment to another. An air barrier will also stop bedbugs from crawling between apartments, hotel rooms, or hospital rooms. Don't forget the holes where a hotel headboard is mounted to the wall: they are a bedbug superhighway.

For existing walls built without an air barrier, caulking the joints at the top and bottom of the baseboard molding can help stop cockroaches and bedbugs from traveling from one room to another. Caulking the joint between the floor and the gypsum board is usually more effective, and less visible, but requires removing and replacing the baseboard molding. Caulking around kitchen cabinets can prevent roaches from using the gap behind the cabinets as a living space located conveniently close to food and water.

Termites can also be kept out of a building with a barrier, but because they chew through wood, plastic, and sheets of lead, and can fit through cracks as small as 0.4 mm (1/64"), a termite barrier is tricky to build. Termite barriers need to be made of very, very fine metal mesh sold specifically for that purpose, or from sheets of galvanized steel or stainless steel. The main challenges to keeping termites out with a physical barrier are the connections between pieces of the barrier and making sure the termites cannot easily find another route into the building by going around the end or side of the barrier. Because of these challenges, it is usually impractical to add a termite barrier to an existing building. But for a new building the difficulty of incorporating a termite barrier into the design and construction is well worth the trouble because termites cause a staggering amount of damage to buildings every year. The value of a barrier will probably increase in the future as poisons are banned, because they are hazardous to people's health, leaving fewer effective options for protecting buildings.

Some termite infestations start when termites fly into attic vents. This can be stopped by installing fine screens on the vents at any point in the building's life. An even better solution is to convert the attic into an indoor, conditioned space, as described in Chapter 16: Building Enclosures, which eliminates the need for attic vents.

Initial infestations by mice and rats occur because a building has holes large enough for them to crawl through, making it realistic to prevent new infestations by stopping up all holes. Mice and rats are easier to stop with a barrier than insects because they need larger holes: mice need a 6 mm (1/4") hole, and rats need a 13 mm (1/2") hole. Mice and rats can chew through wood and gypsum board, but a good air barrier helps reduce food smells that attract them and forces them to start a new hole instead of using or enlarging an existing hole. Their holes can also be closed with metal lathe (metal lathe is shown on Page 327) or steel wool, which they cannot chew through, held in place by plaster or Portland Cement.

Buildings can protect people from mosquitoes if every ventilation system opening has a filter, every window has an intact screen (with no tears or holes) that is also connected to the window with no gaps, every door has weatherstripping, and no other holes exist that mosquitoes can sneak in through. Energy recovery ventilators, as described in Chapter 17: Indoor Air Quality, incorporate filters that will stop mosquitoes from entering through the ventilation system. Mosquitoes can still fly in when people open doors, so in regions where mosquitoes carry deadly diseases people can be protected by vestibules with two sets of doors. This requires the mosquitoes to follow people through not one but two doors. The area between the doors could be protected by electronic mosquito zappers, and the building's ventilation system could be designed to constantly blow air out through the vestibule, making it harder for mosquitoes to fly in. The air blown out would of course have already been filtered on its way into the building.

Pigeons are fairly easy to keep out of buildings because they are too large to fit through small holes. They usually get into buildings through openings that are too high to be easily repaired, such as rooftop ventilation openings or severely rotted eaves. Regular window screens or wire mesh with almost any size holes work well for keeping pigeons out of buildings.

Block Rat Tunnels

The two photos above show openings to rat tunnels. Each tunnel connects the soil near a tree to a hole in a basement wall, typically near openings for pipes and wires. Rats use the tunnels to get between the basement (where they live) and the sidewalk (where they eat garbage).

In the photo at right, a layer of steel wool was buried under the soil (visible around the tree) to discourage rats from digging tunnels. Rats or mice might eventually work their way through steel wool, but not through wire lathe. The holes in the basement should also be found and closed up with cement and metal lathe.

Block the Gap

The photo at right shows a wall being built with shiny insulation on its outdoor side. Wood strips on the outdoor side of the insulation are used to create an air gap between the insulation and the cladding, which will allow the wall to dry, as described on Page 393.

At the bottom of the air gap, a **plastic barrier** is used to block insects from crawling up into the gap from below and making nests.

The photo at left is a close-up of the pest barrier mounted on the wall.

The barrier is the same thickness as the wood strips that will create the air gap, which allows the barrier to fill the gap without leaving any inviting openings.

The size of the holes in the top of the barrier can be seen in the photo at right.

They are large enough to prevent capillary suction but small enough to prevent small animals and most insects from getting in.

The photo at left shows the bottom side of the barrier, which is what an insect will see when looking for a way to crawl into the wall: it is covered with a felt fabric. The holes in the fabric are too small to allow insects to crawl into the wall.

The holes in the fabric and the rest of the barrier are still large enough, however, to allow water to drain out and air to flow through, which will keep the wall dry.

Use Poison Only as a Last Resort

Poison is a popular approach for killing pests but is not effective in the long term. Insects have such short life spans that they quickly adapt and become immune to most poisons. Termite poison is usually applied to the soil, where bacteria can soon break it down and rain washes it away, leaving the soil safe for termites to tunnel through. If mice or rats eat poison and live through the experience, they wise up and don't eat it again. If it kills them, they usually die hidden behind a wall, giving off a strong and unforgettable smell for weeks, which can't be stopped without tearing open walls to find the carcasses. Because poison is not very effective in the long term, and is dangerous to people, it should only be used as a last resort.

Better than Poison

For mice, use traps, or the best trap of all: a cat. Mice communicate with each other with high-pitched squeaking noises that people can't hear but cats can. Unfortunately, most cats are not very aggressive about catching rats, which are best caught with traps.

A safe, effective way to kill insects is to use boric acid, which is only mildly poisonous to people and pets if they eat it but very poisonous to insects, partly because it works as a desiccant. A desiccant is a substance that absorbs water, which is a problem for insects. Complicated animals such as people depend on many valves to control the flow of water and other liquids into, out of, and within their bodies. Insects depend more on absorb-desorb mechanisms, which desiccants interfere with. Boric acid also kills insects by acting as an abrasive that scrapes the waxy coating off the insect's stomach, causing the insect to dry out. In effect, the insect dies of thirst.

Even safer for people is diatomaceous earth, which is a very fine sand, formed from shells of small organisms that died many years ago. It, too, kills insects by scraping the coating off their stomachs. It stays effective for a long time.

Boric acid or diatomaceous earth can be sprinkled into walls before they are closed up. This kills insects where they hide, as well as on their way from one room to another. Walls near kitchens and bathrooms and other sources of water, such as a dripping window air conditioner, should be defended against cockroaches, while walls near bedrooms should be defended against bedbugs. In other words, while any wall is open for any reason, pro-actively apply these to kill insects.

In existing buildings, a puffer can be used to inject boric acid or diatomaceous earth into small openings in walls (see the next page). Bathroom and kitchen walls usually have small holes around pipes, and most rooms have small gaps between the wall and the floor. All these gaps and holes are great places to inject boric acid or diatomaceous earth into the walls.

Boric acid and diatomaceous earth don't work instantly, but they keep working for years longer than toxic pesticides. A typical response from someone who treats a cockroach-infested kitchen with boric acid is, "I put that stuff out a week ago and still have roaches!" But when asked a week or two later, that same person might admit they haven't seen any roaches for a while. Because boric acid and diatomaceous earth kill slowly, there are few dead insects lying around (as they're usually hidden in their nests behind walls). And since both of these substances keep working for so long, they don't have to be reapplied very frequently, which saves time and money.

Sprinkling boric acid into a bathroom wall before the gypsum board is installed is a good way to prevent insect infestations. Even though boric acid is non-toxic, a high-quality respirator should be worn for protection against inhaling any type of fine dust.

Injecting Boric Acid or Diatomaceous Earth into an Existing Wall

① Remove the baseboard molding. ② Use a puffer to squirt boric acid or diatomaceous earth into the wall through the gap between the floor and the gypsum board. The powder should be applied the entire length of any gap. ③ Put a bead of caulk at the junction between the floor and the wall to block transportation routes. ④ Replace the molding.

Keeping Pigeons off Buildings

In the photo at right, an architect and a developer are using models of a pigeon, a wall, and **window lintels** to evaluate lintel designs. The lintel should be too narrow for pigeons to sit on while still being aesthetically pleasing.

The photo below shows a bird's eye view of a light fixture covered with spikes.

Thinking about where birds might want to roost—and then designing a building to discourage their roosting—can save a lot of trouble later.

Models: Chris Benedict, R.A., and Mary Spink. Wall mock-up by Teresa Arana; pigeon by Lisa Barnhardt.

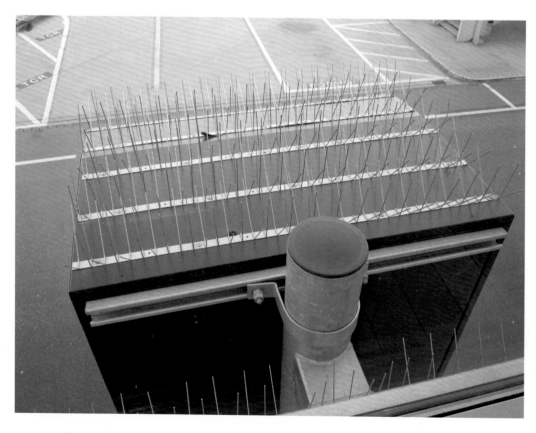

SUMMARY

While it can be tempting to use toxic chemicals to get rid of pests, they are not safe for people and are not as effective, long term, as other strategies. Instead, find ways to make life as difficult as possible for pests. Fight them for every drop of water and scrap of food. Clean up after them, so their smell does not attract more of their kind. Close up openings where they can get into buildings or move around inside of buildings. Use boric acid or diatomaceous earth to kill insects, and use cats to kill mice. Only use pesticides as a last resort.

Chapter 15 **ELEVATORS**

Some people don't give elevators a second thought, but they and the machinery they require take up valuable space and require energy. Time spent waiting for them can disrupt a person's day and should be minimized.

ELEVATORS AND AIR LEAKAGE

An elevator's motor and lights require energy, but the amount of energy they require is minor compared to the amount of energy required to heat or cool air that leaks through the building via the elevator shaft. All the outdoor air moving through the building makes people less comfortable, while adding significantly to the building's heating and cooling loads.

An elevator shaft acts like a chimney, moving warm air up through a building during the winter and cool air down through a building during the summer. The mechanism that moves the air is convection, also known as the stack effect, as explained on Page 80.

Codes in some areas require venting elevator shafts to outdoors, while codes in other areas prohibit this. In other areas, codes allow shaft vents to be closed or mostly closed with motorized louvers that open in response to a smoke alarm sensing smoke. Codes usually also limit the size of the opening where a cable passes through the floor of an elevator machine room.

Some elevator manufacturers require that equipment rooms be heated and cooled, even if codes require those rooms to be vented to outdoors. Buying elevator equipment that does not require installing or operating heating or cooling equipment can save money and energy.

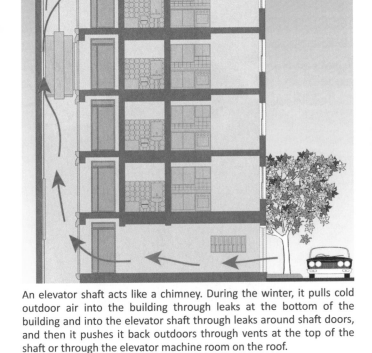

An elevator shaft acts like a chimney. During the winter, it pulls cold outdoor air into the building through leaks at the bottom of the building and into the elevator shaft through leaks around shaft doors, and then it pushes it back outdoors through vents at the top of the shaft or through the elevator machine room on the roof.

This is a typical elevator machine room built above an elevator shaft. The shaft is vented to outdoors with a **louver**. The machine room is cooled with an **air conditioner** during the summer and also has a heater (not shown) for the winter, both of which are a waste of energy.

TWO POPULAR ELEVATOR TYPES

There are two main types of elevators in use today: hydraulic and overhead traction. A hydraulic elevator cab is lifted from below by a piston and cylinder pressurized by hydraulic fluid pumped into the cylinder by an electric pump located in an equipment room. Hydraulic fluid is oil mixed with additives to prevent bacteria from eating the oil. The photo at right shows a hydraulic elevator lifting mechanism located in the bottom of the elevator shaft.

Hydraulic elevators can simplify the structure of a building because the weight of a hydraulic elevator is supported by the soil underneath the cylinder, which reduces the load on the structure of the building. But hydraulic elevators require a lot of electricity.

An overhead traction elevator cab is lifted from above by a cable connected to the top of the cab. The cable wraps around motor-driven pulleys at the top of the elevator shaft, then extends down the side of the shaft to counterweights that hang on the end of the cable. This greatly reduces the load on the motor, thereby saving electricity. The overhead traction machinery is supported by the building's structure.

The photo at right shows the equipment for an overhead traction elevator in a machinery room located at the top of an elevator shaft. The **electric motor** turns a **gearbox**, which turns a **pulley**, which moves the **cable**. An **opening** in the floor allows conditioned air to escape out the top of the elevator shaft, then out any vent to outdoors, which wastes energy.

The **relay board**—a primitive computer made from magnetically controlled switches—dispatches elevator cars to floors, controls cab speed, and opens cab doors.

The photo at right shows a close-up of a conventional overhead traction elevator machine. The cables that lift the cab go through the machine room floor, from where they connect to the top of the elevator cab.

Codes in some areas limit the size of the opening around the cables to a maximum dimension. This is wise because it reduces the amount of air moved through the lobby and hallways, the elevator shaft, and the machine room.

The photo below shows the machine for a newer, more energy-efficient type of overhead traction elevator called a "Machine Room Less," or MRL, elevator. The round green mechanism is the motor and pulley combined. Because the machine is mounted inside the elevator shaft on the wall near the top of the shaft, there is no need for a separate machine room for the motor and pulley. Instead, the elevator shaft is extended a small distance above the roof, as shown in the photo on the next page.

The electronic controls for an MRL elevator can fit in a small space the size of a clothing closet. This can be located wherever space can be found, either at the top or at the bottom of the elevator shaft. The room containing the electronic controls for an MRL elevator is not required to be vented to outdoors, which drastically reduces the heating and cooling loads necessary to condition those rooms.

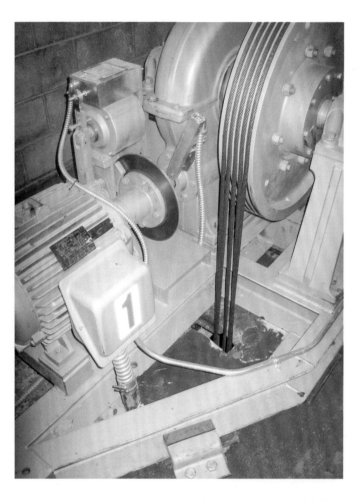

Another advantage of MRL elevators is that they do not have gearboxes. A conventional elevator machine has a gearbox, which requires maintenance in the form of periodic oil changes and replenishment of oil.

The structure at right encloses the top of an elevator shaft containing two MRL elevators. If they were normal elevators, a whole machine room would have to be built on top of the elevator shaft, like the one on Page 363. Using MRL elevators saves rooftop space, reduces the height of the building, and saves the cost of building, maintaining, and conditioning these machine rooms.

The photo at left shows an MRL machine mounted on the wall at the top of an elevator shaft. An air vent connects the shaft to outdoors, as required by code in that area.

The top-floor shaft door slides on a sliding door track similar to the track that is used for a sliding closet door. These doors leak a lot of air between the shaft and each floor. Hopefully someday someone will make shaft doors that do not leak much air.

REDUCING AN ELEVATOR'S ENERGY REQUIREMENT

Until somebody starts manufacturing reasonably airtight elevator shaft doors, there are few good approaches. First, try reducing the size of the vent openings at the top of the shaft or closing them completely—whatever code allows.

Another approach is adding an elevator vestibule, as shown on the next page, which reduces air leakage by stopping the flow of air to the elevator shaft doors. Alternatively, pressurizing the elevator shaft, which code in many areas allows instead of venting to outdoors, prevents it from pulling air through the building. Whereas pressurizing the shaft with hot or cold outdoor air would result in comfort complaints, an energy recovery ventilator (ERV, described in Chapter 17: Indoor Air Quality) can supply conditioned air while one of its fans pressurizes the shaft. The heating or cooling to condition the incoming air comes from air exhausted from the building. The drawing below shows an ERV using room temperature hallway exhaust air to cool hot outdoor summer air, which pressurizes an elevator shaft.

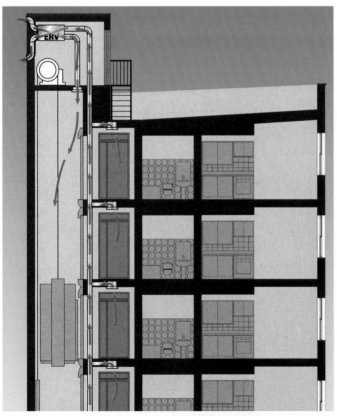

An energy recovery ventilator is using stale ventilation air from this apartment building's hallways to cool incoming fresh summer air, which it uses to pressurize the elevator shaft. Some codes allow pressurizing the elevator shaft as an alternative to venting a shaft to outdoors.

Elevator Electricity Use

The amount of electricity elevators require varies widely. A four-floor[1] round-trip ride on a modern ten-passenger traction elevator that operates on AC (alternating current) electricity requires anywhere from 4 to 45 watt-hours of electricity.[2] The difference in energy required by different elevators depends not so much on speed or carrying capacity but on the electronics that control the motor.

Older elevators that run on DC (direct current) electricity require even more electricity.

As mentioned earlier, a hydraulic elevator requires much more electricity than a traction elevator—at least 110 watt-hours of electricity for the same ride—because its motor lifts the weight of the piston, cab, and passengers straight up against gravity with no help from a counterweight. When the cab is on its way down, its speed is controlled by the hydraulic fluid flowing through a small hole, where friction turns the energy of raising the cab into heat in the hydraulic fluid. The heat escapes outdoors with air leaking through the shaft.

Avoiding installing hydraulic elevators is a good way to reduce elevator electricity use. Hydraulic fluid also impacts indoor air quality, as described on Page 429. And occasionally hydraulic fluid spills and contaminates the soil under a building. These are all good reasons to avoid using a hydraulic elevator.

A traction elevator uses less electricity than a hydraulic elevator because it has a counterweight to counterbalance the weight of the cab. The counterweight goes down and up the shaft next to the cab as the cab goes up and down. Most of the lifting is actually done by the counterweight. The motor only lifts any difference in weight between the counterweight and the cab (and passengers, if any). Most of the lifting the motor does is the result of changes in the weight of the cab as passengers get on and off the elevator.

1   An example of a four-floor ride as described here would be going from the second floor to the sixth floor of a building. Terminology here can be confusing: is a ride from the second floor to the third floor a one-stop ride or a two-stop ride? Avoiding similar confusion is why architects do not describe how many stairs a stairway has; instead, they count the risers (the part your toe kicks on the way up the stairs).
2   A watt-hour is the amount of electricity required to operate a one watt load for one hour. Keeping a 15 watt light lit for two hours requires 30 watt-hours of electricity. Utility companies sell electricity by the kilowatt-hour (kWh). One kilowatt-hour = 1,000 watt-hours.

Energy-Saving Elevator Vestibules

The glass walls and doors in the photos on this page create vestibules that reduce the amount of air the elevator shafts move through the building. The walls and doors block the movement of air to and from the leaky elevator shaft doors, which slows down or stops the movement of air through the shaft.

Elevator vestibules have the added benefit of reducing the spread of smoke in case of a fire.

If a fire starts on one floor, the glass doors will prevent smoke from getting to the elevator shaft doors and being pulled through the shaft to other floors.

Elevator Cab Ventilation

In most locations, codes do not require elevator cabs to have a ventilation fan. Regardless, many elevator cabs are equipped with a fan that moves air in through the cab door and out through the cab roof. Ventilation can also be provided by openings in the top of the cab and near the bottom of the cab's walls like those shown in the photos on this page. As the cab moves up and down, air will move through the holes in the cab, providing ventilation.

If a fan is used, it can be kept off most of the time by a timer or motion sensor. The fan will start running when any call button is pushed, and it will turn off a set amount of time after the cab has stopped moving.

Alternatively, a motion sensor can turn the fan on when it "sees" the elevator door opening and turn it off after the ride. One downside of using a motion sensor is that it would need to be adjusted to not "see" air movement caused by the stack effect or by movement of other elevator cabs sharing the same shaft, which would cause the fan to run when the cab is not occupied.

Elevator Lighting

Elevator lights should, of course, be energy efficient because they will operate many hours per year. Ideally, they should be controlled by a timer or motion sensor that turns them off when nobody is in the elevator. One light should remain on at all times though, in case someone gets stuck in the elevator.

Many designers make the same mistake: choosing a rich, luxurious, dark-colored finish for the elevator interior, chosen after seeing a small sample in a brightly lit room. When the dark material covers all the elevator walls, the cab is too dark, and additional lights need to be added. It is much smarter to choose a lighter, more reflective finish in the first place.

ELEVATOR CONTROL PANELS

The control panel at right is counterintuitive and confusing. Someone who wants to go to the lobby might push "L" without knowing there is another lobby ("LL": Lower Lobby), or they might want to go to the garage, which might or might not be "G" (which could also be ground floor). "M" could mean main floor, or it might mean mezzanine.

The star symbol on the "L" button identifies the floor with the closest accessible exit.

Elevator Quiz
The photo at left shows some obscure abbreviations.

What do "P2," "P1," "LL," "HL," and "BR" mean?

Turn to Page 562 for the answer.

Below Street Level Numbers

The photo at right shows the control panel in an elevator that stops at a hotel lobby and at two parking garage levels. On this control panel, "L" is for lobby, and "G" is for garage.

But which garage level is lower: "G1" or "G2"?

The photo below shows the floor identification sign on one of the same elevator's doorframes, visible from outside the elevator. It identifies the floor as "G1." The handwritten sign inside the shaft says "G1," too, but just above that was a stenciled label someone crossed out, which used to identify that floor as "G2."

Apparently, deciding which garage floor should be "G1" and which should be "G2" confused the people building the elevator, too. They must have come to an agreement, and now pushing the "G1" button sends the elevator to floor "G1." But a passenger still doesn't know which floor "G1" is: the lower garage level or the upper garage level? Arranging buttons "G1" and "G2" side-by-side on the control panel offers no clue about which floor is above or below the other.

People who don't easily memorize numbers may send the elevator to the wrong floor and hold the door while they determine if the floor looks right. Or they might waste even more time looking for their car on the wrong floor and then take another ride on the elevator. All this increases the time other people wait for the elevator, too.

Confusion could be avoided by arranging all three buttons in a vertical row corresponding to the actual positions of the floors.

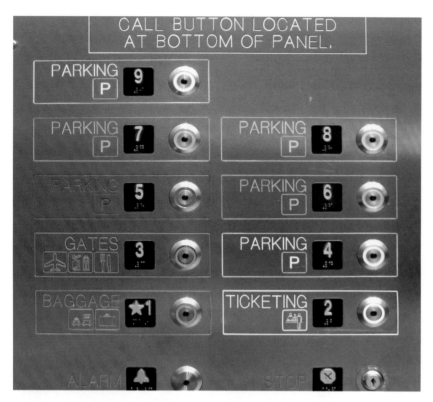

Sensible Control Panel Layouts

The control panel at left, for a parking garage, is color coded. The colored buttons and graphics each correspond to the color painted on the doors and some of the walls on each floor. This is a smart design, which helps people remember where they parked.

The control panel at bottom left has easy-to-understand floor designations. It is simplified by locating the floor buttons by themselves, far from the door opening and closing buttons, key switches, and other controls.

The panel below is even simpler and more intuitive—all the higher floors are above the lower floors. It could be improved by moving the phone call button (at the top) down with the other non-floor buttons.

The simpler and more intuitive a control panel design, the fewer extra trips the elevator will make, and the shorter the wait times will be.

A well-designed control panel can shorten trip times, avoid nuisance stops, and sometimes even avoid the need to install an additional elevator to handle passenger overflow from an elevator with a poorly designed control panel.

The control panel at right shows the street level designated as "0" and floors below the street level designated with minus signs. The floor "-1" is one floor below "0," while "-2" is two floors below "0." It also shows a sketch of the building, to make things even clearer.

The drawings of control panels below show how to arrange floor buttons in the same sequence as the floors, even when space is limited.

Non-floor technical control buttons such as phone, alarm, and testing controls should be located away from floor control buttons and open/close buttons. The reason for this is to make it easier to find floor buttons. Floor buttons should have one look, open/close buttons should have another look, and technical controls should have yet another look, to reduce the time required to find floor buttons.

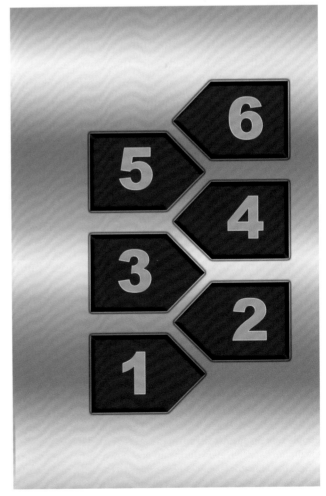

ELEVATOR TRIVIA

Elevator Trivia #1

An overhead traction elevator requires more electricity for a typical down ride than for a typical up ride. This is because elevator counterweights are intended to weigh about as much as a cab filled with half the maximum number of people the cab can hold. This weight, halfway between the weight of an empty cab and a cab filled to its maximum capacity, is chosen because it limits the peak load on the motor and brake. This load will be about equal to the load the motor has to lift when the cab is going down empty because the motor has to lift the difference in weight between the counterweight and the empty cab. A heavier weight would increase the peak load when the cab is going down empty, and a lighter weight would increase the peak load when the cab is going up full. Elevator cabs are less than half full on most rides,[1] therefore the counterweight weighs more than the cab (and any passengers) on most rides. The motor, then, has to lift more weight, and requires more electricity, for a typical down ride than for a typical up ride.

Elevator Trivia #2

Few people, before squeezing into a crowded elevator cab, check the sign in an elevator that warns against exceeding the maximum number of people the elevator can carry. Fortunately, it is almost impossible to overload an elevator with people because an elevator's maximum weight-carrying capacity generally exceeds the weight of the maximum number of people who could squeeze into the cab. One exception might be a basketball team, which could fill the cab not only horizontally but also vertically.

Elevator Trivia #3

Yes, measurements show that some "Door Close" buttons actually do make the door close sooner.

1   Picture people spilling into an office building lobby from an elevator cab packed to capacity during the "down" rush at the end of the workday. If the cab goes up empty, it would have to be filled to capacity for the whole down ride to average half full for the round-trip ride. But it typically picks up a non-capacity number of people on a high floor, then continues down less than full, and only fills completely at a lower floor. This means that even if a few people ride up against the rush, the average load is less than half the maximum capacity, even during up-and-down rushes. At non-rush times, the elevator is almost never filled to capacity, making the average load much less than half the maximum capacity.

The heater on the ceiling of this elevator equipment room is mostly heating air that immediately leaks through the ventilation louver on the wall, which is a waste of energy. A better arrangement would be to use electronics that can survive in an unheated space the way electronics used under the hood of a car can survive.

SUMMARY

Air leaking through an elevator shaft is generally a bigger energy load than the electricity required to run an elevator. To reduce air leakage, holes at the top of elevator shafts should be closed up to the extent required or allowed by code. Elevator equipment that does not require heating or cooling saves the cost of installing heating and cooling equipment and reduces the elevator's energy requirement.

There are two main types of elevators: hydraulic and overhead traction. Hydraulic elevators use much more electricity than overhead traction elevators. They also require hydraulic fluid, which is not good for indoor air quality. MRL elevators, a special type of overhead traction elevator, save the cost of a machine room.

Nuisance stops and wait times can both be reduced by designing more intuitive elevator control panels. Control panels should never leave passengers wondering.

Chapter 16 **BUILDING ENCLOSURES**

INTERACTIONS BETWEEN FLOWS OF HEAT, AIR, AND WATER

Air, heat, and water are flowing through every building in the world right now. The sometimes complicated interactions between these never-ending flows need to be understood to understand building enclosures. Each type of heat movement, each mechanism that moves air, and each way that water moves through a building can only be accurately understood by also looking at how the other of these flows are behaving at the same time. Because a change in one usually causes a change in the others, every decision affecting one of these flows has many results, including many that might be unexpected. When these interactions are not understood or are ignored, the resulting building will do a poor job of controlling the flows of heat, air, and water. All too often, this oversight can cause water damage, which can be expensive to repair.

The movements of light, sound, fire, and pests through buildings are less dependent on each other, which makes it easier to control these functions individually.

A High-Performance Enclosure

A good enclosure controls heat, air, water, light, sound, fire, and pests, as described in previous chapters. Most existing and new enclosures do not do a good job of controlling these flows. Certain segments of the building industry, however, are paying more attention to controlling these flows, and, as a result, some very good building enclosures are being built today.

FOUR BUILDING DESIGN PRIORITIES

Before integrating the information in this book, it is helpful to prioritize the overall goals of building design. First, a building has to look good, otherwise nobody will want to spend time in it or take care of it. Beautiful buildings can be a source of happiness and pride for people. Though designing beautiful buildings is beyond the scope of this book, the information in this book can be used to make beautiful buildings work well and stay beautiful.

Here are the next four building design priorities, in order of importance:

1. Make a building comfortable for people.

2. Make a building safe and healthy for people.

3. Make a building durable.

4. Make a building energy efficient.

The order of the priorities above may seem strange at first, especially putting safety after comfort—but there are good reasons for this.

If people feel uncomfortable in a building, they will change something or demand that someone do something to make them comfortable. Actions taken in the name of comfort often compromise safety, durability, and energy efficiency. Experienced firefighters tell stories of the crazy things people do to keep warm during the winter, which end up burning down the house and even sometimes killing someone. Therefore, for a building to keep people safe, it must first keep them comfortable. This is especially true for people who can't afford high energy costs.

A comfortable building also gives people an incentive to maintain the building over the years and not make radical changes that might make it less safe. A smart design also makes it expensive to undo safety, which helps maintain safety over time. Safety itself is important because any building that is not as safe as it can be might hurt people or make them sick. Stairs should be painted contrasting colors to reduce falls. A safe design resists mold growth because mold can make people sick, and if the mold itself does not make them sick, fighting over the problem will. There is no excuse for not making a building as resistant as possible to the spread of fire and smoke, as well as to collapse from fire. Keeping people safe in a building requires having some sense of what people will do to the building in the future. Predicting people's behavior is notoriously difficult but is a worthy goal. Keeping people comfortable encourages them to leave well enough alone.

Durability is also important. If a building needs a lot of maintenance, even if it is beautiful and comfortable, it will be hard to make it last a long time.

As important as energy efficiency is, it is the last priority on this list because, if there are problems with comfort or durability, people will make changes that compromise the building's energy efficiency.

Fortunately, a good working knowledge of building science can enable all these priorities to be met simultaneously, with few or no trade-offs.

THE HISTORY OF BUILDING ENCLOSURES

The entire history of building enclosures, from the first shelters humans built to the most modern high-performance enclosures, can be divided into three stages:

Stage One Building: No barrier to either heat or air.

Stage Two Building: Barrier to heat but no barrier to air.

Stage Three Building: Barriers to both heat and air.

Dividing the entire history of buildings into three categories is a broad generalization that risks all the usual hazards of generalizing. But this categorization is relatively accurate and is applicable to most locations in the world.

Until recently, some types of building construction happened to leak less air than others, but this was mostly by accident. And it was not that long ago when almost all buildings were built with no insulation at all.

For example, a hut made of animal skins or logs was cold during the winter and hot during the summer because neither of these materials is a good barrier to heat. Not much air leaks through a log or an animal skin, but making airtight connections between logs or animal skins is difficult, which means a house built from these materials probably leaked a lot of air. Therefore, this type of construction offered nothing more than limited protection from rain, wind, and sunlight. For thousands of years, well into the 1900s, uninsulated buildings were the norm in most places, and almost no buildings had an air barrier. Even buildings built with tarpaper stapled to the sheathing in the early 1900s allowed enough air through to be considered Stage One buildings.

Stage Two buildings, with insulation but no air barrier, started being built in large numbers in different places at different times, but by the mid to late 1900s they had become the norm in most cold climates. In parts of the world that get cold, most buildings standing today and most new buildings built today are Stage Two buildings, which means they are potentially problematic.

The Risks of Stage Two Buildings

Insulating something makes one side of it cold. An insulated building enclosure has a warm side and a cold side. Which side is warm and which side is cold depends on the climate and the time of year, but, in both the winter and the summer (especially if the building is air conditioned), one side is cold. And the more insulation that is added, the colder the cold side gets.

Because a Stage Two enclosure by definition has no air barrier, air will leak through it. Which direction the leaking air will move depends on the combined effects of wind, stack effect, and fans. In any type of building in any climate, including a Stage Three building (no air barrier is perfect), some air will leak from the warm side of the enclosure to the cold side many hours each year. The leaking air will move water vapor from the warm side of the enclosure to the cold side. When the cold side of the enclosure (for example, the outdoor side during the winter) cools the leaking air below its dewpoint temperature, water condenses out of the air onto the cold building materials. Or, if the air is not cooled below its dewpoint temperature, it can still be cooled enough to raise its relative humidity high enough to prevent drying of water already in the building materials. The amount of water vapor the air can transport through the air leak is infinite because the flow of water vapor will continue as long as the building has holes in it. This uncontrolled water vapor movement can damage a building.

Stage Two Rot

In the photo of the Stage Two wall at right, the indoor side of the wall and the insulation have both been removed, revealing an area where the wood sheathing has rotted away. What apparently happened is that warm air leaked from the indoor side of the wall through an electric box to the outdoor side, which was cold during the winter. The drawing below shows how the cold wood **cooled the leaking air** below its dewpoint temperature, condensing **water** out of the air, keeping that spot wet, which encouraged mold growth.

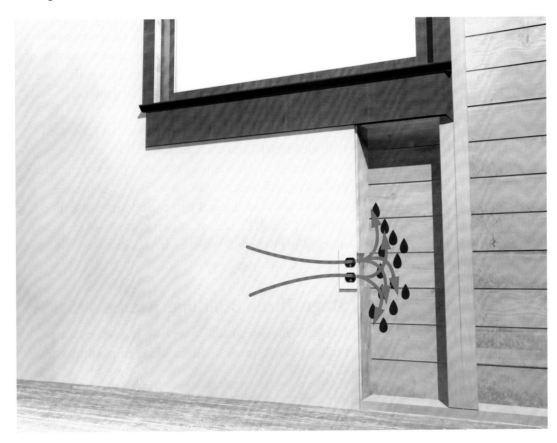

Including a vapor barrier in the wall would not have helped, as it would not have stopped the air leaking through the electric box. A much larger air leak would have negated the benefits of the insulation, in effect reverting the wall to a Stage One wall. This would have improved durability in all but very cold climates, while making the building uncomfortable and too expensive to heat and cool. Airtightening the electric boxes and connecting them to the gypsum board (see Pages 120-122) would have prevented the problem, while improving comfort and energy efficiency.

Other Vulnerabilities of Stage Two Buildings

Insulating a building makes one side of its enclosure cold, which is risky. One reason cold parts of buildings tend to be wet is because evaporating water requires latent heat. Wet building materials encourage mold and pests. The more insulation that gets added, the colder the cold side becomes, and the worse the problem can get. Super-insulated Stage Two buildings can be super-problematic.

Other changes in construction practices introduced since insulation became popular make Stage Two buildings even more vulnerable to mold. One of these changes was the introduction of building materials made from wood (mold's favorite food) chopped up into small pieces, which makes it easier for mold to digest. Each step in the transition from building with whole wood to building with plywood and then oriented strand board is a step toward predigesting the wood for mold to more easily eat it. In addition, the switch from plaster, which is unfavorable for mold growth because of its alkaline chemistry, to paper-faced gypsum board encourages mold because mold loves to eat paper, which is made from small wood fibers. And in the 1970s, lead paint was replaced with latex paint—a good thing for people's health but not good for warding off mold. (Lead paint inhibits mold growth.)

More air leaking through Stage Two buildings than through Stage One buildings can make moisture problems even worse. Old buildings had fewer and smaller electric boxes than new buildings. Plaster walls made a good connection to floors and electric boxes. Stage Two buildings built with gypsum board typically leak a lot of air between the gypsum board and the floor, and between the gypsum board and the electric boxes. Increased air leakage increases the movement of water vapor transported by air leaking from the warm side of an assembly to the cold side.

Further complicating matters, many Stage Two buildings are built with ducts and fans, which create pressure differences that greatly increase air movement through leaks, as shown on Page 483. When the fans are turned off, the ducts are still there, acting as huge holes, and the ducts themselves usually have holes in them that let the air leak wherever the prevailing pressure difference moves it.

Another vulnerability of Stage Two buildings is that the materials they are built with (gypsum board and small pieces of wood) typically have lower water storage capacity than the materials used to build Stage One buildings (stone, brick, and large pieces of wood). This makes Stage Two buildings more vulnerable to water damage, as described on Page 156. Also, in many Stage Two buildings, wood studs and joists are being replaced with metal, which cannot absorb any water.

Many Stage Two buildings are built with a sheet of polyethylene inside the walls to act as a vapor barrier, which greatly increases the time it takes a wall to dry.

All these factors add up to make many newer Stage Two buildings more vulnerable to moisture problems and mold growth than older Stage One buildings.

If an enclosure is uninsulated, it is safe against most problems with water because, during the winter, one side will be warm, and the other side will be warm, too. During the summer, one side will be warm, and the other side will also be warm (even with air conditioning). Both sides warm means both sides will be dry many hours of the year. The only problem: the building will be uncomfortable to live in and expensive to heat and cool. The solution is to insulate, of course, while at the same time protecting the building with an air barrier to prevent air from transporting water vapor from the warm side of the enclosure to the cold side of the enclosure. This is a Stage Three enclosure: insulated and airtightened.

More and more buildings are being built or renovated with air barriers, and some building codes are starting to encourage or even require them.[1] Wherever comfort and energy efficiency are taken seriously, air barrier construction is an integral part of building design and construction. But effective air barriers are still far from the norm. Only time will tell when humans will stop building Stage Two buildings.

Stage Three Buildings Are Less Risky

It is generally safe to add an air barrier to an existing building or to a new building as it is being built. When an

---

1   Fire codes have long demanded that the amount of smoke permitted to pass through fire-rated assemblies be zero. If smoke can't get through, neither can air. In effect, fire codes have long required and still require effective air barriers.

air barrier blocks air from passing through an assembly, it protects the cold side of the assembly from the infinite supply of water vapor lurking in the air on the warm side.

An air barrier has many other benefits. It makes a building more comfortable by controlling heating and cooling loads, humidity, and noise. It will also help keep pests out. It will make a building safer and healthier for people by reducing the potential for mold growth, by helping control fire and smoke, and by helping the ventilation system work better. It will make a building more durable by reducing problems with wind-blown rain penetrating into walls. It will protect metal building components from corroding and masonry materials from being damaged by freeze-thaw or other mechanisms.

In 2007, the United States military (one of the largest builders in the world) got serious about air barriers. Realizing what a large percentage of their budget went to energy costs, and knowing how vulnerable their operations can be to interruption of energy supplies, they made energy conservation a priority.[2] Rather than gradually updating the airtightness requirements for new buildings built each year, they aimed straight at their target of very good air barriers in many of their new buildings. After the initial upheaval associated with the change, the military contractors got on board. Today, very good air barriers are the new normal in the U.S. military.

Building a Stage Three wall does not guarantee a building will have no problems. Far from it. Buildings are increasingly getting more insulation, which makes the cold side of an assembly colder. New materials absorb and store less water, which makes them and the materials touching them more vulnerable to mold growth. Some new materials, such as foam insulation, are less vapor permeable than old materials, which reduces a wall's drying potential. However, it is still much better and safer to have an air barrier than not.

THE LAYERS OF AN ASSEMBLY

A wall needs layers to control the passage of heat, air, and liquid water, and maybe a layer to control the movement of water vapor by diffusion. Some materials act as "smart

"Walls need to breathe" is a meaningless statement because nobody agrees on what "breathe" means. Air leaks? Liquid water leaks? Holes in a wall? In the garment industry, "breathable" can mean a fabric is a barrier to liquid water but not to water vapor. Examples include Gore-Tex® and the high-quality du rag above. Buildings usually benefit from walls that don't include a barrier to water vapor, but that is not what people mean when they say "walls need to breathe." Usually it is a universal excuse for construction defects.

vapor barriers" by varying their water vapor permeability in response to changing humidity: they become more vapor permeable when wet and less permeable when dry. Tarpaper is one example of a smart vapor barrier. Other, high-tech smart vapor barriers have also been developed.

Walls also need a nice-looking layer on the inside, a structure to hold the building up, and an aesthetically pleasing layer on the outside that protects the other layers from sunlight, rain, and physical damage. Roof assemblies and basement wall and floor assemblies have similar requirements.

Naming the Sides of an Assembly

The indoor side of a wall or other assembly is made of materials that are more vulnerable to water damage than the materials used to build the outdoor side. Therefore, it makes sense to call the indoor side of an assembly the "dry side" and the outdoor side the "wet side." The barrier to liquid water can be considered the boundary.

2   Energy efficiency is not a new or unimportant concept in the military. A plane or ship's capacity to travel from its base, spend time accomplishing a mission, and return to base is called its "combat radius" or "time on station."

Sequencing Layers in an Assembly

Proper sequencing of the layers in a wall (or other assembly) is critical. The great building scientist Joe Lstiburek calls the correct sequence the "Perfect Wall." He credits Canadian engineering professor Neil Hutcheon with first describing the concept. Because it is not a specific collection of building materials, but a specific sequence of building materials, it could also be called "The Perfect Sequence." The sequence starts with the exterior cladding, which can be bricks, shingles, stucco, or whatever material is chosen for the outermost layer. Next, just indoors of the exterior cladding is the insulation layer, also called the heat-control layer, the thermal boundary, or the thermal barrier. (No insulation is a complete barrier to heat—insulation only slows heat movement.) The barriers to air and liquid water—which should be complete barriers—go on the indoor side of the insulation. If the assembly includes a barrier to water vapor, it should be in approximately the same location as the barriers to air and liquid water. Next is the structure holding up the wall. Finally, on the indoor side is an aesthetically pleasing layer, such as gypsum board or plaster.

Sequencing the insulation layer on the outdoor side of the liquid water barrier is key. Locating it there insures that whichever side of the insulation is cold at that time of year will be on the wet (outdoor) side of the barrier to liquid water, where any materials that get wet are materials that are less vulnerable to water damage than the materials on the dry (indoor) side of the wall.

The perfect sequence is still not normal practice in the industry, but it has so many benefits that there is no reason not to do it. It helps keep most of the layers of the wall dry throughout the year. It provides a location where the air barrier and the insulation layer can be built without being interrupted by studs, pipes, and wires, and it allows easy visual inspection of the air barrier before other layers cover it up. Locating the insulation on the outdoor side of the structure allows the structure's thermal mass (heat storage capacity) to reduce peak heating and cooling loads as well as annual heating and cooling loads. Locating the insulation layer on the outdoor side of the structure also keeps the structure at room temperature, which protects it from cracking and other problems caused by expanding and contracting with changes in outdoor temperature. Locating the air barrier and the barrier to liquid water

on the indoor side of the insulation and cladding ensures that these barriers last longer. Not only does this sequence protect them from the sun's harmful ultraviolet rays, but it also prevents the stretching and shrinking they would be subject to if they were to heat up and cool down with the outdoor temperature. This sequence also reduces the amount of rain that reaches these barriers.

Wall Sequence Drawings

The drawings on Pages 381-386 show air leaking from the warm side to the cold side of different wall assemblies. When air flows in this direction it gets cooled, which increases its relative humidity, causing condensation or at least reduced drying. None of the drawings show air leaking from the cold side of the wall to the warm side of the wall. Surely air sometimes leaks from cold to warm, but air flowing in that direction will be less harmful because warming the air will reduce its relative humidity, preventing condensation while also facilitating drying.

The direction that air moves as it leaks through walls changes with wind direction, with the season (stack effect gets reversed during winter and summer), and as fans cycle on and off. This makes it unrealistic to try to control or predict the direction of air leaks or to expect air to always travel in the same direction through leaks. Therefore, expect air to sometimes leak in the direction shown in the drawings in any wall that does not have a perfect air barrier. Expecting to build a perfect air barrier, or anything else perfect, and keep it in perfect condition for the life of the building, is unrealistic. Realistically, every wall and other assembly will leak some air, but the perfect sequence will help to protect the assembly.

Each drawing on the following pages shows rough approximations of the outdoor and indoor air temperatures (**hot**, **room temperature**, and **cold**), the temperature of each layer of the wall, and the temperature of air leaking through the wall until it reaches a layer cold enough to condense water out of the air.

The wall on Page 381 has no insulation. If it has no air barrier, it is a Stage One assembly. The walls on Pages 382-385 could be either Stage Two or Three; it doesn't matter which because no air barrier is perfect. Each page explains why each of these walls will have water-related durability problems. Finally, on Page 386, the materials are arranged in the perfect sequence.

No Insulation: Durable but Uncomfortable

The drawings on this page show what happens when air leaks from the warm side to the cold side of an uninsulated wall.

Because the wall is uninsulated, heat moves from indoors through the wall, keeping all the wall's layers close to **room temperature** during the winter. Water will not condense out of the air within the wall because the air is not significantly cooled until it gets to the outdoor side of the wood siding.

The drawing at left shows the same wall during the summer, when the house is cooled by air conditioning. Warm air is leaking from outdoors to indoors—from the warm side to the cold side.

The thermometers show that all the layers of the uninsulated wall stay **hot** during the summer. Water will not condense out of air leaking through the wall because the air is not significantly cooled within the wall.

Insulated on the Indoor Side

The drawings on this page show a wall with **insulation** between the studs, which puts the insulation close to the indoor side of the wall.

The thermometers show that all the layers of the wall on the outdoor side of the insulation, including the **chipboard sheathing**, are cold. Warm indoor air leaking through the wall touches the cold sheathing, as shown at right, and can cause condensation, which leads to mold damage (see Page 377 for an example).

The drawing at left shows the same wall during the summer. The thermometers show that the gypsum board on the cold (air conditioned) side of the insulation is colder than the outdoor air.

Air leaking through the wall from the warm side to the cold side will reach a cold layer within the wall, where water can condense out of the air and cause rot. In this assembly, the first cold layer is the outdoor side of the gypsum board.

Insulated on the Indoor Side with a Vapor Barrier

The drawings on this page show a **water vapor barrier** (a sheet of clear polyethylene) on the indoor side of the insulation. Because it is difficult to connect the polyethylene to other materials, it does little to stop air from leaking through the wall. As explained in Chapter 5: Water - Basic Science, air leaks are the main mechanism for moving water vapor through a wall. So, despite its name, the vapor barrier does little to prevent water vapor from wetting the wall.

Not only does the vapor barrier not reduce wetting significantly, but it also actively reduces drying.

Water absorbed by building materials can only leave the building as a gas (water vapor), not as a liquid. During the winter, diffusion will move water vapor toward dry indoor air unless a vapor barrier near the indoor side of the wall prevents it from moving through the wall by diffusion. Because the vapor barrier will reduce drying, it can contribute to mold growth within the wall.

Insulated on the Indoor Side with a Layer of Housewrap

The drawings on this page show the wall with a layer of housewrap, such as Tyvek® (or a similar product), installed on the outdoor side of the sheathing.

Tyvek® is a barrier to air and to liquid water but is not a barrier to water vapor, as explained on Page 132. Because it is a barrier to liquid water, it can reduce wetting by rain. But because it is not a barrier to water vapor, it still allows drying by diffusion.

Air can leak between pieces of Tyvek® that are not perfectly connected to other materials. When air leaks through the wall from the warm side to the cold side, water will condense out of the air onto the first cold building material it touches. In both examples on this page, the first cold layer the air reaches is on the indoor, or dry, side of the Tyvek®, where water condensing out of the air can damage materials. Tyvek® will not prevent the problem of wetting by condensation, but because it is not a barrier to water vapor, it will allow the wall to dry.

Insulated on the Outdoor Side

The drawings on this page show a wall with a layer of **foam insulation** just inside the cladding. There is no Tyvek®. In the drawing at right, water is condensing on the indoor side of the wet (exterior) side of the wall, which is covered with wood siding (but could be clad with any other water-resistant material). The location of the insulation is keeping all the materials on the dry (indoor) side of the wall warm during the winter, protecting them from condensation all winter.

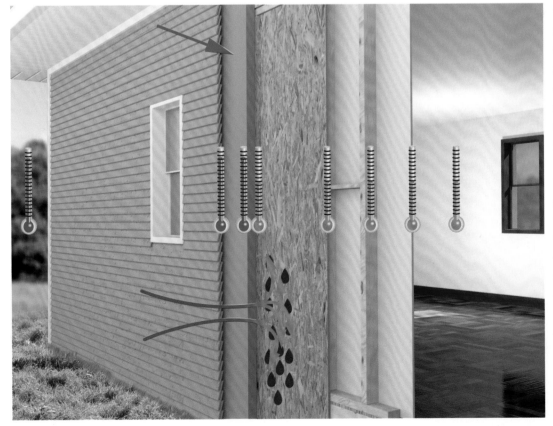

However, the same wall is vulnerable to water damage from condensation during the summer, when materials on the dry (indoor) side of the insulation are colder than outdoor air, and to water damage from rain all year.

When hot, humid summer air leaks from the warm side of the wall to the cold side, water will condense onto the first cold material the air touches, which is the sheathing. In this wall the sheathing is chipboard, which is not water resistant. It will therefore be damaged by the water.

The Perfect Sequence

The drawings on this page show the perfect sequence: a layer of insulation on the outdoor side of a barrier to liquid water (Tyvek®, etc.). If water condenses on the cold side of the insulation, the water will be on the outdoor (wet) side of the housewrap, where all the materials are water resistant. This would also be true without the barrier to liquid water, as shown on the top of Page 385.

A wall built in the perfect sequence would also include an air barrier located in the same place as the barrier to liquid water. Tyvek® connected at all seams would be one example of an air barrier in the same place as the barrier to liquid water. But all the drawings in this series, including the Stage Three drawings on this page, show air leaks because no air barrier is perfect.

The drawing at left shows how the barrier to liquid water located on the indoor side of the insulation is required to achieve the perfect sequence. During the summer, when warm air leaks from the warm side to the cold side, water will condense on the first cold surface in the wall. The first cold surface will be the barrier to liquid water. This sequencing of materials solves the problem shown in the drawing on the bottom of Page 385 and protects the materials on the dry (indoor) side of the wall all year.

What the Perfect Sequence Accomplishes

The perfect sequence does not by itself guarantee that a wall will be durable, but it helps make a wall forgiving of design mistakes and construction defects. It helps reduce durability problems caused by the barriers to air and liquid water not being designed, built, or maintained perfectly. It makes it easier to build a continuous air barrier and a continuous insulation layer. It also helps create a wall that will be durable in any climate: cold, hot, wet, dry, or any combination. These benefits make the perfect sequence essential to good building design.

Stage Three Walls without the Perfect Sequence

A wall can include an air barrier and insulation and not be arranged in the perfect sequence. The wall shown on Page 384 would be an example of this if the pieces of housewrap in the wall were connected to each other and to other materials in a way that created an air barrier. This would be an imperfectly sequenced Stage Three wall, which is still better than a Stage One or Stage Two wall.

But the air barrier needs to be perfect, or nearly perfect, to avoid problems with air transporting warm water vapor to the cold side of the wall. The wall has other disadvantages: much of its thermal mass (see Page 13) is on the outdoor side of the insulation, where it will not help steady indoor temperatures; the structure will be subject to changing size as its temperature follows changes in outdoor temperature; and the insulation is not continuous.

Vapor Barrier or No Vapor Barrier?

Adding a vapor barrier to a wall is like wearing plastic bags for socks. There are times when it will keep the wall (or feet) drier, but it will usually make things worse.

The decision regarding whether to include a vapor barrier or not, as well as how vapor permeable non-barrier materials need to be (their vapor openness varies widely), depends on climate, other materials in the wall, airtightness of the wall, and presence of unusual moisture sources such as a swimming pool. If a wall has no vapor barrier and can dry by vapor diffusion in either direction,

then it will likely be durable in all but unusually cold climates. One unusual moisture source is brick cladding wet with rain. Walls clad with brick can dry with the help of an extra wide gap behind the brick (as wide as 25mm [1”]), as described on Page 393.

Updating Existing Buildings

The same science that applies to new assemblies applies to upgrading existing assemblies:

 - Turning a Stage One assembly into a Stage Two assembly by insulating but not adding an air barrier can make it more vulnerable to water damage than it was when it was a Stage One assembly.

 - Any assembly works better with an air barrier that reduces air leaks through the assembly.

 - Any assembly works better with the layers arranged in the perfect sequence.

Adding an air barrier to an existing building is usually more difficult than building an air barrier into a new building. Much of the difficulty lies in connecting the air barrier in one assembly to the air barrier in another assembly: for example, connecting the air barrier in a wall to the air barrier in a roof. Other challenges include making the air barrier continuous past penetrations for pipes and wires. Much of this difficulty can be avoided by locating the air barrier close to the outdoor side of the building enclosure. Adding insulation to an existing building can be difficult for the same reasons and is also easier to do on the outdoor side of a building's enclosure.

One method of adding an air barrier and insulation to an existing wall assembly is shown on Pages 110 and 111. Methods of adding insulation to the outdoor side of roof assemblies will be shown later in this chapter. It is harder to add insulation to the outdoor side of a basement wall or floor because this requires digging up the soil around a basement wall, or removing and replacing the floor.

An airtight connection between a window and a wall is necessary for the window and wall to form an airtight assembly. Though changing windows will disturb occupants, there are ways to keep disturbance to a minimum. The drawings on the following four pages show one way to minimize disturbance.

Installing Exterior Insulation and New Windows with Minimal Disruption

In the drawing at right, the people are at home reading and playing the guitar. They don't have to know when the workers are arriving. They can stay home or go out whenever they wish.

The drawing at left shows a scaffold erected alongside the building. The existing cladding has been removed, and an installer is installing insulation on the outdoor side of the wall. The installer could also be adding an air barrier and/or a barrier to liquid water under the insulation, unless the existing building already has these barriers.

Here, the installer has almost finished insulating the outdoor side of the wall. The process is so quiet that the people inside the building will hardly know any work is being done.

3

At left, the completed insulation is installed on the outdoor side of the building.

Any type of cladding can be installed on the outdoor side of the insulation, which makes a retrofit like this a good opportunity to make an ugly building look better. If the front of the building already looks attractive, it might be worth installing exterior insulation on only the other three sides and simply installing extremely energy-efficient windows on the front.

4

At right, the installer is putting in a new window on the outdoor side of the original window while the original window is still in place. The installer is doing the work from outdoors.

The installer will be careful to connect the new window to the air barrier and to the barrier to liquid water, making those barriers continuous across the window.

In the drawing at left, the installer is finishing work upstairs. The building now has new windows, new insulation that is continuous, new cladding, and maybe even new barriers to air and to liquid water. All of this was done without any work being done within the apartments, and nobody had to schedule work with the residents.

All that will remain to be done is removing the old windows and fixing the interior wall.

At right, the installer is working inside the first floor apartment, removing an old window.

Next he will use plaster and paint to make the wall where the window was removed look nice.

This part can be done in any weather and whenever access to indoors is available.

Of course, if desired, the old window can be left in place so the building will have two sets of windows, as shown on Page 297.

When access to the upstairs room is available, the old window can be removed, and the wall can be refinished there, too.

At no point during this process was the building open to the elements.

Not needing to interrupt residents' schedules until the last step greatly reduces the cost of a retrofit like this.

Materials for the Perfect Sequence

The building in the photo below has a layer of **Tyvek®** serving as a barrier to liquid water and, depending on how well the connections were made, maybe a barrier to air. Next comes **foam insulation**. Part of the building is clad with **bricks**, the upper part with **siding** that is manufactured to look like wood, and another part with wood/polymer composite **panels**. The cladding visible on the outdoor side of a perfect wall can be anything an architect or owner thinks will look nice. Page 393 shows the cladding on more walls built in the perfect sequence.

It is usually best to use one material as both the barrier to air and the barrier to liquid water. Possibilities include a cement/acrylic product brushed onto concrete blocks, a housewrap such as Tyvek® (connected with very good tape), a fully adhered membrane (rubbery sheets with a strong adhesive back), a barrier applied to the sheathing at the factory (see Page 108), or one of the many barriers sold in cans and applied by spraying, rolling, or brushing.

The insulation needs to be a type that is resistant to damage by water because it will get wet when (not if) rain leaks through the cladding. The types of insulation most commonly installed directly behind cladding are foam and mineral wool. Foam can be sprayed on or installed as sheets. Mineral wool has many advantages over foam: it will not burn or melt in a fire, is not vulnerable to damage from the sun's ultraviolet rays, is flexible enough to lie flat on a not-perfectly-flat wall, is often made from industrial waste, is insect resistant, and is easy to recycle.

There are many examples of perfectly sequenced walls in this book, including at the top of Page 30, where a wall covered with a grey cement/acrylic brush-on barrier to air and liquid water is being insulated with mineral wool behind brick. On the bottom of Page 30, a wall is being covered with a barrier to air and liquid water, then insulated with foam, and then clad with brick. On the bottom of Page 106, a wall is being covered with a fully adhered membrane, then foam insulation, and then stone.

The Benefits of an Air Gap behind Cladding

The photo at right shows a wall being built with an air gap between the **foam insulation** and the **stone cladding**. The photo below shows a wall with a gap between the **foam insulation** and the **wood siding**.

A gap (10 mm [3/8"] is generally enough) serves many purposes. First, it provides a place for liquid water to drain. All cladding should be expected to leak some water, so when (not if) water leaks through, it can drain down the back of the cladding and out the bottom of the wall, perhaps through weep holes. The gap also provides a place for water vapor diffusion to spread the water out away from the leak, reducing wetting in the vicinity of the leak. It also reduces wetting of the wall from water stored in cladding diffusing through the wall. Most importantly, as long as the gap has small openings to outdoor air at the top and bottom, air will circulate by convection, absorb water vapor, and leave the wall, taking water vapor with it. The bottom opening should include an insect barrier as shown on Pages 358-359.

Without the gap, liquid water would penetrate deeper into the wall. Liquid water leaking through the cladding would immediately wet the insulation, which puts water one layer closer to the dry side of the wall. Capillary suction between the cladding and the insulation could wet additional parts of the wall. Eventually, water pressure could build up between the cladding and the insulation, forcing water deeper into the wall. An air gap behind the cladding is beneficial for any above-ground Stage One, Two, or Three wall, perfectly sequenced or not, in any climate.

The design of aluminum siding and vinyl siding includes an air gap, which is one reason why those types of cladding do a good job of preserving walls. A layer of mineral wool insulation, as shown on the top of Page 30, can allow enough air movement to eliminate the need for a gap. The wall at the top of Page 401 is being built with an air gap behind the siding.

Fire Safety

If fire gets into the gap it will reach Stage Two quickly because the gap has insulation on one side and no opening infrared radiation can escape through. Some building materials that will not burn out in the open should not be considered safe against burning inside a gap behind cladding. One way to reduce the hazard is to interrupt the gap with a horizontal barrier of fireproof material at each floor, plus vertical fireproof barriers spaced a similar distance apart.

Special Concerns for Basements and Roofs

A similar sequence can be used to improve the performance of roof assemblies (discussed in more detail on Pages 400-401) and basements, which are different from above-ground walls in a few important ways.

One difference is that basement and roof assemblies generally do not benefit from an air gap, although sometimes a gap for liquid water to drain along the side of a basement wall is beneficial, and sometimes roofs incorporate air gaps to keep them cool to prevent ice dams (see Page 423).

Another difference is that roof assemblies generally dry toward indoors only because they have a barrier to liquid water on the outdoor side, which is almost always also a barrier to water vapor and to air. This makes it important to not add another vapor barrier on the indoor side of a roof assembly because, if water gets in, it won't escape toward outdoors and won't dry out for a very long time.

Basements and floor slabs are also different from walls because they will forever touch soil that will be relatively wet (by capillary suction) forever. Walls get wet intermittently, roofs get wet frequently, but basement walls and floors get wet all the time from touching soil and almost never dry toward outdoors.

Including a barrier to water vapor or a barrier to capillary suction in a basement wall or floor assembly will not reduce drying to the outdoor side of the assembly because soil is almost never dry enough to absorb water from building materials, even in a desert. But a barrier to water vapor and capillary suction can prevent a significant amount of wetting of the basement wall because soil is almost always wet. Any material that is a barrier to water vapor will probably also be a barrier to capillary suction because a barrier to water vapor has holes too small to allow groups of water molecules through.

The Perfect Sequence for Basements

The photo below shows an example of the perfect sequence for a basement wall. On the outdoor side of the structure (the steel-reinforced concrete) is a black troweled-on barrier to air, water vapor, capillary suction, and liquid water. It is similar to the material applied to the wall in Drawing 7 on Page 215. The barrier to air will probably not be necessary unless the concrete cracks, but concrete does crack, and the air barrier might stay connected across small cracks. On the outdoor side of that is the pink-colored foam insulation. (Some types of foam insulation are vulnerable to insects chewing on it for food or to make a place to live.) Because this is a basement wall, there is no cladding on the outdoor side of the insulation, and there might or might not be an aesthetically pleasing layer added to the indoor side of the wall. Otherwise, the sequencing of the layers is the same as in the perfect wall.

The drawings on Pages 396 and 397 show why it is better to put insulation on the outdoor side of basement walls and floors than on the indoor side. Digging up a yard to install insulation on the outdoor side of an existing basement wall can be expensive, but it is usually the best way to make the basement healthy and comfortable and the only way to avoid chronic dampness that can otherwise be treated only by operating a dehumidifier.

The house in the photos on this page has an uninsulated basement floor and uninsulated basement walls. The masonry walls conduct a lot of heat to outdoors during the winter, which is why the basement is white in the infrared photo below. As a result of the lack of insulation, water condenses out of indoor air onto the basement floor all summer. The basement floor and walls also have no barrier to capillary suction, so the floor and walls are wet all year.

This problem can only be solved by digging up the basement floor and insulating underneath it, and by digging up the soil around the perimeter of the house and insulating the outdoor side of the basement walls. Before the insulation is added, barriers to capillary suction and to air, as shown on Page 394, should be installed on the outdoor side of the basement walls. Without this work, any walls, stairs, or furniture that touch the basement floor or walls will get wet and grow mold.

Insulating on the Indoor Side of the Assembly Can Increase Wetness

In most climates, soil stays at a colder temperature than indoor air all year starting at about two meters (six feet) below the surface. The drawing at right shows an uninsulated basement wall and floor kept warm by the air in the basement, which is heated by the building's heating system. This warming discourages—but does not always stop—water from condensing out of the air onto the basement walls and floor.

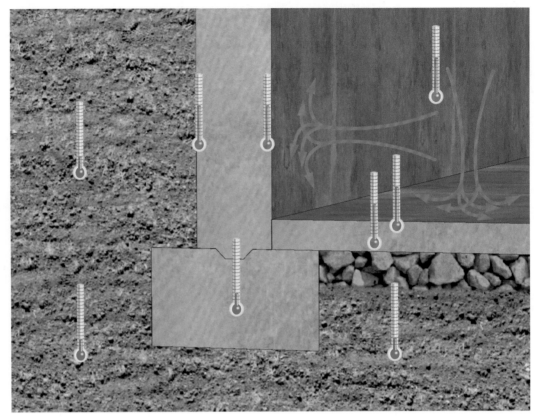

At left is a basement wall with **insulation** on the indoor side and a **wood floor** on top of the uninsulated concrete floor. The insulation and wood reduce the flow of heat from the heated basement air to the basement walls and subfloor. Therefore, the walls and floor cool to close to the temperature of the soil, which is often below the dewpoint temperature of indoor air. Air leaking from indoors through to the concrete carries water vapor with it, which condenses on the cold concrete, causing mold to eat any wood or paper parts of the wall and floor.

Insulating on the Outdoor Side of the Assembly Solves the Problem

The drawing at right shows a basement wall and floor with blue foam insulation on the outdoor side. The wall and floor will be warmer than if they were uninsulated or insulated on the indoor side. Because the insulation is on the exterior, indoor air will keep the walls and floor close to room temperature, which at all times of year is above the indoor air's own dewpoint temperature. This will prevent water from condensing on the basement walls and floor, while also keeping them warm enough to help evaporate any water they absorb from the soil.

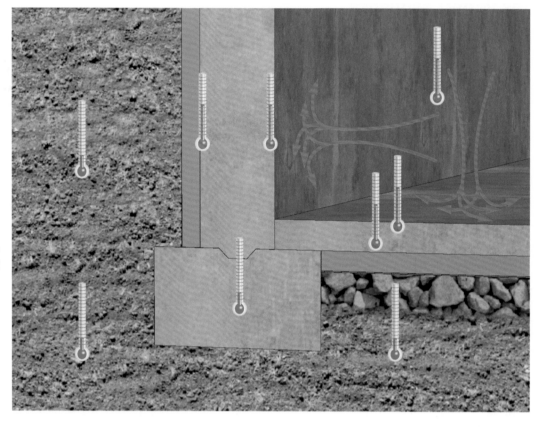

Where digging deep enough to expose the whole basement wall is impractical, a "**skirt**" of foam insulation can be buried in the soil, extending out far enough to require heat escaping from the basement wall below it to travel a long distance through the soil (around the end of the skirt) to get to cold outdoor air which will carry it away. In effect, the soil itself is being used as a very thick layer of low-quality insulation, which keeps the wall below the skirt close to room temperature.

Retrofitting an Existing Basement with the Perfect Sequence

Heat conducted from an uninsulated basement to soil will cool the indoor side of the basement wall or floor. In most parts of the world, the temperature of the soil is colder than the dewpoint temperature of indoor air for many hours each year.

The lack of insulation is a problem that causes many basements and floor slabs to get wet by water condensing out of indoor air, or to not dry after getting wet by water leaking through walls or by capillary suction from the soil. Insulation on the wrong (indoor) side will make the problem much worse. Ventilation might make the symptoms go away during the winter but will make the problem worse during the summer.

Winter air in all but maritime climates is so dry that there is no chance of water condensing out of winter air onto a basement wall or floor. As explained on Page 220, dry outdoor winter air moved through a building can remove an almost infinite amount of water.

But ventilating a basement with humid outdoor summer air will only make a basement wetter because water will condense out of the summer air onto the cool basement floor and walls. Ventilating a basement with outdoor summer air in a dry climate might or might not help, depending on how dry the outdoor air is.

The problem is illustrated clearly in the photo on Page 154, which shows condensation forming on a basement floor with just a little insulation (a rug) on the indoor side. Many a basement throughout history has not had water problems until the indoor side of its concrete walls was covered with a nice-looking finish, which acts as a small amount of insulation on the wrong (indoor) side of the assembly, keeping the wall cold and therefore wet for months each year.

The room in the photo at right used to have this problem. It is a bedroom on the lower floor of a two-story house. The people who owned the house started sneezing and getting headaches whenever they slept there. They were reacting to mold that was eating the underside of the wood floor, which rested on an uninsulated concrete slab, which itself rested directly on the soil.

If the house had had a very good air barrier, they could have kept the windows closed during the summer and hoped the cooling system would keep the indoor air dry enough to stop the mold. But that was not possible because it was an old Stage One house that had been insulated but not airtightened over the years, making it a Stage Two house. A dehumidifier would have helped, but they knew capillary suction and air leaks would probably wet the floor faster than the dehumidifier could dry it.

As soon as they understood the basic science, the couple decided to have the bedroom floor replaced. The new floor included gravel to act as a capillary break, followed by a polyethylene vapor barrier,[3] then foam insulation, then concrete, and then wood. The wall is still insulated on the wrong (indoor) side, but otherwise the job was a success. The owners' sneezing and headaches disappeared, and soon they insulated on the outdoor side of the basement floor throughout the house.

3   The polyethylene can go either above or below the foam. Some people put it above the foam to stop the foam from floating up in the wet concrete. But a good mason mixes concrete with a low water-to-cement ratio, which avoids this problem while increasing the quality of the concrete. The concrete below is properly mixed.

Model: Simon Menzies. Photo: Timothy Greenfield-Sanders.

Insulating Both Sides of an Assembly

If an assembly has enough insulation on the outdoor side, additional insulation can be safely added on the indoor side to take advantage of the otherwise wasted hollow space inside the wall without causing condensation problems. The amount of insulation that can be safely added depends mostly on climate. In colder climates, more of the insulation needs to be on the outdoor side. In a very cold, arctic-type climate, almost all the insulation needs to be on the outdoor side.

The same is true for a wall, a roof, a basement wall, a basement floor, or a slab-on-grade. Some amount of insulation can be safely added to the indoor side of the assembly if the outdoor side of the assembly is also insulated. The more insulation on the outdoor side, the greater the amount of insulation that can safely be added to the indoor side. And, the colder the climate, the greater the amount of insulation that needs to be on the outdoor side.

The Perfect Sequence for Roofs

The perfect sequence for a roof has an attractive layer on the indoor (ceiling) side, then the structure, then a barrier to liquid water (and to air), then an insulation layer, and finally an outer layer that protects the insulation and the waterproof layer from foot traffic and ultraviolet light. Because the waterproof layer is on the indoor side of the insulation, it is protected from stretching and shrinking with changes in temperature. The combined effect of all this protection helps the waterproof layer last a long time.

Roof shingles are not a perfect barrier to liquid water. A shingled roof assembly should have another barrier to liquid water on the indoor side of the insulation, such as tarpaper or, better yet, a fully adhered membrane.

The **barrier to liquid water** (roofing paper) on the roof below is being covered with a **dimpled mat**, which forms a gap for water to easily drain through (because this is a "flat" roof). Two layers of **insulation** are laid down with

The photo above shows roof pavers made from recycled car tires. The pavers are used instead of gravel to hold down the insulation.

seams staggered between layers, and then a **fabric** keeps gravel from falling down to the barrier to liquid water. Finally, **gravel**, which has proven its durability over millions of years, protects the other materials from wind blowing them away, foot traffic, and ultraviolet light.

In the photo at right, insulation is being added to the roof of the house shown on Page 29.

The insulation is being laid on top of the existing roof shingles. It would have been better to remove the old shingles to prevent any toxic chemicals in them from getting into the house and to replace them with a barrier to air and to liquid water, such as a fully adhered membrane.

Photo: Timothy Greenfield-Sanders.

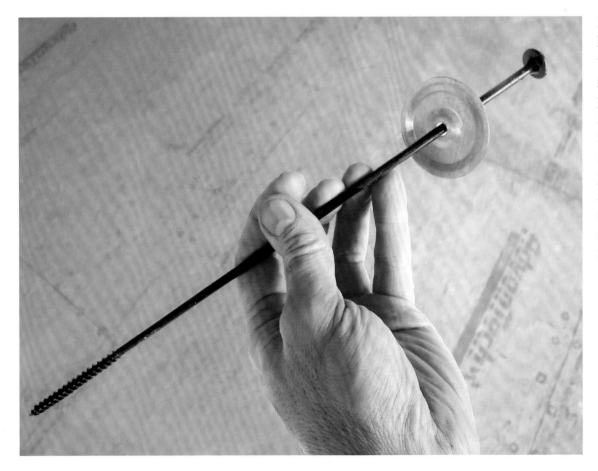

Long screws like the screw in the photo at left go through the plywood and the insulation and into the roof joists (rafters). The plywood layer makes it easy to attach new roof shingles with nails.

Continuous Layers across Assemblies

It is obvious that the structure of a roof needs to be connected to the structure of the walls because the walls support the roof and keep it from falling down or blowing away in a strong wind. Likewise, it is obvious that the structure of the wall needs to be connected to the foundation that supports it from underneath. What is sometimes less obvious is that the layers that control heat, air, and liquid water also need to be connected to each other. These layers need to form continuous barriers, with no gaps, including at corners and at connections to windows and doors. The same applies if the enclosure includes a vapor barrier: it needs to be continuous.

Each layer of an assembly should connect to the same layer in adjoining assemblies. Described another way, each layer needs to continue uninterrupted across connections between assemblies. For example, the air barrier layer in a wall assembly should connect to the air barrier layer in a roof assembly.

Connecting all these barriers across assemblies can be difficult; it is one of the most challenging parts of designing and building a building.

A complete plan for a building enclosure identifies what will provide structural support, as well as what layers of which materials will control heat, air, and liquid water. One drawing showing the layers within the wall and another showing the layers within the roof are not enough. The drawings should also show how the layers connect at internal and external corners, to windows and doors, and across connections between assemblies.

Large amounts of heat will escape through the gaps between the "assemblies": the hat and jacket, gloves and jacket, jacket and pants, and pants and boots.

The different pieces of insulation connect to or overlap each other, which prevents heat from escaping between "assemblies." Model: Oscar Su.

The Pencil Test

One good way to think about continuous layers in a building enclosure is to imagine using a pencil to trace a layer around a plan of the entire building without lifting the pencil from the paper (except where doors and windows perform their functions).

The red line in the drawing at right represents a layer in the walls connecting to all the doors and windows.

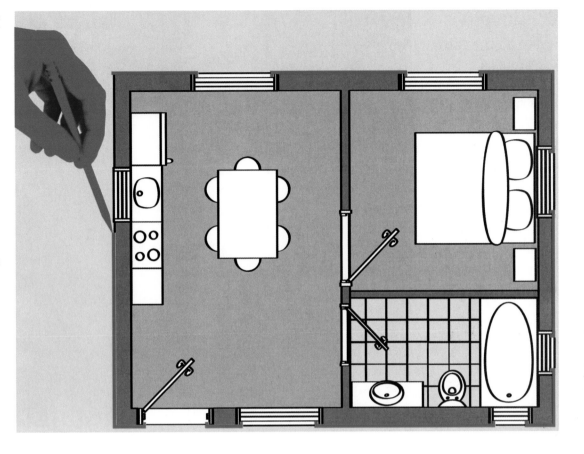

The schematic drawing at left shows insulation on the outdoor side of a wall continuing up and over the parapet wall at the edge of the roof and connecting to the insulation on the outdoor side of the roof, creating a layer of insulation that is continuous (counting the windows as part of that layer).

The barriers to air and to liquid water (also including windows) should also be continuous across assemblies, enclosing the whole building.

Continuous Insulation over a Parapet

The parapet under construction in the photo at right is being insulated with white foam on both sides.

The photo below shows the layer of white foam continued over the top of the parapet.

The building will have a continuous layer of insulation covering the exterior wall, the sides and top of the parapet, and the roof.

In the photo at left, some of the foam on the indoor side of the parapet has been covered with **stucco**.

Note that the design does not depend on the stucco to protect the parapet from air leaks and liquid water leaks. The yellow brushed-on material in the photo above is a more effective barrier to air and liquid water. It is located where other layers will protect it from UV light (which can damage foam) and from stretching and shrinking caused by changes in temperature.

The photo at right shows the same parapet covered with **metal coping** to protect the foam from UV light and to help the parapet shed water. The waterproof layer of the roof is getting covered with a dimpled mat, then blue foam insulation, then a black fabric, and then concrete paving stones.

Blue foam insulation also covers the parapet wall up to the bottom of the flashing.

The materials in the building's roof, parapet, and wall are arranged in the perfect sequence.

On the parapet, the yellow brushed-on barrier to liquid water and air is outside the structure and inside the insulation. On the wall (not shown) and roof, the waterproof layer (which is also the air barrier) is outside the structure and inside the insulation. The barrier to air, the barrier to liquid water, and the barrier to heat (the insulation layer) are continuous across the roof assembly, the parapet wall assembly, and the exterior wall.

ENCLOSE THE WHOLE BUILDING

No part of any building should be partly indoors and partly outdoors. This is why attics, basements, and underfloor crawl spaces[4] are bad ideas, unless they are conditioned (heated, cooled, dehumidified, ventilated) and completely enclosed.

An attic is problematic because it is the intersection of flows of air, heat, and water vapor from indoors and outdoors, and maybe from leaky ducts, which at some point in time will combine in the worst possible way, causing condensation. The only space more problematic than an attic is a crawl space, which is the intersection of flows of air, heat, and water vapor from indoors, outdoors, and the soil, and maybe from leaky ducts, plus liquid water from the soil, which will more frequently combine in the worst possible way. Whenever there is a question about whether to leave part of a building partly outdoors (unconditioned), the answer is no. The whole building should be a fully conditioned indoor space.

Crawl Spaces

In his 1865 book, The Handbook of Household Science, Edward Youmans, founder of Popular Science magazine, quoted a contemporary named Dr. Buchanan who had strong opinions on cellars and crawl spaces. Condemning them, Dr. Buchanan proposed a plan for building a house that would avoid their evils, which included "noxious emanations," among other things:

> While I would condemn cellars and basements entirely, the common plan of building, in the absence, must be condemned also. The house being built above the surface of the earth, a space is left between the lower floor and the ground, which is even closer and darker than a cellar, and which becomes, on a smaller scale, the source of noxious emanations. Under-floor space should be abolished as well as cellars and basements. The plan that I have adopted with the most satisfactory success, to avoid all these evils, is the following: Let the house be built entirely above the ground; let the lower floor be built upon the surface of the earth, at least as high as the surrounding soil. If filled up with any clean material a few inches above the surrounding earth, it would be better. A proper foundation being prepared, make your first floor by a pavement of brick, laid in hydraulic cement, upon the surfaces of the ground. Let the same be extended into your walls, so as to cut off the walls of your house with water-proof cement, from all communication with the moisture of the surrounding earth. Upon this foundation build according to your fancy. Your lower floor will be perfectly dry – impenetrable to moisture and to vermin; not a single animal can get a lodgment in your lower story. By adopting this plan, your house will be dry and cleanly; the atmosphere of your ground floor will be fresh and pure; you will be entirely relieved from that steady drain upon life, which is produced by basements and cellars,-and if you appropriate the ground-floor to purposes of storerooms, kitchen, &c., you will find that the dry apartments thus constructed are infinitely superior to the old basements and cellars. And if you place your sitting and sleeping rooms on the second and third floors, you will be as thoroughly exempt from local miasma as Architecture can make you.[5]

Dr. Buchanan's advice is still relevant today. Not only is it a good idea to avoid crawl spaces, but also his prescription to use waterproof cement on walls near the earth makes it clear that he understood that a building needs a barrier to stop capillary suction from transporting water from soil into a building. (Modern methods of stopping capillary suction are shown on Pages 214 and 215.) His plan to put the house slightly above the surrounding soil prevents damage from surface water on a rainy day. His urging to abolish all basements, presumably uninsulated in his day, no longer needs to be followed because insulation can now be installed on the outdoor side of a basement, including underneath the basement floor.

Problems with existing crawl spaces can be remedied by insulating between the crawl space and both the soil and outdoors, airtightening against air leaks between the crawl space and the soil or outdoors, and controlling liquid water flow into the crawl space. Described another way, make the crawl space a fully conditioned, indoor part of the building. With new construction, build on top of an insulated basement or an insulated floor slab (slab-on-grade). When raising a building above the ground to avoid damage from floods, the building can be built on piles or concrete walls that are completely outdoors, below an insulated and airtightened underside of the building.

---

4   As used in this book, the term "crawl space" refers to a space under the lowest floor of a building that is too short to stand up in.

5   Dr. Buchanan, quoted in Edward L. Youmans, The Handbook of Household Science (New York: D. Appleton & Co., 1865 [1857]), Page 202.

The drawing at right shows wind blowing hot, humid outdoor air through a vented crawl space. The soil under the building stays cooler than outdoor air all summer. Radiant heat movement from the floor of the house to the soil (the uninsulated floor of the crawl space) cools the floor of the house, often below the dewpoint temperature of the air, which can cause condensation on its underside. More ventilation with hot, humid summer air will usually make the problem worse.

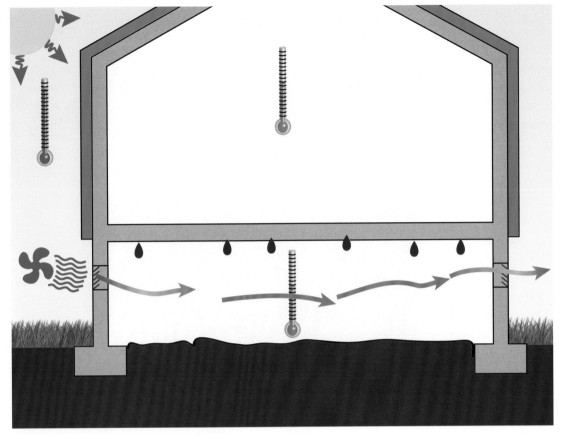

Insulating the house's floor, as shown at left, can make the problem in the crawl space worse by keeping the underside of the floor colder. This causes more condensation on the underside of the floor, which causes mold, which rots the floor from underneath and can make occupants sick.

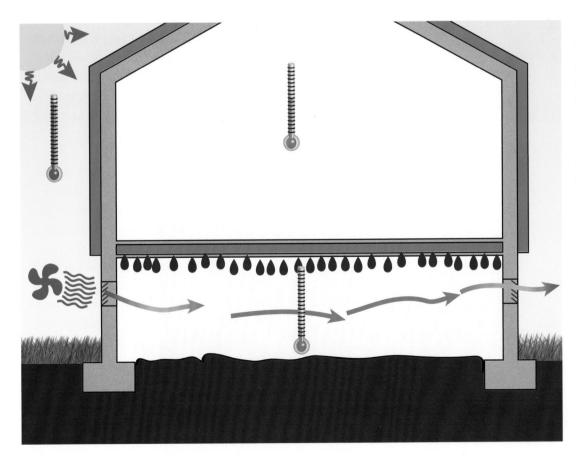

The photo at right shows a crawl space that has this very problem.

A pool of water is sitting on top of the soil of the crawl space, which keeps the relative humidity in the crawl space very high.

The fiberglass insulation between the floor joists was not installed well to begin with and is now falling down in places.

The fuzzy white stuff in the photos at left is not cobwebs. It is mold growing on the underside of the insulation and floor joists.

Mold may not only eventually destroy the structure of the floor but also pose a serious health hazard to residents of the building.

No doubt the people living in this building experienced the "noxious emanations" and "local miasma" Dr. Buchanan referred to.

How Insulation Worsens the Problem

In the close-up at right, little mold is growing on the warm, upper part of the joist. Fuzzy white mold is growing lower down on the joist because less heat is conducted to that part of the joist from the house above. Crusty white mold is growing on the bottom of the joist, which is coldest because it faces the soil in the crawl space, which cools it by absorbing more infrared radiation than it emits. Without insulation above it, the bottom of the joist would be warmer—and less moldy. But removing the insulation would also make the building uncomfortable and expensive to heat and cool.

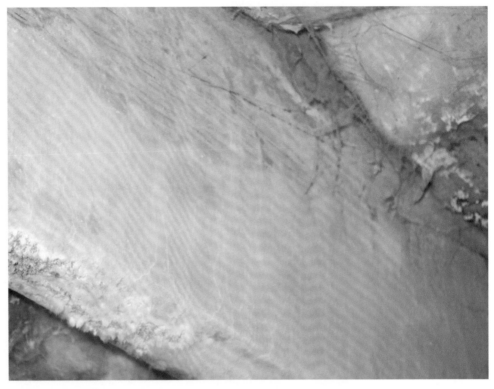

Insulating a wall or roof makes the outdoor side of the assembly colder during the winter and warmer during the summer. Insulating a floor above a crawl space makes the outdoor side of the assembly colder during the winter, too, but it also makes it colder during the summer because of radiant heat movement to the soil.

In the photo at right, mold is growing below **where the insulation was** before it fell down. No mold is growing on the wood above where the insulation was because that part was warmed by the floorboards above. This shows that insulation worsens the problem.

Venting Crawl Spaces

The house in the photo at right has a crawl space with **ventilation openings** that allow outdoor air (and rain and pests) to pass through.

The brown staining on the wall is a clue that the lawn sprinkler system has probably been spraying water directly into the ventilation openings, making the crawl space even wetter than it otherwise would be.

The sprinklers should be moved.

The house in the photo at left has **vents** that let air through the crawl space and also has a **vent** that lets air through the attic.

Closing off the vents would keep the crawl space and attic drier at most times of year in most climates but is generally prohibited by code. The solution is to not build a crawl space or attic in the first place or to convert the attic or crawl space into a fully conditioned indoor space, for which code would not require venting.

The Solution: Conditioning Crawl Spaces

The drawing at right shows what happens during the winter when a crawl space is a fully conditioned (heated, cooled, ventilated, dehumidified) part of the building and the vents to outdoors are closed up: nothing.

It doesn't get cold, no condensation occurs, no mold grows, and no one experiences "local miasma"[6] or "noxious emanations."

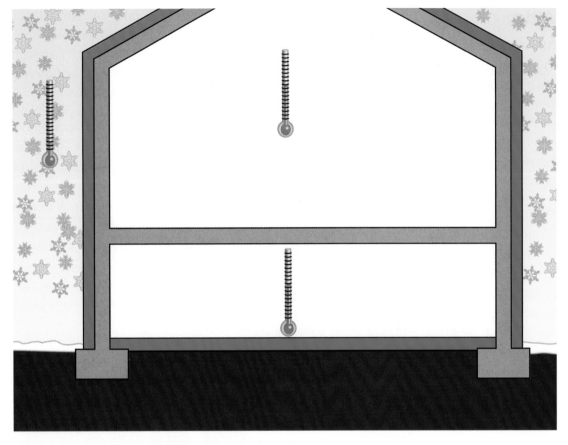

6   The miasma theory said that people caught disease from a "miasma," which was "night air" or "bad air" rising from soil or rotting organic matter. The theory was popular from ancient times until germ theory became more accepted in the late 1800s. The only part of the idea that was correct was that "night air" makes people sick, which it still does wherever mosquitoes are active at night.

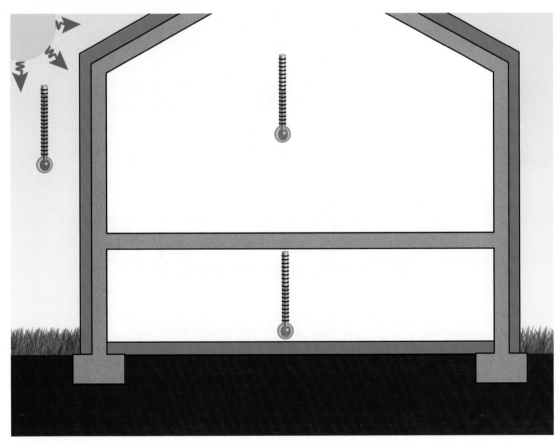

The drawing at left shows what happens during the summer when the vents to outdoors are closed up and a crawl space is a fully conditioned part of the building: also nothing. No damage to the building occurs, and nothing harms the health of the people in the building.

New buildings should not be built with crawl spaces. They should be built with insulated basements or with insulated floor slabs.

Attics

Attics can also be problematic because they are partly indoors and partly outdoors. Some codes require venting attics to outdoors. During some times of year in some climates, ventilating an attic can make it drier, depending on insulation, ceiling airtightness, and other factors. But at other times of year, ventilating an attic can make it wetter. No matter the climate, ventilating an attic is never a safe and reliable strategy for avoiding moisture problems.

Ventilating an attic is sometimes thought to save energy during the summer by moving hot air from the attic to outdoors. However, most summer heat movement from the roof to the top-floor ceiling is via radiant heating, not conduction through attic air. Therefore, ventilating an attic is not an effective strategy for reducing summer energy use. In addition, cold outdoor air leaking through the attic vents increases winter energy use, making attic ventilation an ineffective way to try to save energy at any time of year.

A better name for an attic might be "a duct cover" because, besides occasional use as a storage space where old junk collects dust, it serves little other purpose. The need to cover heating and cooling ducts can be avoided by not having them at all. Chapter 18: Heating and Cooling explains the advantages of heating and cooling without ducts. Ventilation air can be distributed throughout a house with ducts small enough to fit inside walls. If a house does not have large ducts, it won't need an attic.

Steeply pitched roofs look nice and shed rain very well, but the area under a roof can be put to better use. It can be included in a house as a conditioned space, often giving top-floor rooms beautiful high ceilings, such as those shown in the photos on Page 529. Or, this space can be used to create extra conditioned rooms.

Converting an attic into a conditioned space avoids code requirements for an attic vent, as well as all the problems with vented attics described on the next few pages.

If this house were to have an attic covering its ductwork, the air in the attic would be very hot during the summer, which would increase the energy required to cool the house. The attic would not be much warmer than outdoors during the winter, which means it would not save much heating energy. Leaving uninsulated ductwork outdoors is not recommended either, but is not all that different from enclosing it in a ventilated attic.

The lighter color of the siding around the attic vent at right is evidence that a lot of air has been flowing out of the vent for many hours every year and that the air coming out of the attic vent has a different temperature than the outdoor air. The mechanisms that cause the difference in color are described on Page 22. The house is in a climate that gets cold during the winter and hot and humid during the summer. Warm air probably leaks from the living space into the attic and then out the attic vent many winter hours per year.

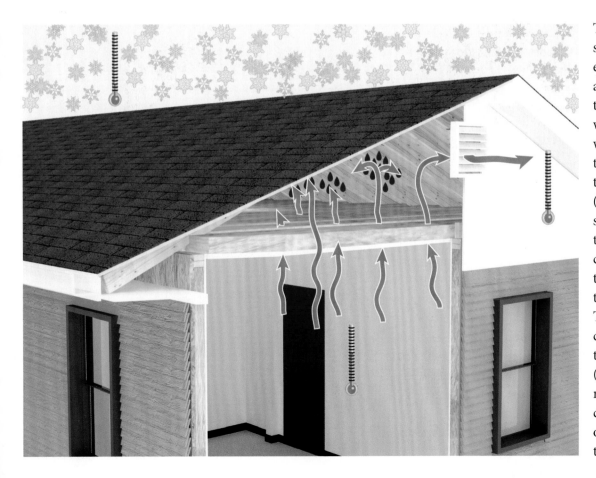

The drawing at left shows the stack effect moving warm air from a house to the attic during the winter. When the warm air touches the underside of the cold roof deck (the wood the shingles are nailed to), the air gets cooled, maybe to a temperature lower than its dewpoint. This can cause condensation on the underside (indoor side) of the roof deck, which can lead to rotting or to water dripping through the ceiling.

Rotting Roof Decks

The photo above shows a new plywood roof deck (the plywood sheathing the shingles are nailed to) that replaced the old rotted one.

The photo at right shows mold growing on the new roof deck after only six months.

The reason the new roof deck is rotting away so quickly is that when the new roof deck was installed, money was saved by not running the bathroom exhaust ducts through the attic and out through the roof. Instead, the exhaust fans blow warm, humid bathroom air directly into the attic, which of course causes condensation on the underside of the roof deck, leading to mold growth. (One of the bathroom fans is shown on Page 102.)

The old roof deck was replaced when it was about thirty years old. Because of the water vapor blown into the attic by the bathroom exhaust fans, the new roof deck will probably have to be replaced in just a few years.

The photo on the top of the next page shows a close-up of the new roof deck.

The photo at right shows a close-up of the new roof deck. The black spots are mold.

Rust is visible on some of the nails used to attach shingles to the roof deck. The nails extend through the plywood with their points inside the attic. Because nails conduct heat better than plywood, water condenses on them in cold weather. The rust visible on the nails is evidence that water has been condensing on them.

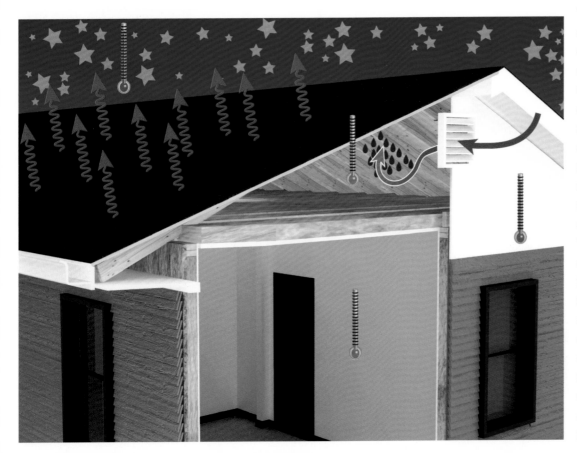

The drawing at left shows another source of water vapor that can condense on and damage a roof deck over an attic: wind moving humid air into an attic on a summer night. Radiant heat movement from a roof to a clear sky, also known as "night sky cooling," can cool a roof to a temperature lower than the temperature of the warm outdoor air. When humid air coming in the vents touches the underside of the cool roof deck, condensation can form on its underside.

Ice Dams

Ice dams are formations of ice that build up along edges of roofs after snowfall. They form when heat from the building melts snow on the roof, and the liquid water drains toward the edge of the roof and freezes on the eaves, which are cold because there is no heated building underneath the eaves. (Eaves are the roof overhangs that extend past the wall.) Ice dams almost never form on unheated buildings.

Ice dams are problematic because they block the flow of liquid water draining off the roof. With the water's downhill route blocked, water builds up on top of the shingles. Shingles overlap each other, with nothing to prevent water under pressure from getting in between them and then underneath them.

The heated house at left in the photo below has an **ice dam** on the eaves. However, there is no ice dam on the **eaves** of the unheated garage at the right.

The roofs of heated buildings get warm enough to melt snow because the stack effect pulls warm air through air leaks and through the insulation (especially in Stage Two buildings), regardless of the insulation's position: on the attic floor or on the underside of the roof deck. If heating ducts are located in an attic, some heat is always conducted through the insulation on the ducts, and some hot air almost always leaks out from connections between pieces of ducts.

There are various strategies to prevent ice dams, but they have had mixed success. Vents that move cold outdoor air along the underside of the roof deck might keep the roof cool enough to prevent snowmelt and are required by code in some places. But these vents work best on a roof with a simple shape that gives air a straight path from the eaves to the peak at all parts of the roof (see Page 421), which is unusual. Other strategies include the use of either sheet metal in place of shingles (to improve waterproofing and encourage ice to slide off) or electric heating wires mounted on the shingles (see Page 422).

The photos on this page show other **ice dams.**

In both photos, there is no clear path for water to drain down from the roof to the gutter: the ice gets in the way.

The ice dam in the photo at right was still in the process of forming when the photo was taken. The photo below shows an ice dam after most of the snow on the roof has melted.

Ice dams and the leaks that they cause ruin many ceilings every year and also damage joists, roof decks, and eaves. The weight of the ice damages many gutters, too.

Icicles at the edges of roofs are usually caused by the same mechanism that causes ice dams. Icicles are dangerous—falling icicles injure and kill people every year.

These drawings illustrate the mechanism that forms ice dams.

The drawing at right shows snow falling on a roof and room temperature air from inside the house leaking up through the attic insulation, melting the snow on the roof. The water from the melted snow, shown as blue drops between the snow and the roof, runs down (blue arrows) to the cold part of the roof above the eaves, where it freezes.

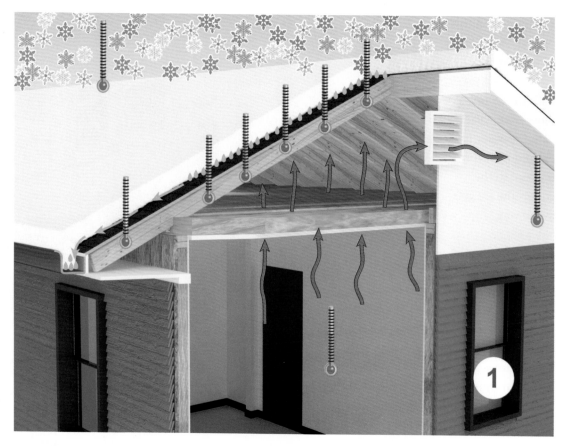

The drawing at left shows the ice where it collects in the gutter and on the roof above the eaves. Icicles are also forming.

The drawing at right shows the ice dam advancing further up the roof. Water building up behind the dam leaks through gaps between the shingles and then through the eaves. Some of the leaking water refreezes and forms icicles on the underside of the eaves. But before it does that, the water can damage water-sensitive materials in both the eaves and the wall.

The drawing below shows the water collecting above the eaves and leaking through the roof and attic into the house.

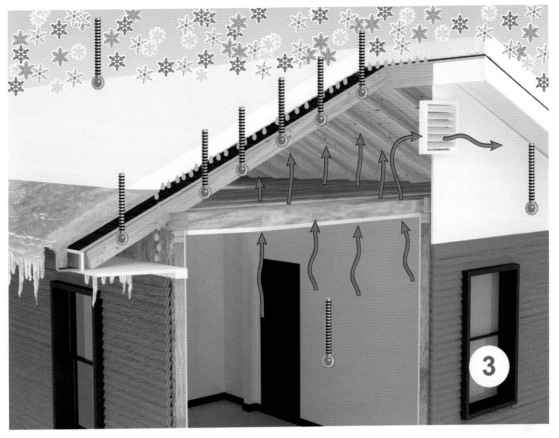

In theory, ice dams can be prevented with air vents between the attic and outdoors, an air barrier and an insulation layer between the living space and the attic, and almost no air leaks from any ducts in the attic. In reality, achieving and maintaining all these things, especially the air barrier (because framing at the roof/wall junction is complicated), is unrealistic.

Venting under the Roof Deck

The photo at right and the drawing below show roof vents that circulate outdoor air along the indoor side of part of the roof deck. The air enters at **soffit vents** (see drawing at bottom of page) under the eaves, is driven by the stack effect upward through the **foam channels** along the underside of the roof deck, and leaves the house via **ridge vents** at the peak of the roof. The foam channels are sometimes called attic rafter vents, baffles, or attic ventilation channels.

The goal is to keep the roof deck above the living space as cold as the roof above the eaves to prevent heat from indoors from melting the snow when the outdoor air temperature is below freezing, thereby preventing the formation of ice. These vents can also prevent condensation from forming on the underside of the roof deck on humid summer nights (as shown on the bottom of Page 415), while also hopefully extending the life of the shingles by cooling them during hot summer days. (The vents move outdoor air, which is cooler than the shingles when they are exposed to midday sun.)

However, these vents only work when they can extend from the eaves to the roof peak, which is only possible on simple roofs such as the one shown below and the one shown on the top of Page 421. Most roofs, such as the roof shown on the bottom of Page 421, are too complicated to allow vents to run continuously from the soffit to the peak on all areas of the roof.

The drawing at right is an aerial view of a roof vented with air entering the soffit vents and leaving via the vents at the peak of the roof (ridge vents).

Few buildings are designed with roofs that are this simple.

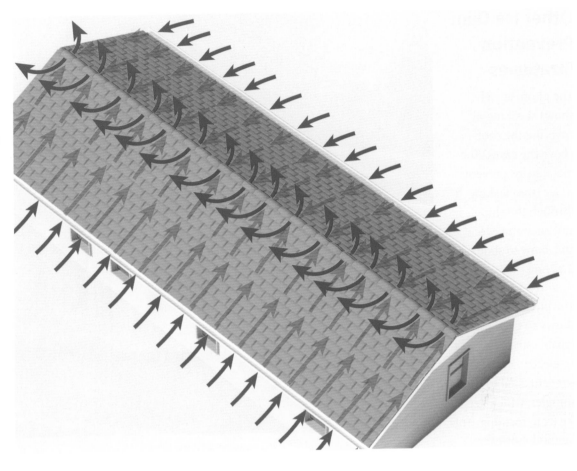

The drawing at left shows a more typical roof with many areas that can't have channels that run continuously from the eaves to the peak.

On roofs that have these complex shapes, it is unrealistic to expect vents on the underside of roofs to stop all ice damming.

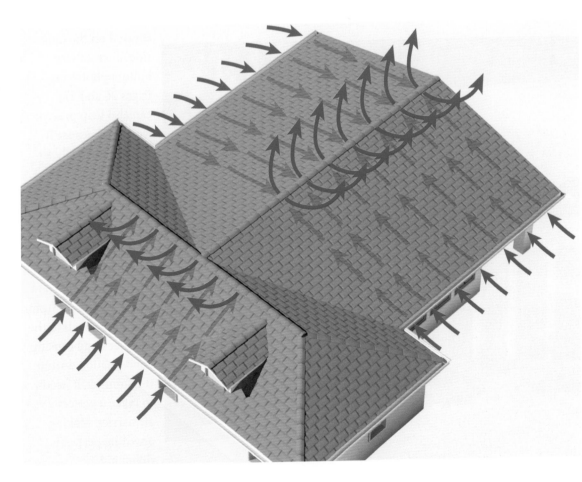

Other Ice Dam Prevention Strategies

The photo at right shows sheet metal covering the roof above the eaves. The metal helps prevent water from leaking through the shingles and encourages ice and snow to slide off the roof.

The photo below shows an even more reliable strategy: an electric heating wire attached to the shingles, which keeps ice from forming. This method, however, requires a lot of electricity.

Foam insulation sprayed on the indoor side of a roof (see bottom photos on Pages 26 and 27) can also help prevent ice dams because it is simultaneously a barrier to heat and a barrier to air. However, it will be interrupted by roof joists, which will conduct heat and thereby melt snow. And, to prevent warm, humid air from leaking through to the roof deck and causing condensation during the summer, it needs to make a perfect air barrier. Making anything perfect is difficult.

The Perfect Sequence for Roofs

The photo at right shows the best solution: a perfectly sequenced Stage Three roof (same roof as at the top of Page 401). It is covered with an air barrier—located where it will prevent warm air from passing through the insulation and melting snow—and then a continuous layer of insulation. Because there is no insulation in the eaves, sunlight warming the walls (see shed on Page 39) and heat conducted through the walls will warm air, which will rise up and melt ice on the eaves.

Photo: Timothy Greenfield-Sanders.

Surprisingly, snow has significant insulating value. A thick enough layer of snow on a roof can provide enough insulation to melt the snow underneath (with heat slowly passing from indoors through the insulated roof), causing ice damming. In areas with very heavy snowfall, one solution is a roof vented as shown on Page 420 built on top of a Stage Three roof.

Eliminate the Unconditioned Attic

A large portion of the house at left is occupied by attics. Attic vents let outdoor air in, which makes attics not very useful space. They also let in termites (they can fly), embers from nearby fires, humid air, and wind-blown rain and snow, which can cause water damage. Making an attic a fully conditioned space with a perfectly sequenced Stage Three roof helps prevent ice dams, adds useful, high-ceilinged rooms (as seen on Page 529), makes the house more comfortable, and saves energy.

PLUMBING VENTS

When waste water goes down a drain pipe, it pushes on the air in the pipe ahead of it and pulls on the air behind it. Without a way to relieve this pressure, the air can push or pull the water out of a fixture's P trap (the low spot in each drain, visible under a sink, which holds water to block sewer gas from escaping), allowing sewer gas to escape from the sewer into the living space. This not only smells but can also make people sick. In many areas, codes require extending pipes out the roof to act as vents to relieve the pressure. Some codes also require the building's main drain pipe to be vented before it enters the sewer.

Plumbing vents are useful, but they cause a small but steady loss of heating or cooling energy when wind or convection moves air in one roof vent pipe and out the other, or between the sewer vent and the roof vent pipes. The pipes themselves also conduct heat directly through the building's enclosure. The photo at right shows snow melted around two plumbing vents. Much more snow melted around the chimney, but the amount melted by heat from the plumbing stacks is still significant. Each pipe penetrating the roof is also a source of a possible water leak through the roof.

The photo at left shows five plumbing vents extending through a roof. Note that not all of them are the same diameter pipe. A careful reading of codes sometimes reveals that vents can be smaller than some people think.

These five vents could have been combined into a smaller number of vents, as shown on the next page.

Combine Plumbing Vents

The drawing at right shows three plumbing vents, each extending separately out through the roof. This requires waterproofing around each of the three pipes. Plus, each pipe is a pathway for a small but never-ending flow of heat between indoors and out.

The drawing at left shows the same three plumbing vents connecting into one vent pipe. Codes generally allow this, with limitations. A vent pipe is not allowed to go downhill and then uphill, or water will collect in the low area, blocking the flow of air. And vent pipes have to be large enough to handle the number of connected fixtures. But the benefits of combining vents usually outweigh the cost of the additional pipe. Plus, one pipe looks better than three.

Buildings should be aesthetically pleasing, or nobody will want to spend time in them or cherish them or take good care of them.

SUMMARY

A good building enclosure is both aesthetically pleasing and comfortable, healthy, and safe for the people inside it. At the same time, it is also durable and energy efficient. It has continuous layers to control heat, air, and liquid water. The perfect sequence for the layers locates the insulation immediately outdoors of the layer or layers that control air and liquid water and just indoors of the cladding. Adding insulation to a building is not inherently safe, but adding an air barrier generally is (unless combustion appliances depend on leaks for combustion air).

No part of a building should be left partly outdoors and partly indoors. This means attics and crawl spaces should be omitted from designs for new buildings. In existing buildings, they should be modified so they are fully conditioned indoor spaces. This might sound radical at first, but it will make a building more comfortable, healthy, durable, and energy efficient.

Many buildings have lasted centuries without being built in the perfect sequence—and without any barriers to air or heat and with crawl spaces and attics. But modern building materials and modern standards of energy efficiency make these practices increasingly risky. It is much safer to build a Stage Three building completely enclosed by an enclosure with continuous layers arranged in the perfect sequence.

A building enclosure should be continuous and should enclose the whole building.

Chapter 17 **INDOOR AIR QUALITY**

CAUSES OF POOR INDOOR AIR QUALITY

Despite the enormous impact air quality has on people's comfort, health, and safety, air inside buildings can and often does contain poisons not found in significant concentrations in outdoor air.

Old Poisons in Old Buildings

Evidence that asbestos sickens and kills people has been accumulating since at least the 1800s. Yet asbestos was still being used in pipe insulation, floor tiles, floor tile adhesive, plaster, stucco, ceiling texture, siding, and other materials until well into the 1900s. Arsenic and lead were recognized as poisons, too, yet paint still contained arsenic until the early 1900s and lead until the late 1900s.

Important changes came in the 1970s. Asbestos and lead were both mostly banned in many places, and good-quality water-based paint started to replace oil-based paint. But many other uses of these and other toxic chemicals took longer to eliminate. Plumbers were still soldering drinking-water pipes with lead in the 1980s; pouring bottles of mercury into pressure gauges in the 1990s (often spilling some on the floor in the process); waterproofing custom shower enclosures with sheets of lead until the end of the 1990s; and installing pressure switches containing mercury until about 2010. In the past, when people disposed of something containing mercury there was little choice but to throw it in the garbage. Now there are places for recycling mercury, and nobody would think of using lead to solder water pipes.

These poisons are present in old buildings and will be unless they are removed. Except for the lead in pipes and peeling paint, they seldom harm people unless they are disturbed, which typically happens during construction. Unfortunately, this is fairly common. Tearing down buildings or parts of buildings generates dust. Depending on the age of the building, that dust often contains lead and asbestos. When people inhale the dust they can get lead poisoning from the lead dust and lung cancer from the asbestos.

It is safest to assume that all dust is toxic. Any dust particles small enough to penetrate deep into a person's lungs do harm just by being there. Lead, asbestos, and other chemicals are each also harmful in their own ways. The best protection is to minimize the amount of dust generated and to wear a high-quality respirator whenever a significant amount of dust of any type is in the air.

This thermostat, shown with its cover removed, reliably switches electricity by tilting a **glass vial** containing a **drop of mercury**, which flows to the end of the vial where two wires are located. Mercury is a great conductor of electricity, but it is poisonous. The mercury doesn't harm anyone unless the glass vial breaks open. Therefore thermostats containing mercury should be handled with care. Special recycling facilities handle thermostats and other devices containing mercury.

The photos on this page show asbestos pipe insulation. Asbestos became popular for good reasons: it is inexpensive, lightweight, strong, fireproof, and highly insulating. The ancient Greeks used it for lamp wicks because it did not burn. If it were not so deadly, it would still be popular today.

The pipe elbow (right-angle turn) in the pipe at right is covered with a plaster-like asbestos insulation. The straight parts of the pipes in all the photos on this page are covered with "aircell," which is corrugated cardboard treated with asbestos. The missing insulation has probably fallen to the floor, where unsuspecting people walking by will disturb it, causing it to become airborne and easily inhaled.

Asbestos that is loose enough to become airborne, called "friable" asbestos, should be removed by a trained professional wearing protective gear. Almost all asbestos pipe insulation is now old enough to be friable and therefore should be removed from the building by trained personnel and disposed of in a special facility.

The photo below, of a grocery store in North America in 2017, shows someone weighing an apple on a scale hung from a **pipe covered with aircell**. Asbestos was such a popular material for so long that it will be around for a long time.

Modern Poisons in Modern Buildings

Causes of air quality problems in new buildings include volatile organic compounds, fine dust, carbon monoxide, cleaning chemicals, hydraulic fluid, mold, insecticides, and low humidity.

"Volatile organic compounds," usually abbreviated as VOCs, are released from carpet, paint, plywood, chipboard, and many other materials. New types of carpets do not emit anywhere near the variety or the quantity of VOCs that old carpets did, but carpet padding sometimes emits more than the carpet. Most materials have gotten better, but even materials labeled "Low VOC" can put out new chemicals that are not on the standard lists of chemicals that are banned or discouraged. And no matter how safely a building is built, furniture brought into the building can emit VOCs in large quantities.

One of the most problematic VOCs found in buildings is formaldehyde. It is found in many building materials such as plywood, and it is found in larger quantities in materials containing a lot of glue, such as chipboard and oriented strand board. People exposed to large concentrations get itchy eyes and noses, and sometimes headaches. People exposed to lower concentrations usually do not notice any symptoms, but even mild exposure is linked to asthma and allergic reactions. Formaldehyde is also a known human carcinogen. Indoor levels are usually highest in new buildings and gradually decrease with time. However, in a building of any age, high humidity levels can degrade urea-formaldehyde glue, causing increased off-gassing of formaldehyde.

Formaldehyde is one of many chemicals known as aldehydes. They are not only included as ingredients when products are manufactured (often as part of an adhesive); they are also emitted by cutting wood that has not been dead a long time and created by mold growth, drying paint, and combustion.

Fine dust, also known as particulate matter (PM), is created in large quantities by combustion—for example, by burning fuel in cars, boilers, furnaces, and even gas cooking stoves. The most dangerous dust particles are the ones small enough to penetrate deeply into people's lungs. These are generally too small to be caught by air filters or by the human body's upper respiratory system (nose and throat). Particulate matter is strongly linked to lung cancer, cardiovascular disease, and other health problems.

Another poison emitted by a gas stove is carbon monoxide. As soon as a burner on a stove is lit, significant quantities of carbon monoxide (CO) are produced. When a pot of cold water is put on the stove, the flame produces much more carbon monoxide because the pot cools the flame, interfering with complete combustion. Long-term low-level exposure interferes with the central nervous system; high concentrations are deadly.

Cleaning chemicals are often the biggest source of poisons in a building. This hazard can be reduced by choosing cleaning products that are less toxic, using smaller amounts of cleaning products, and choosing wall and floor finishes that are easy to clean.

Another contaminant in indoor air is fumes from hydraulic fluid, which can leak from the lifting mechanism of a hydraulic elevator, as shown below. Hydraulic fluid is oil mixed with bacteria-killing chemicals. If the air in an elevator cab or in the vicinity of an elevator has a lingering smell of oil, the fluid is probably leaking. An overhead traction elevator, which uses cables to lift the passenger cab from above, eliminates the need for hydraulic fluid.

Water itself of course is not toxic, but all leaks, no matter how small, can cause mold and pest infestations, which can have a harmful effect on indoor air quality. (Too little water vapor mixed with indoor air can also cause health problems, as described on Page 147.)

Hydraulic fluid leaks down the piston of a hydraulic elevator. The surface of the piston exposes indoor air to hydraulic fluid from the bottom of the elevator shaft to just underneath the floor of the passenger cab.

MAKING INDOOR AIR AS HEALTHY AS POSSIBLE

The key to healthy indoor air quality is to not add poisons to the building in the first place. After that, remove whatever poisons can safely be removed.

Don't Poison the Air

Chemical air "fresheners" work by emitting strong chemicals that mask odors or deaden the smell receptors in our noses. Candles and incense may seem safe, but no matter how "natural" they are, they produce soot particles and carbon monoxide.

Avoid carpets, as they are impossible to clean completely, and vacuuming with a normal vacuum cleaner fills the air with dust fine enough to penetrate deeply into a person's lungs. If the building has a central vacuum system (a system with suction pipes hidden inside walls), venting the exhaust directly outdoors will prevent fine dust not caught by the filter from spreading within the building, as shown below.

Instead of toxic cleaning chemicals, baking soda, vinegar, or soap and water should be used whenever possible. A building that is built with surfaces that are easy to clean won't need toxic cleaning chemicals.

Steam-heated radiators are uniquely bad for air quality because they get hot enough to pyrolyze dust, as shown in the photo on the bottom of Page 84. And because steam heat so frequently overheats buildings, it can encourage people to open windows during the winter, causing indoor humidity levels to drop to unhealthy levels. A healthier alternative would be radiators heated with hot water, since hot water radiators normally don't get as hot as steam radiators and are easy to control with a thermostat on each radiator, which prevents overheating.

Furnaces, boilers, water heaters, fireplaces, wood stoves, and any other combustion appliances should all be the sealed combustion type, as described on Pages 516-520.

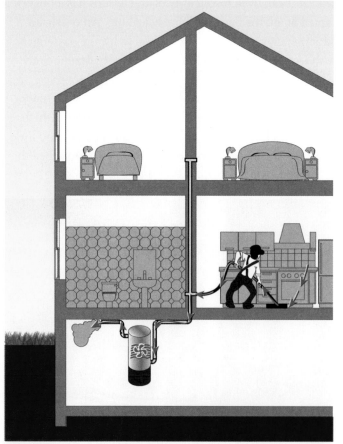

This central vacuum system filters large dust particles out of the air. The small particles normal vacuum cleaner filters cannot catch are exhausted into the house. The smallest particles are the most dangerous to people because they can penetrate deep into the lungs.

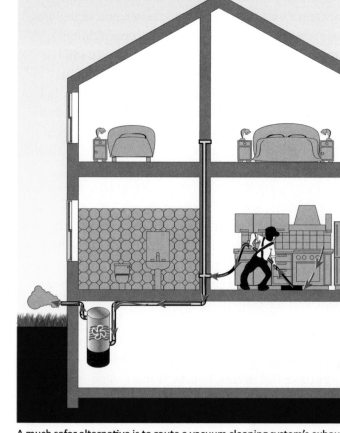

A much safer alternative is to route a vacuum cleaning system's exhaust air outdoors, which will prevent fine dust from spreading indoors. The air duct that goes outdoors should automatically close tightly when not in use, to prevent air leakage through the building's enclosure.

Making it hard for pests to live in a building, as described in Chapter 14: Pests - Applied Science, can reduce or eliminate the temptation to use pesticides.

Controlling humidity will prevent mold and reduce infestations of insects and rodents. An air barrier built into the building enclosure will help the ventilation system work better while controlling humidity and will also help keep dust and pollen out of the building. Think of the steps involved in drying a flooded building (see Pages 222-227) beforehand, just in case.

To limit VOCs, choose building materials and furniture containing the smallest possible quantity of VOCs.

One clue to a material's toxicity is smell: if it smells, don't buy it, and don't bring it indoors. If it is already indoors, get rid of it. New cars and other new products can have a characteristic "new car smell," or "new plastic smell," which is the off-gassing of many chemicals used during manufacturing, probably none of them good for people's health. Not that many years ago, new buildings had a

strong smell, too. Fortunately, the smell is becoming less strong in both cars and buildings because manufacturers are using chemicals that are less volatile.

Not all poisons smell, though. Asbestos, lead, mercury, and many other poisons have no smell at all. Most toxic chemicals that do smell are still harmful to people in concentrations that are too low for people to smell. Look at labels, read up on products, and reward manufacturers that make healthy products by buying their products.

Run an Exhaust Fan When Cooking

Cooking with electricity is much healthier than cooking with gas. A gas flame emits particulate matter and carbon monoxide, and also emits water vapor, which can cause mold. An electric induction stove uses less electricity than an electric resistance stove, and it also offers more accurate control of heat. When cooking with any type of stove or oven, ventilate near the stove with an exhaust fan.

Don't Live in a Garage

A building with an "attached" garage, more accurately described as a "built-in" garage, can have good indoor air quality unless the garage is filled with cars and gasoline, lawn mowers, fertilizer, and maybe other poisons including pesticides. When a car is started in the garage, it exhausts significant amounts of carbon monoxide into the garage, even if the garage door is open and the car is driven out of the garage immediately. Many carbon monoxide alarm "false alarms" have been traced to cars that were driven out of the garage long before, sometimes hours before the carbon monoxide alarm went off. If the garage is attached to the house, the house's air quality can be improved by storing gasoline and other chemicals in a shed that is not connected to the house and by parking the car outdoors.

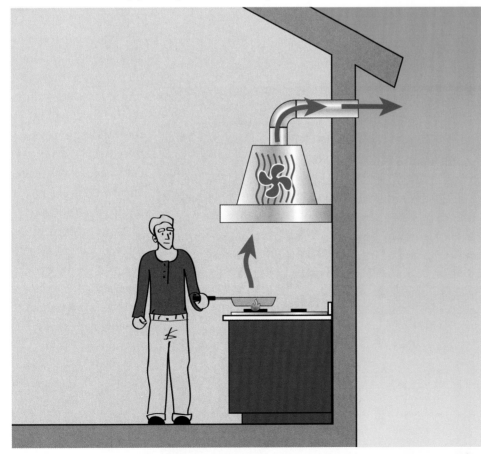

A fan should be used to move cooking exhaust outdoors, especially when using a gas stove. When not in use, the exhaust duct should be closed to prevent air leaks. Automatic dampers are available, which close by gravity and open from the fan pressure. The hood above the stove (which is where the cooking exhaust goes) can be equipped with a thermostat to turn the fan on and off automatically.

Those are houses on the street at right, but it is hard to see the living spaces because the garages are the dominant feature.

The garages are connected to the houses and are most likely not separated by a good air barrier. Because of this, the residents will probably breathe some carbon monoxide and other dangerous chemicals. It is much easier to include an air barrier when a building is built than to add it later.

The photo at left shows an apartment building on top of a garage. The solid white wall on the lower half of the building encloses the garage. During cold weather, the stack effect will create an air pressure difference that will push air up through the garage and against any air barrier separating the garage from the apartments, moving car exhaust through any leaks.

Holes in the garage wall would both allow wind to remove car exhaust and eliminate almost all the pressure difference generated by the stack effect.

The photo at right shows an **air handler** in a garage that is built into a house. An air handler is a box that contains a fan and uses an external source of heating or cooling to heat or cool the air it blows through ducts.

An air handler located in a garage will almost certainly move gasoline fumes and carbon monoxide from the garage into the house. No air handling equipment, including ducts, should be located in a garage.

The garage in the photo at left is separated from the house by a short breezeway, which goes a long way toward improving air quality in the house.

To prevent air leaks from the garage to the house, the air barrier around the house needs to be carefully continued where the breezeway roof connects to the house.

REMOVE AIRBORNE POISONS BY VENTILATING

First, sources of poisons in indoor air should be eliminated, as described above. Then a ventilation system should be used to remove whatever poisons remain. All buildings that people spend a significant amount of time in should be ventilated. As defined in this book, a ventilation system removes stale indoor air and delivers fresh outdoor air.

How Much Fresh Air is Necessary for Healthy Ventilation?

The question about how much to ventilate (called the ventilation rate) has been a topic of much debate in the building industry over the centuries. The lower limit on the amount of ventilation a building can have without generating complaints is generally the point just before which people notice an objectionable odor. Depending on indoor humidity, temperature, and other factors, the first odor people usually object to as ventilation rates are reduced is body odor. Codes generally require an amount of ventilation that safely exceeds the amount necessary to prevent such odors from being noticeable.

Higher ventilation rates are better than lower ventilation rates for removing both odors and poisons from indoor air. But, as described in Chapter 6: Water - Applied Science, a higher wintertime ventilation rate lowers indoor relative humidity, which can make the indoor air uncomfortable and unhealthy for people. During the summer, a higher ventilation rate can raise indoor relative humidity, which, in addition to being uncomfortable for people, can cause mold growth, pest infestations, and increased off-gassing of formaldehyde. Ironically, body odor complaints can increase when indoor relative humidity increases due to a higher summer ventilation rate. Lower ventilation rates are better for controlling humidity in both winter and summer, but higher ventilation rates are usually better for controlling poisons at any time of year. So, low or high: which is best?

Common sense says the higher the ventilation rate, the better. The recorded history of common sense applied to ventilation rates goes back to at least 1824, when the English engineer Thomas Tredgold wrote his book about heating and ventilating buildings. He wrote:

That a pure atmosphere is necessary to preserve health I need not attempt to prove by reasoning; it is a truth universally known and acknowledged; but it will be proper to examine and estimate the effects of those causes which render confined air impure and unfit for supporting life. It has been remarked, that "the salubrity and healthy state of the air depend, in a great measure, on the quantity of oxygen gas it contains, and this quantity appears to exist in all places exposed to a free atmosphere, and the influence of winds. But the same uniformity of composition does not prevail in the confined air of dwelling houses, crowded theatres, and hospitals that are badly ventilated."* Yet, the chemist who wrote this remark was not able to detect an appreciable difference between the air of an hospital and that of an open situation. And the same thing is averred by other chemists. Seguin tried the air of an hospital, the odor of which was disagreeable, but it gave him the same result as the external air. The researches of Priestly, De Marti, Gay Lussac, and others, all tend to establish the same result; which is, that the composition of the atmosphere is essentially the same every where.** If you allow these experiments to be correct, they only prove that a deadly poison may be diffused through the atmosphere which the art of the chemist cannot detect, but of which we have better evidence than is given by the nicest tests of the analytical chemist, in the pale visages and weakly constitutions of the inhabitants of confined and crowded cities; in the unhealthiness of particular districts, and in the important alterations which a change of residence often produces in individuals unaccustomed to such changes. If there be no variations in the quantity of oxygen, some other means should be taken to enable us to know what the difference consists in. Perhaps it is the presence of foreign ingredients: these should be tested for.[1]

* Philosophical Mag. Vol. L. p. 433.

** Dr. Murray's System of Chemistry, Vol. 11. p. 37. Dr. Thomson's System of Chemistry, Vol. 111. p. 178.

The scientists Tredgold refers to are Joseph Priestly, who discovered oxygen and other gases; Antonio de Martí y Franqués, who developed better ways of measuring

1   Thomas Tredgold, <u>Principles of Warming and Ventilating Public Buildings, Dwelling-houses, Manufactories, Hospitals, Hot-houses, Conservatories, &c.</u> (London: Josiah Taylor, Architectural Library, 1824), Pages 68–69.

oxygen concentration in air; Gay Lussac, who did early research into the chemical composition of water; and Armand Seguin, who was Antonio Lavoisier's lab assistant and research subject when Lavoisier discovered that the heat produced by the human body is produced by the same chemical reaction as combustion. So, scientists have been investigating the difference between fresh and stale air since at least the founding of modern chemistry.

The belief that "a pure atmosphere is necessary to preserve health" is still "a truth universally known and acknowledged" in modern times and is usually interpreted as the higher the ventilation rate, the healthier people will be. Tredgold apparently felt the need to defend his opinion in 1824, as he included two footnotes in one paragraph on the topic of indoor air. Opinions on the topic are still strong, and debates about the best ventilation rate continue today.

It is still challenging to do quality research on how ventilation rates affect people's health. That is because it is challenging to measure people's health in isolation from "the unhealthiness of particular districts" or to isolate the effect of ventilation rates when studying "the important alterations which a change in residence often produces in individuals."

The debate over ventilation rates will probably continue over the centuries and will continue to be complicated by the difficulty of comparing more effective ventilation systems with less effective ventilation systems. The question of what is the best ventilation rate is probably not the best question to ask. It is probably better to focus on getting a ventilation system to work effectively.

The **supply air grill** and return air grill for this cooling/ventilation system are located too close to each other. The air will go directly from the supply air grill to the return air grill without providing much ventilation (or cooling) to any part of the room except the corner. The problem could be solved by shortening the return air duct, which would move the return grill further away from the supply grill, forcing the air to cross the room on its way from supply to return.

Focus on Quality, Not Quantity

The effectiveness of ventilation systems varies wildly. Some remove the amount of stale air they were designed for and replace it with fresh outdoor air; many do not. Some move air to and from where intended; many do not.

Many systems, including the one in the photo above, deliver no ventilation when the thermostat is not calling for either heating or cooling. Most, probably including the one above, serve as a large hole in the building enclosure when they are turned off, which leads to all the problems associated with uncontrolled airflow.

Ventilation air is best supplied at one end of a room, apartment, or house, and removed from the other end. In the photo above, the **supply air grill** is so close to the return air grill that the air in the rest of the room remains stagnant.

A ventilation system that works well and moves the code-required amount of air is generally better than a badly working system designed for a higher ventilation rate.

A True Ventilation System Moves Stale Air Out of a Building and Supplies Only Fresh Outdoor Air

A ventilation system should not compromise anyone's comfort. If it does, someone will find a way to disable it, leaving people indoors with no ventilation. One type of ventilation system that is usually "disabled" more hours than it operates is a window.

Windows provide ventilation without compromising comfort when the wind speed and outdoor temperature are within narrow limits. At all other times, sensible people will close the windows. When open windows do provide ventilation, they have a 50 percent chance of moving ventilation air in the correct direction and a 50 percent chance of moving ventilation air in the wrong direction, such as from a bathroom or kitchen through the rest of the house. On a day with little or no wind or stack effect, windows will not move sufficient ventilation air in either direction. Because windows also admit pollen, dust, rain, and noise, as well as uncontrolled amounts of dry, cold, hot, or humid air—and sometimes even criminals—people close them at times. This leaves them with no ventilation.

Ventilation systems should be operating whenever people are in a building. They should deliver only fresh outdoor air, and send stale air outdoors. A surprisingly large number of "ventilation" systems are still being designed and built to move stale air around within a building, hopefully diluting it with some outdoor air before it gets delivered to people in another part of the building. Codes generally permit this, even in hospitals, but this is unhealthy because it can spread diseases.

HOW TO VENTILATE

Ventilation systems can be divided into three broad categories:

1. Ventilation as one of the functions of an HVAC system.

2. Exhaust-only ventilation systems.

3. Energy recovery ventilation systems.

Constant or Intermittent Ventilation?

Codes generally offer a choice between a small ventilation system operating continuously and a large ventilation system operating intermittently.

A small system operating constantly is usually the best choice for houses, apartment buildings, and hospitals because people are usually in those buildings at all times of the day and night. Other types of buildings where occupancy is intermittent, such as schools and offices, are usually best served by ventilation systems that turn on and off, with dampers that automatically close the ducts when the system is not operating.

1. VENTILATION VIA AN HVAC SYSTEM

An HVAC (heating, ventilation, air conditioning) system combines ventilation with heating and cooling, all delivered by the same ducts. HVAC systems have many disadvantages. They require more space, make more noise, and use more energy than other types of systems, and they often require expensive and complicated electronic controls to work properly. They also have a poor record of delivering comfort—often overheating or overcooling a building or parts of a building—and a poor record of delivering ventilation. One reason is that it is difficult to deliver the desired amount of ventilation air using the same air that heats or cools a building.

HVAC systems are also generally the most expensive type of system to install, operate, and maintain.

HVAC systems are primarily found in office buildings and hospitals and are described in more detail on Pages 478-481.

An HVAC system uses air to move heat into rooms during the winter or out of rooms during the summer. Because air does not hold much heat, an HVAC system must move a very large amount of air. The air moved is mostly used air from inside the building, heated or cooled as appropriate and mixed with some percentage of fresh outdoor air.

As mentioned earlier, this is not a very healthy option because if a sick person sneezes in one room, the HVAC system moves the viruses to all the other rooms in the building served by the same HVAC system. (See the drawings on Pages 438-439.) Large buildings are usually served by multiple HVAC systems, but each system still circulates used air through multiple rooms, which means that all the people in those rooms share the same air (and viruses).

Yet the need for a ventilation system to deliver only fresh air from a clean source has been known for some time. Florence Nightingale, the English social reformer and founder of modern nursing, had strong opinions about fresh air:

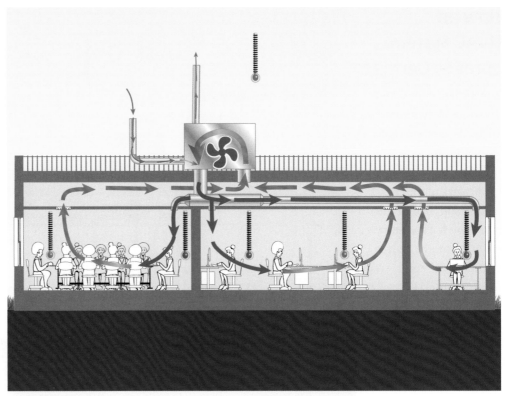

The HVAC system above is moving a large amount of air to provide heating. A small percentage of outdoor air is mixed with the air moved by the HVAC system, which is mostly used air.

The very first canon of nursing, the first and the last thing upon which a nurse's attention must be fixed, the first essential to a patient, without which all the rest you can do for him is as nothing, with which I had almost said you may leave all the rest alone, is this: TO KEEP THE AIR HE BREATHES AS PURE AS THE EXTERNAL AIR, WITHOUT CHILLING HIM. Yet what is so little attended to? Even where it is thought of at all, the most extraordinary misconceptions reign about it. Even in administering air into the patient's room or ward, few people ever think, where that air comes from. It may come from a corridor into which other wards are ventilated, from a hall, always unaired, always full of the fumes of gas, dinner, of various kinds of mustiness; from an underground kitchen, sink, washhouse, water-closet, or even, as I myself have had sorrowful experience, from open sewers loaded with filth; and with this the patient's room or ward is aired, as it is called – poisoned, it should rather be said. Always air from the air without, and that, too, from those windows, through which the air comes freshest. From a closed court, especially if the wind do not blow that way, air may come as stagnant as any from a hall or corridor.[2]

2   **Florence Nightingale, Notes on Nursing: What It Is and What It Is Not** (New York: D. Appleton and Company, 1860), Pages 12–13.

Florence Nightingale's advice is still relevant today. Not only is delivering stale air unhealthy, but moving stale air around a building is expensive and wasteful. It wastes both space (necessary for the large ducts and fans required to move stale air) and energy (required to operate much larger fans). Larger ducts and fans themselves are also more expensive. They also make much more noise than a small system that moves fresh air only. Systems that circulate used air around a building should be avoided. Instead, systems that deliver fresh air only should be used.

A ventilation system that delivers only fresh air has the built-in advantage that it is easy to tell if the system is working: put a hand near an air intake or exhaust grill, and, if air is moving, the building is being ventilated.

A system designed to move stale air diluted with a percentage of fresh air has the disadvantage that it is difficult for anyone, even a trained professional with sophisticated test equipment, to know if the ventilation system is actually providing any fresh outdoor air. Simply feeling air moving out of a grill doesn't determine if the air is fresh or stale or offer any information about how well an HVAC system is distributing fresh air to various parts of a building.

How an HVAC System Spreads Germs

This series of four drawings shows how an HVAC system that circulates used air spreads disease. The red arrows represent **hot air** supplied to the offices by the rooftop HVAC unit, the purple arrows represent **room-temperature indoor air**, and the blue arrows represent **cold outdoor air**.

① The drawing at right shows a person in the office at far right sneezing out some **viral particles**.

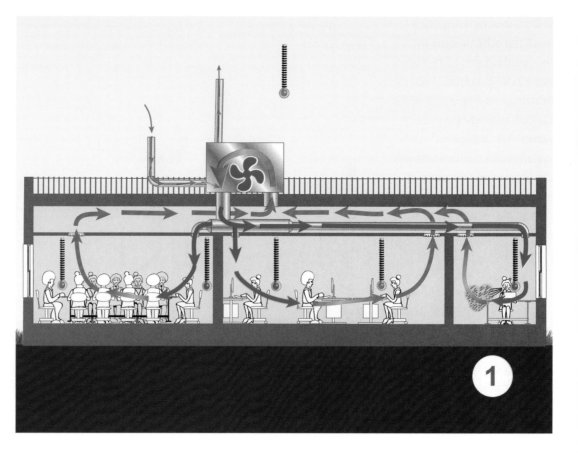

② The drawing at left shows the viral particles drawn into the hollow ceiling cavity (used as an air return path in many HVAC systems) and entering the HVAC system air handler.

The HVAC air handler exhausts a percentage of the air and the viral particles to outdoors. But as it heats (or, during the summer, cools) the stale indoor air, it also mixes viral particles with the hot (or cold) air that will be supplied to all the offices.

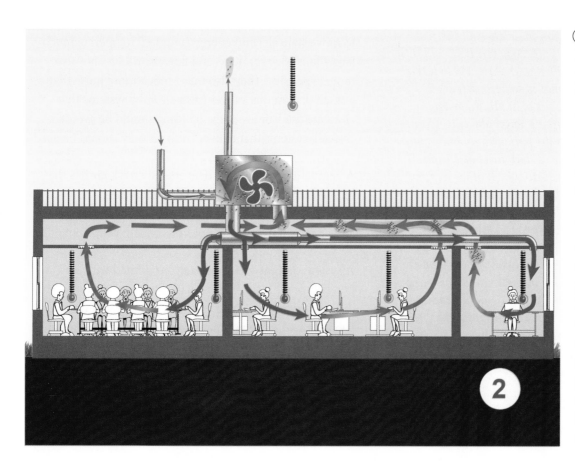

③ The drawing at right shows the HVAC unit distributing most of the return air, plus a percentage of fresh outdoor air, into the supply ducts. The return air contains the viral particles, which are spreading through the supply ducts to unsuspecting people in other offices.

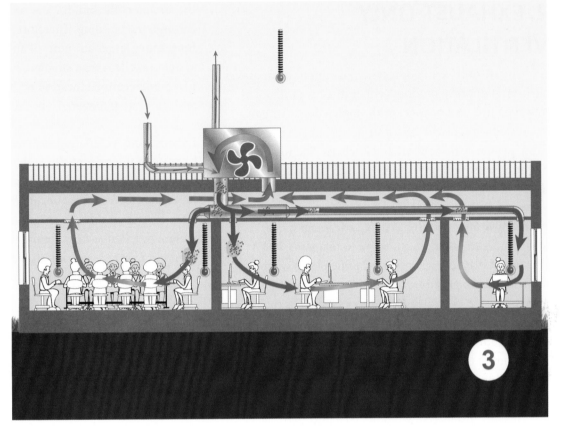

④ The drawing at left shows that the viral particles have spread throughout the air in all three rooms.

In reality, the HVAC system is a germ-spreading machine. This is a large disadvantage over types of ventilation systems that do not circulate any used air.

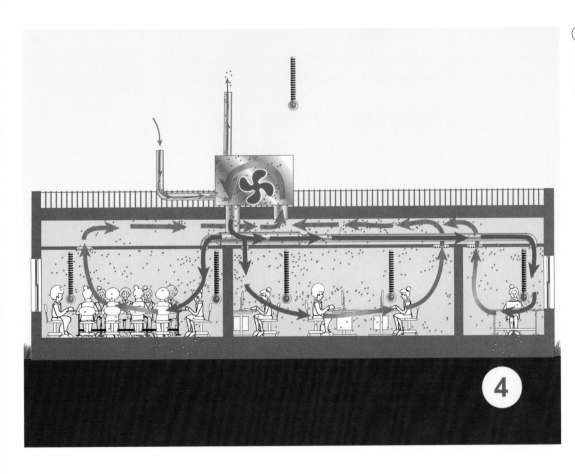

2. EXHAUST-ONLY VENTILATION

An exhaust-only ventilation system is simple: a fan moves air from indoors to outdoors either directly (with a fan mounted in a wall or roof) or through a duct. Air gets exhausted from places where air needs to be exhausted from, primarily bathrooms and kitchens. Suction created by the exhaust fan moves fresh air into the building through holes in the building enclosure.

An exhaust-only system has many advantages: it is inexpensive to install, inexpensive to maintain, and effective at exhausting air from specific places where it needs to be exhausted from. It has the disadvantage of moving heated or cooled air outdoors, which is replaced by new outdoor air that has to be either heated, cooled, or dehumidified. It is also not possible to filter dust and pollen out of the incoming supply air when it enters the building through many small holes. Sometimes air is supplied by "trickle vents," a kind of intentional leak, usually installed in windows (see next two pages). Another disadvantage is that it is difficult to control where

the air enters the building, as well as which path it takes through the building. Therefore, an exhaust-only system must move larger amounts of air to be as effective as a system that delivers a smaller amount of fresh outdoor air to a predetermined location within the building, such as an ERV system (covered later in this chapter).

Exhaust-only ventilation systems are very common because of their simplicity and low cost. They are used in many single-family houses, which have exhaust fans for each bathroom, maybe another exhaust fan for the kitchen, and no other ventilation equipment except windows. Exhaust-only ventilation systems are also used in many apartment buildings, with fans on the roof connected by ducts to bathrooms and kitchens throughout the building (see Page 443).

Exhaust-only systems can be operated continuously or intermittently. If they are operated intermittently, they should be equipped with a damper to close the duct when the system is not in use.

A supply-only system with a fan supplying fresh air is theoretically possible and would be similar to an exhaust-only system operating in reverse. But there is a very good reason to not use supply-only ventilation: codes and common sense generally require exhausting air from bathrooms and kitchens. For this reason, true supply-only ventilation systems are almost never used. Some systems that supply fresh air to an HVAC system are called "supply-only" systems, but in this book they are considered part of an HVAC system.

An exhaust-only ventilation system usually pulls fresh air through leaks in the building enclosure, wherever they might be. This gives the occupants of the building little choice about where their air supply comes from.

Ventilation Systems Work Better with Air Barriers

Moving air where it is intended to go requires a container with strategically located openings. The container prevents unplanned air movement; the openings allow planned air movement.

The drawing at right shows a kitchen **exhaust fan** pulling air through unintended leaks from the bathroom and kitchen in the apartment next door, as well as from the stairway. An air barrier would prevent this.

Trickle Vents

A **trickle vent** is installed in the window at left. For buildings with an exceptionally good air barrier and exhaust-only ventilation, trickle vents can act as planned air leaks. If installed in one window in each bedroom, they allow outdoor air to pass through the bedroom, then through the rest of the house, and out the bathroom and kitchen exhaust systems. The air moves from the cleanest part of the house to the dirtiest, from the driest to the wettest, and then out. If the air barrier is not exceptionally good, a trickle vent is not necessary.

The photo at right shows a trickle vent beneath a hotel room window. A trickle vent typically includes a rain hood and an insect screen on the outside. The indoor air inlets usually direct air up toward the ceiling or out to the sides, away from where it would cause a person discomfort. Some trickle vents also incorporate a moving part that automatically partly blocks the opening on a windy day to restrict air flow to a predetermined limit.

Some trickle vents can be manually closed to stop the flow of air. The photo at left shows the same trickle vent as in the photo above, with the airflow closed off.

This allows people to close the vent when it is too cold or windy. The disadvantage of this kind of trickle vent is that people might close it when it would be better to maintain ventilation airflow, which is most of the time.

Exhaust-only ventilation systems are common in apartment buildings, too. A typical design (see drawing at right) uses a fan on the roof to pull air up through vertical ducts running the height of the building, with a connection to each bathroom and kitchen.

This design has many disadvantages, including the hazard of smoke and fire spreading through the ducts, the likelihood of sound transmission through the ducts, the loss of the floor area occupied by the ducts, and the difficulty of achieving the desired airflow from each of the connected floors. Any leaks in the ducts increase the hazard of smoke and fire spreading, while allowing the fan to pull large amounts of air from random locations. In a tall building, there are even more disadvantages. A lot of energy is required to move air a long distance, and it is difficult to locate vertical ducts in the same location when rooms have different layouts on different floors.

A better alternative would be an individual ventilation system for each apartment. Ventilation systems for individual apartments are described in Chapter 21: Ventilating, Heating, and Cooling an Apartment Building.

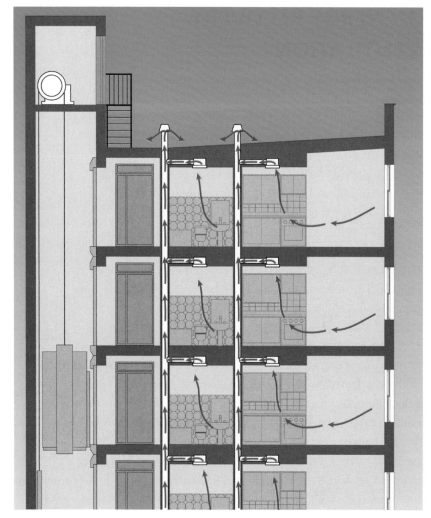

The photo at left shows snow melting on the roof around an apartment building's rooftop exhaust fans. Much of the air coming out of those fans is pulled from apartments into the ducts through leaks in ducts—which increases the amount of conditioned air that is sent outdoors (in this case, heated air). When the fans pull extra air from an apartment, the extra air flowing through the apartment makes people feel cold and dry (during the winter) while wasting energy. At the same time, other apartments, especially those on lower floors, might not be getting enough ventilation. Individual ventilation systems in each apartment wouldn't be as vulnerable to problems caused by leaking ducts.

3. ENERGY RECOVERY VENTILATION

An "energy recovery" or "heat recovery" ventilation system uses a ventilator that recovers energy from the stale exhaust air and uses it to either heat up or cool down incoming fresh air. The two airstreams do not mix. The system uses two separate sets of ducts: one to move stale air outdoors and another to deliver fresh air indoors. The stale exhaust air does not pollute the incoming fresh air—only the energy is transferred via a heat exchanger.

For example, during the winter, heat in the room-temperature exhaust air is transferred to the incoming cold air. The incoming fresh air will be close to room temperature, and the exhaust air will be cold.

One important advantage of an energy recovery ventilator, known in the industry as an ERV, is that it captures most of the energy that was used to either heat or cool the exhaust air. This means the building can have smaller equipment to heat and cool it. Because the ERV uses two sets of ducts, it actually removes stale air from where it needs to be removed and delivers fresh air to where it needs to be delivered. This allows it to be effective at a lower ventilation rate than other systems.

One disadvantage of an ERV is that it uses more electricity than an exhaust-only system because its fans need to move air through a filter and a heat exchanger. However, because an ERV system allows the building's heating and cooling systems to use less energy, it yields an overall energy saving in any climate where a building needs a significant amount of heating or cooling.

ERVs come with a basic air filter to protect their internal components but can be equipped with a better filter that can remove pollen from incoming outdoor air. For people with pollen allergies, a building with this type of filter and an air barrier is probably the best way to keep pollen out of the house.

ERV systems are more expensive to install and maintain than exhaust-only systems but less expensive to install and maintain than ventilation equipment that is part of an HVAC system. ERVs can be incorporated as part of an HVAC system but are best used in a ventilation-only system.

Buildings with high ventilation loads, such as schools and office buildings, cannot use exhaust-only ventilation because the high rate of outdoor air leaking into the building would cause comfort complaints. For these types of buildings, an ERV system is the simplest system possible because it preconditions (heats or cools, and humidifies or dehumidifies) incoming ventilation air without incorporating any complicated heating or cooling equipment.

The simplicity of an ERV system also avoids the need for the more technically demanding design and installation skills required to get more complicated ventilation systems to work effectively.

An ERV is easy to find space for: different types can go indoors or outdoors, wherever a convenient space can be found.

ERVs and HRVs are available in all sizes, from small enough for a single apartment to large roof-mounted units for large office buildings.

ERV vs. HRV

Energy recovery ventilation equipment comes in two types: ERVs and heat recovery ventilators, known in the industry as HRVs. They are very similar devices, but they handle water vapor differently.

Depending on psychrometric conditions in the two airstreams (supply air and exhaust air), one of the two airstreams can get cooled below its dewpoint temperature, causing water vapor to condense out of the air within the ventilator. HRVs have a drain pipe that will transport the condensate (condensed water) to a nearby drain.

ERVs handle water vapor in a different way. The heat exchanger plates are made of a special Tyvek®-like material that transfers water vapor from the airstream with the highest specific humidity to the airstream with the lowest specific humidity (even if no condensation occurs). During the winter, when outdoor air is usually drier than indoor air, water vapor is transferred from the exhaust air to the incoming air, keeping the indoor humidity higher than it would be with an HRV or with exhaust-only ventilation. During the summer, if a dehumidifier or air conditioning system is keeping indoor air drier than outdoor air, some of the water vapor from incoming warm, humid air gets transferred to the stale exhaust air, keeping the indoor air drier than it would be with exhaust-only ventilation or with an HRV.

The advantages of an ERV are its moisture-handling ability and the lack of a condensate drain pipe. The lack of a condensate drain saves the cost and complication of connecting a pipe to a drain. It also means an ERV can be installed in any position, which can make it easier to hide. However, HRVs can be more durable, are usually a little less expensive, and can recover a little more heat than an ERV. Calculating which uses less overall energy is complicated and depends on the climate, the target indoor humidity level, and operating hours (is the system switched off or to low speed in a school at night, when the outdoor temperature is coldest?). One answer is to choose a slightly oversized ERV, with the savings from not installing a drain paying for the larger equipment, and to adjust it to only move the required amount of air, so its slightly oversized heat exchanger will recover more heat. Another answer would be to follow the climate-specific advice of an equipment manufacturer. If indoor humidity gets high during the winter because of unusual indoor moisture sources, or because of a climate where outdoor air is humid during the winter, an HRV would be a better choice because it will reduce winter indoor humidity levels.

Complication: Ice Forming inside the Ventilator

One complication with both ERVs and HRVs is the possibility of ice forming in the heat exchanger during the winter. Because stale exhaust air is warming the incoming fresh air, ice will not form until the outdoor temperature gets far below the freezing temperature of water.

Some ERV and HRV equipment prevents icing with a defrost mode that circulates stale exhaust air back into the fresh air supply for some minutes each hour. This is acceptable in an application such as a school

gymnasium where exhaust air gets supplied back to the same gymnasium it came from but would be a problem in a house or apartment where bathroom or kitchen exhaust would be circulated back into bedrooms. Another complication of preventing icing this way is that if the ERV or HRV is serving multiple rooms, and is in defrost mode during a fire, it can move smoke from one room to another. Codes generally require smoke alarms, smoke dampers, and other safety devices on any ducted system that could move smoke from one room to another in a fire. A safer approach is the type of ERV that cannot possibly move smoke from one room to another.

Ice will damage some ERVs but will only temporarily block the flow of air in other ERVs. In some climates, the outdoor air is only cold enough to cause ice to form for 10 to 20 hours per year, which will occur only at night. If equipment is being selected for a building that is not occupied at night, it would be smart to save money and choose equipment that will freeze up for a few night hours per year, when nobody will be affected by the lack of ventilation (if the manufacturer says their equipment will not be damaged by the ice).

A view of an **ERV** with the cover removed, showing the **heat exchanger**, two **air filters**, and two **fans**. The ERV is connected to two **insulated ducts** (connecting the ERV to outdoors, in both directions) and two uninsulated ducts (connecting the ERV to indoors, in both directions).

How an Energy Recovery Ventilator Works

Two **fans** in the ERV move stale indoor exhaust air outdoors via one pathway through a **heat exchanger** and fresh outdoor air indoors via a different pathway through the same heat exchanger. During the winter (shown at right and below), the heat exchanger moves heat from the room-temperature exhaust air to the cold incoming air. During the summer, the heat exchanger moves heat from the warm incoming air to the room-temperature exhaust air, which cools the incoming fresh air.

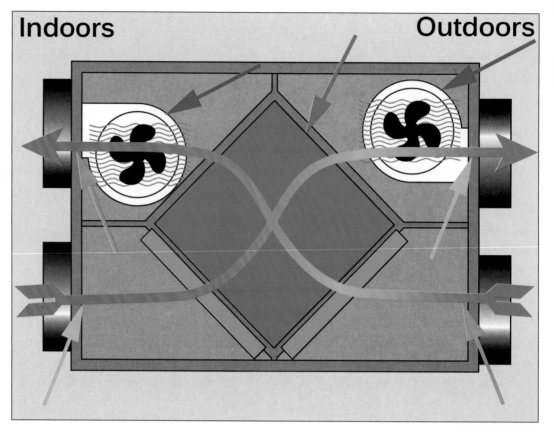

Indoors   **Outdoors**

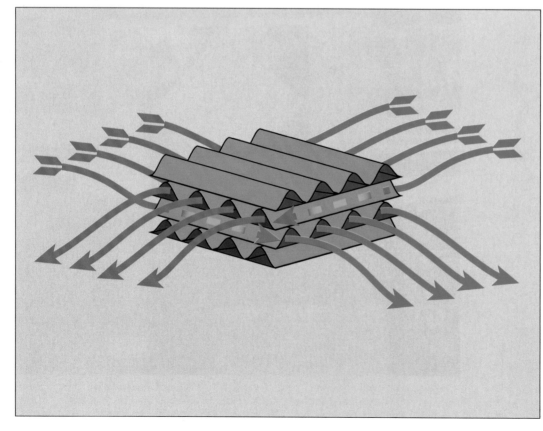

Exhaust air travels out through one set of channels while fresh air travels in through another set of channels. This allows heat to transfer while preventing the two air flows from mixing.

Different ERVs use different designs, but the heat exchanger is generally made of a composite material that not only conducts heat but also transfers water vapor from the airstream with the higher specific humidity to the airstream with the lower specific humidity.

During the summer, the ERV cools the incoming hot fresh outdoor air to almost the same temperature as the indoor air. The ERV not only saves a lot of energy—the incoming fresh air is being cooled by the exhaust air—but also is much simpler, smaller, and quieter than an air conditioner of a similar capacity. Described another way, the ERV eliminates much of the cooling system capacity that would otherwise be required to cool and dehumidify incoming fresh ventilation air.

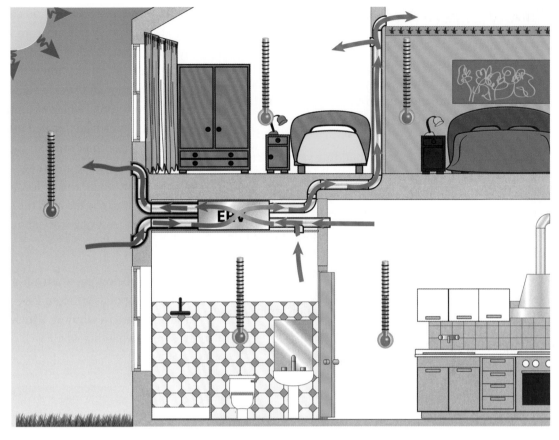

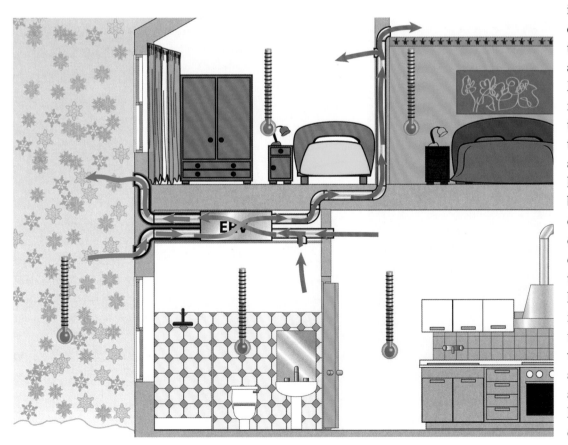

During the winter, the ERV warms the incoming cold fresh outdoor air to almost the same temperature as the indoor air. Modern ERVs can recover 80 percent to 90 percent of the temperature difference and 50 percent of the humidity difference between indoor and outdoor air. Not only does this save a lot of energy—allowing the use of a smaller heating system—but it is much simpler to heat incoming ventilation air with an ERV than with a furnace, electric heater, or other type of equipment.

An ERV's Fresh Air Supply

An ERV system is the simplest ventilation system that exhausts stale air from kitchens and bathrooms and delivers fresh air to deliberately chosen locations. The source of fresh ventilation air should be chosen carefully, so the air is as clean and healthy as possible.

The quality of outdoor air near a building varies widely. Air near the ground is much dustier than air one floor higher. It is unhealthy to take ventilation air from areas close to a chimney, a kitchen exhaust vent, an air discharge vent from a central vacuum cleaner, a plumbing vent (as shown on Page 424), or garbage storage. The roof is also not a healthy place because the sun's ultraviolet rays cause roofing materials to decompose and emit toxic gases. More than one building with ventilation air intakes located on the roof has been evacuated for weeks because the building filled with strong chemical odors when the roof was replaced.

Exhaust-only systems offer no choice of where air comes from because they pull air from whichever leaks offer the least resistance that day, depending on wind and the stack effect. (The exception is buildings that have a very good air barrier and trickle vents.) HVAC systems usually take air from roofs, where equipment is often located, but HVAC equipment located indoors can be connected via ducts to healthier outdoor locations. ERV and HRV systems also have the advantage of offering a choice of where the air intake will be located. A good location for a fresh-air intake is through the side wall of the building, preferably at least one story above the ground to reduce dust.

The photos below show a fresh-air intake on the second floor that supplies air to an ERV system. The intake is located close to a window, which makes it easy to clean the screen when it gets dirty.

This fresh-air intake is located on the wall of the second floor, where the outdoor air is much cleaner than it is lower down.

The air intake is also located where it is easy to see, access, and clean. Model: Isca Greenfield-Sanders.

The photo at right shows the opposite side of the same house. The **stale-air exhaust from the ERV**, the **plumbing vents**, and the **clothing-dryer exhaust** are all located near each other. Except for the ERV exhaust, all of them are far from windows. The kitchen exhaust and the boiler exhaust are at the far end of the house.

The fresh-air intake's location on the opposite side of the house puts it far away from all these sources of pollution.

The photo at left shows the screen of an ERV's fresh-air intake clogged with dirt.

As nasty as this looks, it is better than having all that dirt pulled into the building through holes that have no filters. The screen prevented all that dust and dirt from entering the house, and the filter in the ERV caught even more of it.

The screen is easy to remove and clean with soap and water.

The Best Location for an ERV

ERVs can go wherever there is space and access for a vacuum cleaner's hose to reach for periodic cleaning. A ceiling is usually best.

The photo at right shows an ERV installed in the ceiling near the entrance of an apartment that is under construction. The ceiling will be lowered in that area for fire sprinkler pipes anyway, so the space is perfect for the ERV and its ducts. The photo below shows an ERV installed above a bathroom ceiling in a small house. The ERV is accessed by a door from the hallway outside and above the bathroom door. The photo below right shows an ERV and ductwork installed above what will soon be a bathroom.

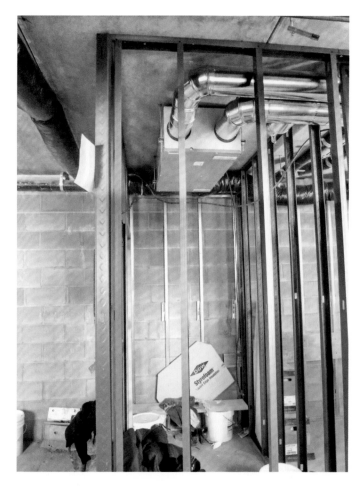

It is advantageous to locate an ERV close to outdoors.

The two drawings on this page show an ERV operating during the winter. The ducts between the ERV and outdoors are filled with cold air and are insulated, yet some heat is conducted through the insulation from the house to the air in those ducts.

Heat conducted from the house to the exhaust air is lost outdoors, while heat conducted from the house to the fresh (cold) incoming air duct reduces the energy recovery effectiveness of the ERV.

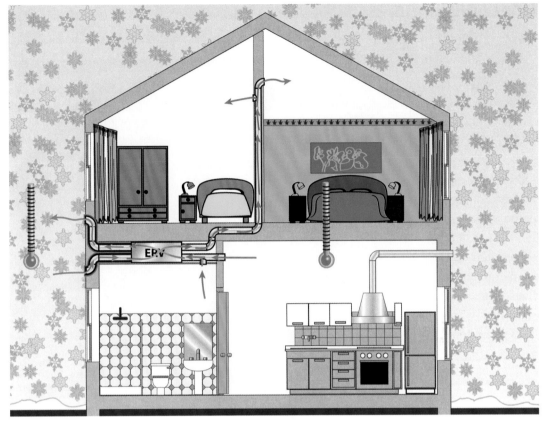

In the drawing at left, the ERV is located closer to outdoors than it is in the drawing above.

This is an improvement that will save energy because the ducts containing cold air (or warm air during the summer) are shorter and therefore will absorb less heat from indoors. And the resulting increase in the length of the ducts between the ERV and the indoor air inlets and outlets will reduce the amount of noise transmitted through the ducts from the ERV to the inside of the house.

ERV Configurations

ERVs are available with air duct connections arranged in a variety of physical configurations. This allows installing the ducts in a way that minimizes their length and the space they occupy. It also helps minimize the number of places ducts must cross each other, which saves space, too.

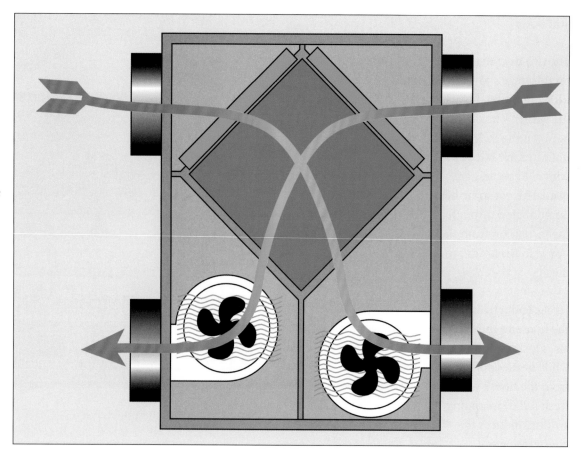

Some ERVs can be reconfigured after purchase, which makes it convenient to make last minute changes in duct layout. Other ERVs are fixed.

The ERV at left is configured with all of the inlet and outlet ducts located on its short ends (like the ERV in the photo on Page 445), instead of on its long sides. It performs the same functions as the one above, but finding space for it and the ducts might be easier.

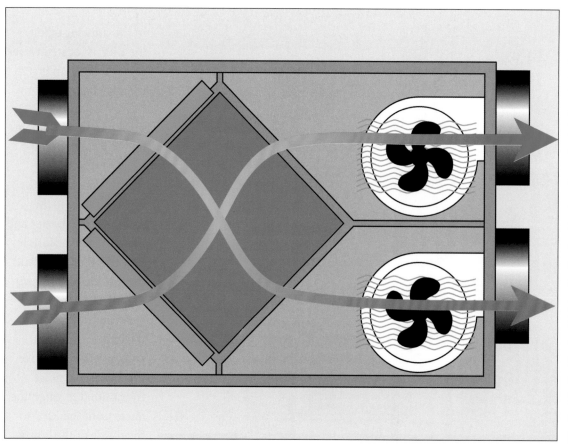

ERV Air Filters

The photo at right shows a foam air filter covering the air intake to an ERV's heat-exchange core. Whenever it gets dirty, the filter can be removed, washed in water, and replaced.

It is best to choose an ERV model that comes with washable air filters, as this reduces maintenance cost and waste associated with disposable filters.

The photo at left shows an ERV filter getting rinsed in a sink. The filter prevented all the dirt in that water from polluting the air in the house.

Close Off All Ducts When Not in Use

The photos on this page show the fresh-air intake to an ERV with the ERV's cover removed. The connection to the fresh-air intake duct is equipped with a **motorized damper**, which automatically closes off the flow of air when the ERV is not in use (when the fans are turned off).

In the photo at right, the damper is open.

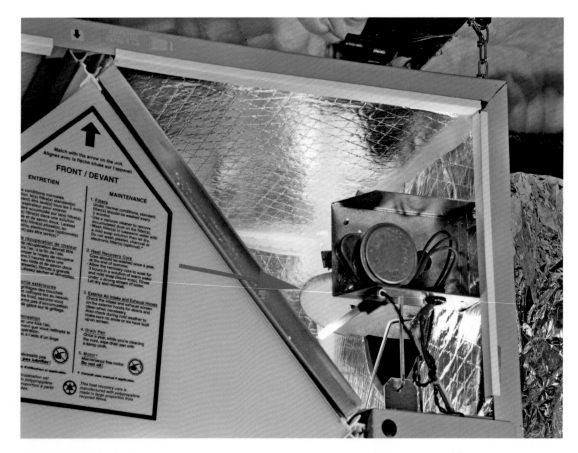

ERVs that ventilate houses and apartments should operate 24 hours per day and therefore do not need dampers. Office and school ventilation systems should be turned off when the space is unoccupied and therefore should have dampers in the ERVs or the ducts to prevent the ventilation system from acting as a hole in the building when it is turned off.

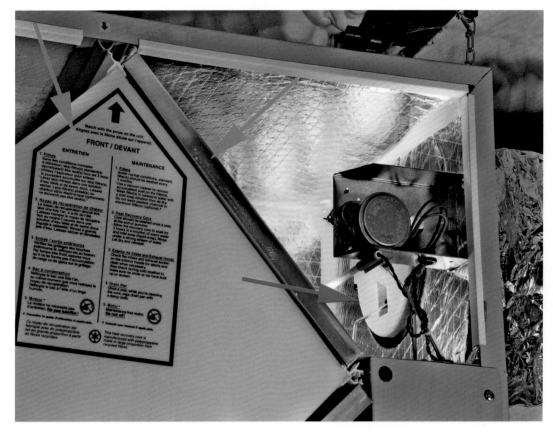

In the photo at left, the **damper** is closed. Also visible are the **heat-exchange core** and the **filter** on the fresh-air intake that keeps both the core and the indoor air clean.

An exhaust-only fan in a bathroom or kitchen should also be equipped with a damper that closes automatically when the fan is off. Various types of dampers are closed by springs, gravity, or an electric motor when a stove cools off or a bathroom fan is turned off.

WHICH VENTILATION SYSTEM IS BEST?

Which system to choose depends on a building's specific needs, but there are some general principles.

While HVAC systems can filter incoming air, they are generally not a good choice because they are complicated and expensive, circulate used air, require a lot of energy, and often require connections to sophisticated fire and smoke alarm systems. They also usually require complicated control systems, large ducts, and large, noisy fans that cost a lot to operate, especially for providing ventilation when no heating or cooling is required.

Exhaust-only systems are the least expensive systems to buy and install, take up the smallest amount of space, and do not have any filters to clean. They are also the most cost-effective option in climates where buildings need little heating or cooling. In climates where buildings need a significant amount of heating and cooling, exhaust-only is not a good choice for schools and office buildings because they pull large amounts of cold or hot outdoor air in through leaks in the building. Exhaust-only systems are practical for apartment buildings or single-family houses located in any climate because the smaller amount of ventilation air required in these types of buildings is usually not enough to cause discomfort as it is pulled in through leaks. However, exhaust-only systems do not heat or cool incoming air. Instead, they add the entire load of heating or cooling incoming ventilation air to the building's heating or cooling system.

For most buildings in most climates, an ERV system is the best choice. An ERV system offers the greatest flexibility in choosing where fresh ventilation air comes from, and it also filters the incoming fresh air. For buildings that require more ventilation air than an exhaust-only system can pull through leaks, an ERV not only is the least expensive type of equipment to buy but also requires the least amount of maintenance. In any climate that needs a significant amount of heating or cooling, the cost savings associated with the reduction in heating and cooling equipment size that an ERV system allows can more than offset the cost differential between an ERV system and an exhaust-only system. It will also save energy compared to an HVAC system or an exhaust-only system.

Chapters 19-22 provide specific recommendations for ventilation systems in different types of buildings.

Ventilation and Energy Consumption

If an exhaust-only ventilation system is replaced with an ERV system, during the winter the incoming cold fresh air is heated to almost room temperature by the exhaust air, which saves most of the energy that would otherwise be required to heat the incoming fresh air. During the summer, if a cooling system is operating, the ERV system will save energy by cooling the incoming fresh air to almost room temperature, saving most of the energy that would otherwise be required to cool the incoming air. Likewise, an ERV will save about half of the energy required to dry the incoming fresh air during the summer and humidify the incoming air during the winter. How much energy an ERV will save compared to an exhaust-only system depends on weather: none if the indoor and outdoor temperatures and humidity are equal, more in colder, hotter, drier, or more humid weather.

An ERV system reduces the load on a building's heating and cooling systems (and reduces the size of the heating and cooling equipment a building requires), but an ERV system requires more electricity than a simple exhaust-only system. In effect, an ERV reduces a building's energy needs by shifting a small part of the energy load from the heating and cooling systems to the electric motors that turn the fans in the ventilation system. An ERV sized to serve a single-family home might require 60-90 watts of electricity (to recover perhaps thousands of watts of heat), while an exhaust fan might require half as much. Sixty watts is not a lot of electricity compared to some other things, such as a window air conditioner that requires 750 watts, but many ventilation systems run continuously, making small differences important over time.

Predicting how much it will cost to ventilate, heat, and cool a building is complicated by the need to consider different prices for different forms of energy. Generally speaking, buying energy in the form of electricity costs more than buying it in the form of fossil fuel. One reason for this is that most electricity today (2017) is produced by burning fossil fuel, and the second law says that an electricity-generating plant cannot be 100 percent efficient. For more information on different energy sources, see the Appendix on Page 564.

VENTILATION SYSTEM DESIGN

Duct Length

Regardless of the type of ventilation system, short ducts are better than long ducts (except when it comes to noise control). The longer a duct, the more it costs, the more space it occupies, the larger the fan needs to be, and the greater the amount of energy the fan will require. Also, a long duct usually has one end exposed to a different air pressure in a faraway part of the building, which complicates the task of moving the correct amount of air.

Also, the longer a duct, the greater the chance it will pass through a demising assembly and need protection against spreading smoke or fire. Fire dampers, smoke dampers, and other technologies can reduce—but never eliminate—the possibility of smoke or fire spreading through a duct.

The office buildings shown on Pages 478, 480, 481, and 558 are examples of buildings with ventilation systems that require air to be moved long distances. In large buildings, ventilation ducts can be shortened by using multiple small ventilation systems throughout the building instead of one large system: for example, individual systems for each classroom in a school (Pages 532-533), each apartment in an apartment building (Pages 536-540), or each floor of an office building (Pages 551-555).

Another way to shorten ducts is by locating the outdoor air intake and exhaust openings close to the space being ventilated (but a safe distance from each other). This often means locating ventilation openings on building walls, as shown on Pages 448, 449, 536, and 537, instead of running long ducts to the roof, as shown on Page 443.

Duct Location

Ducts should be located indoors, as advised way back in 1824 by the English engineer Thomas Tredgold:

> In other cases air pipes of tinned iron, or sheet zinc, or earthen tubes, may be employed for distributing fresh air, placed within the building that no heat may be lost.[3]

3   Thomas Tredgold, <u>Principles of Warming and Ventilating Public Buildings, Dwelling-houses, Manufactories, Hospitals, Hot-houses, Conservatories, &c.</u> (London: Josiah Taylor, Architectural Library, 1824), Page 175.

This advice is still relevant because ducts are still sometimes located outdoors (as shown on Page 412). All ducts should be located completely indoors, which means they should not be in an attic or a crawl space either.

Duct Insulation

All ducts that bring in outdoor air to any type of system need to be insulated to prevent condensation. And, because exhaust air from an ERV is at about the same temperature as outdoor air, the exhaust duct from an ERV should also be insulated to prevent condensation.

To prevent warm humid air from passing through the duct insulation and condensing on whichever side of the insulation is cold at the moment, the insulation should be covered with barriers to air and to water vapor. A sheet metal duct that is airtightened and covered on the outside with fiberglass insulation, which is then covered with an air and water vapor barrier, meets this requirement.

Exhaust-only ducts and ducts between an ERV or an HRV and indoors do not need to be insulated because these ducts contain air at or close to room temperature.

Duct Material

Many ducts are made of thin sheets of steel, which have the advantages of being inexpensive, thin (taking up almost no room), smooth (reducing friction and fan energy), and easy to cut with heavy scissors and connect with screws. Some ducts are made of fiberglass boards, which serve as their own insulation. Other ducts are flexible like vacuum cleaner hoses, which makes them easy to install, but most of these have high resistance to airflow because their inner surfaces are bumpy.

Ducts and Air Leaks

All ducts and all connections between ducts and other equipment, including walls and ceilings where supply and exhaust grills are located, should be made as airtight as possible. One method is shown on Pages 458-459.

Close Unused Ducts

All outdoor air ducts should have dampers that automatically close when not in use. They can be built into equipment, as shown on Page 454, or installed in ducts.

Ducts and Noise

Air moving through ducts can create or carry sound. Duct sound can generally be divided into four categories:

1. Noise generated in one room and transmitted to another, as shown in the drawing below left.

2. Velocity noise, which is caused by air moving quickly.

3. Equipment noise created by a fan or other equipment and transmitted through the air in the ducts.

4. Vibrating ducts caused by vibration from fans or other equipment.

Sound transmission from one room to another sounds like whatever the sound is in the other room, such as an alarm clock (see below left). Long distances between duct openings, as shown in the drawing below right, can reduce sound transmission from one room to another.

Velocity noise sounds like a whistling or whooshing noise. This type of noise can be avoided by using ducts (and grills) large enough to keep the air moving slowly.

Noise generated by equipment usually sounds like a humming or buzzing noise. When caused by a fan, it is fairly constant. When caused by a compressor, such as the refrigerant compressor in air conditioning equipment, it usually turns on and off or gets louder and then less loud. Equipment noise is louder closer to the machinery generating the noise. There are many ways to reduce equipment noise: choose smaller and quieter equipment, mount the equipment on vibration-absorbing supports (see Page 286), or increase the length of duct between equipment and duct openings to rooms. Other solutions include avoiding round ducts (sound waves stay intact in round ducts better than they do in ducts with other shapes) and using flexible duct material (as shown connected to the top of the ERV on Page 445). The rough-shaped interior surface of most flexible ducts breaks up sound waves, and the flexible walls absorb sound.

Vibrating equipment can cause nearby sheet metal ducts to vibrate, creating a buzzing which is louder closer to equipment. A flexible connection between equipment and ducts can absorb the vibration. Duct vibration can also be prevented by a rigid or semi-rigid connection between the duct and a heavy, structural part of the building.

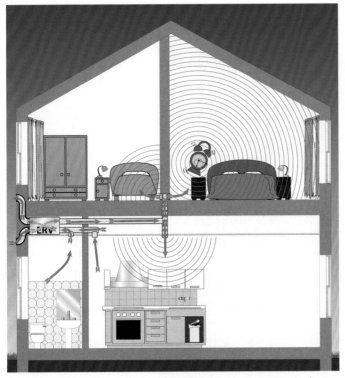

Sound from the alarm clock is traveling into one duct opening in the top right bedroom, through short pieces of duct, and into both the other bedroom and the kitchen. The ducts between the different rooms are very short, which increases sound transmission.

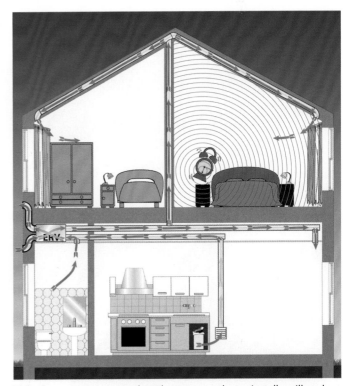

This duct arrangement, though more costly to install, will reduce the amount of sound traveling from one room to another. The ducts between rooms are longer, requiring sound to travel through a long duct and past at least one elbow before entering another room.

Airtighten Ducts and Connections

As mentioned earlier, all duct connections should be as airtight as possible. Duct tape does not do a good job of airtightening ducts. These two pages show a good way to airtighten sheet metal ducts.

First, duct mastic is brushed onto all the seams, including the longitudinal seams, as shown in the photo at right.

In the photo at left, fiberglass mesh is layered on top of the wet mastic.

The fiberglass mesh will add strength to the mastic at the seam the same way mesh adds strength to the brush-on airtightening products being applied in the photo on Page 107 (bottom left) and the photo on Page 110 (bottom).

After the mesh is applied (no need to wait for the mastic to dry), a second layer of duct mastic is applied on top of the mesh.

The combination of duct mastic, mesh, and another layer of mastic produces a high-quality joint that can be expected to stay airtight for many years.

Factory-Made Ventilation Systems

Manufacturers offer complete ventilation systems including flexible ducts, junction boxes, grills, silencers, and connectors that make fast, airtight connections. Buying a factory-made system is easier than assembling a system from parts made by different companies.

The photo at left shows part of a factory-made system that has ducts small enough to fit inside walls (two ducts are necessary to provide enough ventilation for some rooms).

The Right Air-Supply Grill Makes a Difference

The grill in the photo at right will be installed on a ceiling or wall, but it will not send air skimming along the ceiling (or wall) where nobody will notice it. This is because it has short blades that do not extend past the surface of the grill. Much of the air will blow straight out away from the grill, directly into the room, where people will notice it. This can cause comfort complaints.

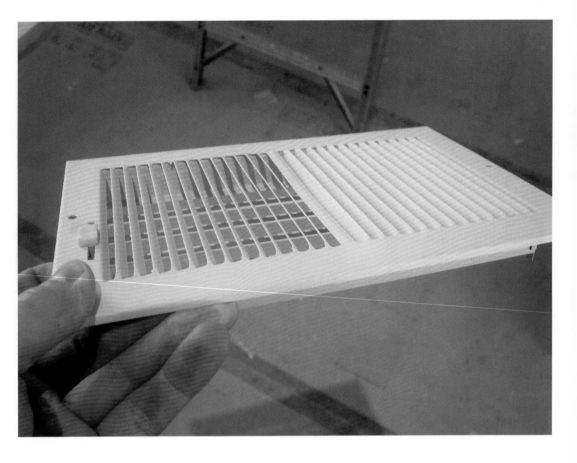

The short blades increase the chance of air being blown directly onto a person, as shown at left.

During the winter, blowing air on a person can make the person uncomfortable, even if the air is warm. During the summer, cold air might feel refreshing at first but is likely to cause discomfort before long. Even if the blowing air makes one person comfortable, it is unlikely multiple people will all be comfortable. The safest way to avoid comfort complaints is to not blow air directly on people.

The ceiling grill in the photo at right has long, curved blades that extend out past the surface of the grill. The shape of the blades causes the air to blow out along the ceiling and hug it for some distance away from the grill. As shown in the drawing below, the air travels along the ceiling and eventually reaches the people in the room but doesn't blow directly on them.

This type of grill should not be mounted on a wall because someone could get hurt by the protruding blades.

As the air skims along the ceiling, it heats or cools the ceiling, turning that part of the ceiling into a radiant heating or cooling surface. This can make the room feel more comfortable than a room heated or cooled by blowing hot or cold air directly into the room (from either a wall or the ceiling). Directing an airstream along the ceiling will not change the amount of heating, cooling, or ventilation air delivered, but it will improve comfort.

Ventilation Supply and Return Locations

In all types of buildings, common sense and codes both dictate removing stale air from bathrooms and kitchens. Codes and common sense also dictate that this exhaust go directly outdoors and not be mixed with fresh air supplied to the building.

Fresh outdoor air is best delivered to parts of a room or building far from where exhaust air leaves. The photo on Page 435 is an example of what should not be done: locating the air-supply grill close to the return (exhaust) air grill. The longer the fresh air has to travel within a room or a building the better, so that more of the building gets the benefit of ventilation air flowing through it.

In houses and apartments, fresh air should be supplied to the bedrooms, from where it can move through the hallways, living room, and dining room on its way to the exhaust outlets in the kitchen and bathrooms. Fresh outdoor air should never blow on someone sleeping or sitting, as moving air—even warm moving air—can cause discomfort, especially during the winter. Delivering air to a bedroom closet works well if there is a space for the air

to pass under the closet door, if the door is louvered, if the door is left open, or if there is no door.

In schools, air should be both supplied to and removed from each classroom. Putting the fresh outdoor air supply near the classroom door is a smart idea because the air will not blow on anyone. Exhaust air should be removed from the opposite end of the room so as to insure that air will circulate through the whole room.

In open office areas, fresh outdoor air can be supplied to hallways, and stale air can be exhausted from offices furthest from the hallways and from copy machine areas (to remove the chemicals). Offices and meeting rooms surrounded by walls are similar to classrooms, needing both supply and return in each room, with the supply air introduced where nobody will be sitting: near the door.

Dust Storms in Desert Areas

In desert areas, dust carried by wind can completely fill the air, covering everything in its path. The inside of any building in the path of a dust storm will be covered with dust, even if the windows are closed. The dust comes into the building with air leaking in through leaks in the building's enclosure and through ventilation ducts.

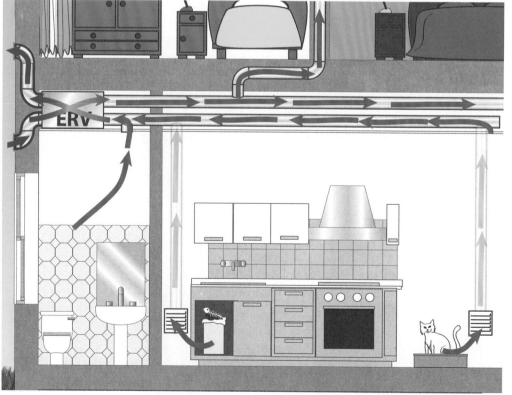

Some people attempt to keep the dust out by using a ventilation system to pressurize the building with a constant supply of filtered air that is blown into the building with a fan. This approach will not work because the wind applies much more pressure to the leaks on the windy side of the building than any realistically sized fan can create, and a filter will clog after a few seconds in a dust storm.

The best solution to the problem of dust entering a building is to make the enclosure as airtight as possible and filter incoming ventilation air.

This ventilation system is effective because it is designed to remove stale exhaust air from three areas that can be particularly smelly: the cat box, the garbage, and the bathroom.

DEHUMIDIFYING

Mold grows in many buildings, especially newer buildings, which can and does make people sick. The solution is to keep indoor humidity from getting too high. For reasons explained in Chapter 5: Water - Basic Science, indoor humidity is usually low during cold weather but tends to be high during warm weather. In the past, air conditioning systems have usually done a decent job of keeping indoor humidity low enough during the summer to avoid problems. But that is changing.

Stage One buildings, as defined on Page 376, tend to have few problems with humidity. One reason is that during warm weather, a lot of heat enters the building through its enclosure, which causes the building's cooling system to run many hours each day to keep the building cool enough for people to be comfortable. While the cooling system is removing heat from the air inside the building, it is also removing water vapor (which condenses on the cold part of the cooling system and runs down a drain).

Stage Two buildings tend to have more problems with humidity because the insulation in the enclosure (usually helped a lot by good windows) reduces the amount of heat that gets inside the building during warm weather, causing the cooling system to run for fewer hours each day. Because the enclosure of a Stage Two building has no air barrier, air leaks in the enclosure will continue to allow water vapor to get into the building during all hours when outdoor humidity is high. This includes hours when the building's cooling system might not be operating—for example, during summer nights. Interactions between air leaks in the enclosure, the cooling system, and mold-sensitive modern building materials, such as paper-faced gypsum board, can cause mold problems with Stage Two buildings in any climate, even a desert climate.

If all else is equal, a Stage Three building will have less of a humidity problem than a Stage Two building because the air barrier in its enclosure will reduce the amount of water vapor that leaks into the building.

But, depending on climate and how a building is designed and built, even Stage Three buildings can accumulate water vapor that the cooling system won't be able to remove. As buildings become more energy efficient, the problem will only get worse.

Increased levels of insulation in new building enclosures reduce summer heat gain. And, because summer heat gain is usually dominated by sunlight entering a building through the windows, new windows with low-e coatings, more panes of glass, gas fill, and better frames greatly reduce the number of hours a cooling system needs to operate each day. Shading windows from solar gain also reduces cooling load, leaving the building defenseless against high humidity for ever longer periods of time.

Better lighting fixtures are also making the problem worse. Buildings are now being designed and built with all LED lighting, which generates only a small fraction of the heat generated by older types of lighting. The reduced heat output from energy-efficient lighting further reduces the number of hours the cooling system will need to operate.

But even the best Stage Three buildings will still gain water vapor from ventilation air and from internal sources such as cooking, showering, and breathing. As buildings become more energy efficient, the amount of heat a cooling system needs to remove from a building to keep people comfortable is gradually being reduced, in some cases to zero. However, the amount of water vapor that needs to be removed from inside a building is not being reduced by nearly as much and cannot be reduced to zero by even the best building enclosure. High moisture levels resulting from reduced cooling loads can cause mold to grow in a building.

Differences in climate complicate the problem of predicting which buildings are likely to have mold problems. Mold growth is facilitated by relative humidity higher than about 85 percent in the immediate vicinity of its food for a few days, which is hard to predict based on average outdoor humidity levels. In some climates, the problem hours occur mostly at night, when the lower outdoor air temperature and the lack of solar gain cause the cooling system to turn off, while the ventilation system continues to bring water vapor into the building. In these climates, operating the cooling system during the day will often dry out the building enough to avoid problems.

Other climates have many consecutive nights and days when outdoor humidity is high enough to cause problems, but the outdoor temperature remains low enough to prevent a cooling system from operating for days or weeks at a time, leaving the building defenseless against mold.

High humidity problems can occur in desert climates because some desert areas have a short monsoon season. Some parts of the world are dry for all but a few weeks, when the climate turns cool and damp, or rainy. Cool weather keeps a building's cooling system from operating, and the high humidity causes mold to flourish. In a climate like this, some people might think they sneeze at a certain time of year because of pollen, but they are really sneezing because of mold growing inside their house.

One way to dry out a wet building is to operate the building's cooling and heating systems simultaneously, as described on Page 224. But while this is a good solution for a one-time problem such as a flood from a broken pipe, this is not a good solution for the long-term problem of a building "flooded" by water vapor from incoming ventilation air. This is because running both the cooling and heating systems for months at a time would make a building uncomfortable while also using too much energy. (The same can be said for adding heat by going back to incandescent lights, single-pane glass, and uninsulated walls.) And, depending on climate and design, many buildings don't need and don't have a cooling system.

The solution is to use a dehumidifier. A dehumidifier is a mechanical device that removes water vapor from air.

TYPES OF DEHUMIDIFIERS
Stand-Alone Dehumidifier

The simplest type of dehumidifier is a stand-alone model (see photo below), available at any appliance store. They plug into an electric outlet, rest on the floor or a shelf, condense water from the air, and drain it into either a container built into the dehumidifier or a drain hose.

Draining water into the container built into the dehumidifier has a drawback: someone has to empty it frequently, or the dehumidifier will shut off. Connecting a drain hose from the dehumidifier to a sink drain allows the dehumidifier to operate continuously, with no container to empty. To prevent sewer gases from escaping, the drain hose should be connected to the sink drain upstream of the drain's P trap (see close-up photo). Most models are equipped with a dehumidistat (like a thermostat, but for humidity), which senses humidity in the air and turns the dehumidifier on and off as necessary.

One disadvantage of stand-alone dehumidifiers is that they tend to be noisy. One solution is a timer to operate the dehumidifier when people are not around. Another disadvantage is that a stand-alone dehumidifier can only dehumidify air that it can circulate through itself with its built-in fan. In an open basement, the fan and convection (dehumidifiers produce heat) will circulate air throughout the basement but not through upstairs rooms. In a house with a furnace and ducts used for heating and cooling, the dehumidifier can operate in one upstairs room, and the furnace fan can circulate dry air through the house. A better solution, however, is a ducted dehumidifier.

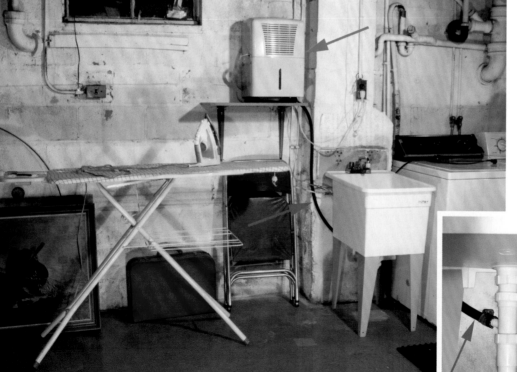

This stand-alone dehumidifier is connected with a hose to the drain of a sink. It can dry the air continuously, without anyone ever needing to empty a container of water.

Ducted Dehumidifier

Dehumidifiers are also available with a built-in fan and connections for ducts that can be used to circulate dry air around a building. The ducted dehumidifier at right is connected to two ducts: one **duct** to move air from the house to the dehumidifier and another **duct** to move air from the dehumidifier to the house. The dehumidifier is powered by **electricity**. The water the dehumidifier condenses out of the air leaves through a **drain pipe**.

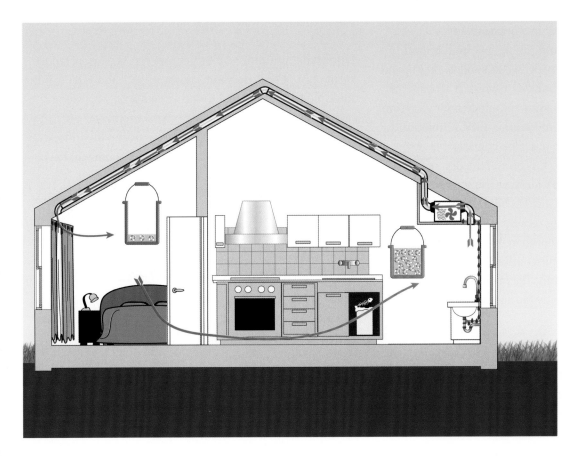

In a house, the dehumidifier can pull air from a common area such as a kitchen or living room and deliver dry air to the bedrooms, as shown at left. As the air circulates through the house, it effectively dries the air throughout the house.

One disadvantage of most dehumidifiers is that they also add a significant amount of heat to the air. A type of dehumidifier called a "cooling dehumidifier" solves this problem.

Cooling Dehumidifier

A cooling dehumidifier has a built-in fan and connections for ducts (see next page) but is different from a normal ducted dehumidifier in one critical way: it rejects heat outdoors. A dehumidifier produces both the latent heat given off by condensing water and the heat generated by its own operation. (In accordance with the first law of thermodynamics, all the electricity entering the dehumidifier leaves the dehumidifier as heat or noise.)

Both stand-alone dehumidifiers and normal ducted dehumidifiers add heat to the air they've removed water vapor from. The combination of removing water vapor and adding heat can make people more comfortable in a building, for reasons explained in Chapter 1: Heat - Basic Science. But during hot, humid weather, people can be made even more comfortable by removing both heat and water vapor from the air.

A cooling dehumidifier rejects heat outdoors with a piece of equipment that is basically the same as the outdoor part of a split type air conditioner. The air blown through ducts by a cooling dehumidifier is unusual in a psychrometric sense: not only is the relative humidity of the air low, but the air is also cool—cooler than the air in the building.

Many people dream of living in a house that is comfortable without air conditioning, but high humidity shatters that dream for many people as soon as they spend a night trying to sleep in a puddle of sweat. If a house has a good enclosure, decent shading to reduce solar gain into the windows, energy-efficient lighting, ERV ventilation, and a cooling dehumidifier, it will be comfortable. As soon as someone walks into this house, the dry and not very hot air will immediately increase evaporative cooling from her lungs and skin. Instead of being noisy—as houses with air conditioning usually are—the house will be quiet. It will also feel cooler than it really is, which will keep a wider variety of people comfortable than a house that is cooler but more humid. The house can also have high ceilings made possible by the absence of large ducts, as shown on Page 529.

Because a cooling dehumidifier does remove some heat from a building, it is, strictly speaking, still a cooling system. But it avoids many of the problems that many air conditioned buildings have, such as dampness and overcooling. In combination with a good enclosure, energy-efficient lighting and appliances, and maybe some strategically located trees, a cooling dehumidifier eliminates the need for a conventional cooling (air conditioning) system in most buildings in most climates. Depending on climate, construction, personal preference, and other factors, some people might not be comfortable with a cooling dehumidifier alone. A cooling dehumidifier can be used in combination with another cooling system. A thermostat can operate the cooling system on very hot days, while a dehumidistat can operate the cooling dehumidifier at times when the indoor air is humid but not very hot, such as during summer nights.

A cooling dehumidifier has many advantages. It is quieter than a conventional dehumidifier because the noisiest part (the compressor) is relatively quiet and is located outdoors. It is also much more likely than a conventional cooling system to keep air too dry to support mold growth. A cooling dehumidifier saves energy by allowing the summer indoor temperature to be higher than it would need to be to keep people comfortable in more humid air, which saves energy by reducing the movement of heat from outdoors to indoors. And a cooling dehumidifier saves space with ducts that are a fraction of the size required for a normal cooling system (because air can hold a lot of water vapor but not much heat).

Ducted dehumidifiers of both types can be connected to furnace or HVAC ductwork, as can ERVs and HRVs. But multiple fans connected to the same ducts, with some operating at some times while others are turned off, can have unpredictable results. The controls can be difficult to configure and operate because the furnace fan will have to operate when only dehumidification is desired. It is generally simpler and better to install a separate system of small ducts for a ducted dehumidifier because dedicated ducts have a good chance of working as intended.

ERVs that Also Cool or Dehumidify

ERVs are now available with a cooling mechanism, which provides cool, dry ventilation air. ERVs are also available with a dehumidifier built in, which is ideal for buildings with radiant cooling systems. Many new equipment combinations will be introduced in the future, complete with all the advantages and disadvantages of combining multiple functions into one piece of equipment.

The cooling dehumidifier at right removes water vapor and heat from the air. The heat leaves the house through a piece of equipment located outdoors. The outdoor part of the system looks and functions like the ductless split outdoor unit on the top of Page 499.

The cool, dry air circulating through the ducts not only removes water vapor from the house but also cools it a little.

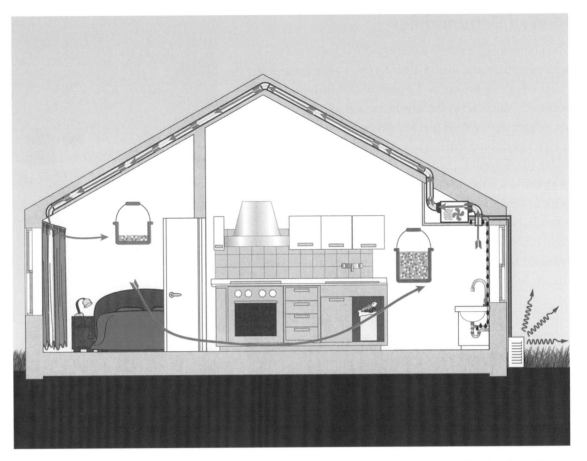

Like the ducted dehumidifier, the cooling dehumidifier above and at left is connected to **two ducts**, a **source of electricity**, and a **condensate drain**.

Unlike a dehumidifier that does not also cool, it is also connected to **two small tubes** that contain refrigerant. The refrigerant moves heat from indoors to outdoors the same way an air conditioning system does. (This is explained on Page 511.)

In-Wall Dehumidifier

The photo at right shows a **dehumidifier** mounted permanently in the wall. Called an "in-wall dehumidifier," it has a built-in dehumidistat control that turns it on automatically whenever the relative humidity in the air is high (the control can be adjusted for a particular level). The dehumidifier has a drain pipe that carries the water condensed out of the air to a nearby drain. Other than being a little deeper than the thickness of a normal wall, this dehumidifier takes up virtually no space. To accommodate the extra thickness, the dehumidifier at right is mounted in the wall of a closet that contains a furnace. The back side of the dehumidifier can be seen at the top left of the photo on the top right of Page 518.

The **air grill** on the same wall is unrelated to the dehumidifier—it is part of the path air takes on its way back to the furnace in the closet.

SUMMARY

Clean, fresh indoor air is crucial for keeping people healthy and comfortable. The most effective way to improve indoor air quality is to avoid bringing poisons into the building in the first place and to remove any poisons that happen to be in the building—including those that are in furniture, carpets, and even building materials. After removing poisons from the building, it is important to ventilate with fresh outdoor air, not stale indoor air.

Kitchen stoves, especially gas stoves, emit soot and carbon monoxide. Both kitchens and garages should be well ventilated. Garages should be built away from living spaces, as they often contain carbon monoxide, as well as gasoline fumes and sometimes even fertilizer and pesticides. Air handlers for a building's heating, cooling, or ventilation systems should never be located in a garage.

A ventilation system cannot work as designed unless the building incorporates a good air barrier to prevent air from moving to and from where it is not intended to move. Without an air barrier in the building, a ventilation system adds chaos to randomness.

The simplest ventilation system, which is an exhaust-only system, simply pulls air in through leaks and exhausts stale air from areas such as bathrooms and kitchens. A heating, ventilation, air conditioning (HVAC) system supplies heating and cooling, as well as ventilation. Though an HVAC system usually supplies a small percentage of fresh outdoor air, it is mostly circulating stale indoor air, which is not the healthiest option. The best ventilation systems use an energy recovery ventilator (ERV), which recovers energy from stale exhaust air, transferring it to the incoming fresh air. ERVs can also transfer water vapor from exhaust air to fresh incoming air during the winter (so indoor air is not too dry) and transfer it from humid incoming fresh air to the exhaust air during the summer (so indoor air is not too humid). ERVs also enable a choice of where fresh air is taken from and where it is supplied to.

Various types of dehumidifiers can remove water vapor from indoor air, which improves summer comfort while keeping indoor air healthy by preventing mold growth.

Chapter 18 **HEATING AND COOLING**

WHY IS IT IMPORTANT TO UNDERSTAND HEATING AND COOLING?

Heating and cooling (air conditioning) systems have an enormous impact on people's comfort, health, and safety. They also impact a building's durability and energy use.

The type of heating and cooling system that keeps people the most comfortable and uses the smallest amount of energy is a good building enclosure that incorporates barriers to heat and air. But regardless of how well the enclosure reduces a building's heating and cooling needs, most buildings in most climates will need at least some additional heating or cooling (or dehumidification instead of cooling, as described on Pages 463-468).

Heating and cooling systems have an enormous impact on a building's energy use. Much of the energy that enters a building first moves through the heating or cooling systems. Choosing appropriate systems and designing them well is especially important in larger buildings.

The energy profile of a small building is typically dominated by the building enclosure, and the energy profile of a large building is typically dominated by the mechanical systems. For example, in a one-room building, all the rooms are always at the same temperature because there is only one room. There is never a problem with one room being hotter or colder than another room. Therefore, the only way to save energy—while keeping the room comfortable—is by improving the building enclosure. A two-room building could have different temperatures in each room, but opening the door between the two rooms would help even out the temperatures. But the larger a building is, the more challenging it is to keep temperatures even enough to prevent overheating or overcooling.

Two rooms that appear to be identical might need the same amount of heating or cooling at one point in time but then require different amounts of heating and cooling at a different time. This may be due to differences in solar heat gain; differences in internal heat gain from lights, appliances, and people; better or worse airtightening; and other factors. It also may be due to differences in the amount of outdoor air leaking through a room caused by changes in wind speed and direction, the amount and direction of the stack effect, and other factors.

A building that illustrates these design challenges well is a tall apartment building. Rooms on one side get sun while rooms on the other side get no sun. The wind blows outdoor air through leaks into apartments on the windy side of the building, through the hallway, then through apartments on the other side of the building, and then back outdoors. This causes some rooms to have a constant flow of cold or hot outdoor air (depending on the season), while others receive air that has already been heated or cooled by the mechanical systems. Some rooms are high up where the wind is strongest, while others are down low where the wind is weaker. The stack effect moves air from outdoors into some rooms, through other rooms, and back outdoors from other rooms. All these factors cause the loads on the mechanical system to vary wildly from time to time and from one part of the building to another.

In large buildings, heating and cooling systems also tend to be more complicated, which increases the challenge of getting them to work as intended. Also, in larger buildings it is more challenging to deliver the correct amount of heating and cooling to rooms that are far away from the heating and cooling equipment.

KEEP IT SIMPLE

The more complicated a mechanical system is, the less likely it will work as intended. Complicated systems are vulnerable to problems created at the design stage, during installation, while adjustments are made at start-up, or later, with maintenance. Simple systems are less vulnerable to problems because it takes less time and expertise to get them working properly.

The more complicated a mechanical system is, the more complicated the controls need to be. A simple heating system in a house is usually controlled by a wall thermostat. A window air conditioner can be controlled by one or more knobs built into the unit. But many mechanical systems designed and installed today, especially HVAC systems, are so complicated mechanically that they need sophisticated digital controls that require software custom configured for an individual building. Like computers, digital HVAC controls can achieve many amazing feats; also like computers, digital HVAC controls sometimes don't perform as desired and don't always work years after the original software was written. The simpler a system is mechanically, the simpler the controls can be, and the more likely the system will work as intended and stay working for a long time.

One way to keep mechanical systems simple is to ventilate with a separate ventilation-only system. Keeping the ventilation system separate from the heating and cooling system (or systems) means that if a system breaks down or does not work as intended, finding and fixing the problem is much simpler. For example, if air is blowing out of a duct connected to a heating and ventilation system, it is difficult for anyone, even an expert, to know how much of that air comes from outdoors. If air is blowing out of a duct connected to a ventilation-only system, it is easy to know how much of it comes from outdoors: all of it.

Later chapters provide examples of ways to heat, cool, and ventilate different types of buildings.

EQUIPMENT SIZING

Properly sizing a heating or cooling system requires calculating the peak load for each room in the building.

The peak heating load is the amount of heat that needs to be supplied to a room to keep it comfortable during the coldest and windiest night of the year. Historical weather data can predict the coldest outdoor temperature fairly accurately. Record-breaking cold nights that may occur in the future are not that significant because those records are usually exceeded for only a few hours, which is not long enough for a building to cool down significantly. Calculating the peak heating load is fairly straightforward: add together the amount of heat required to warm up air that enters through a ventilation system, the amount required to heat air that enters through leaks, and the amount expected to move from indoors to outdoors through all surfaces exposed to cold temperatures (calculated by knowing the area and the heat conductance of those surfaces).

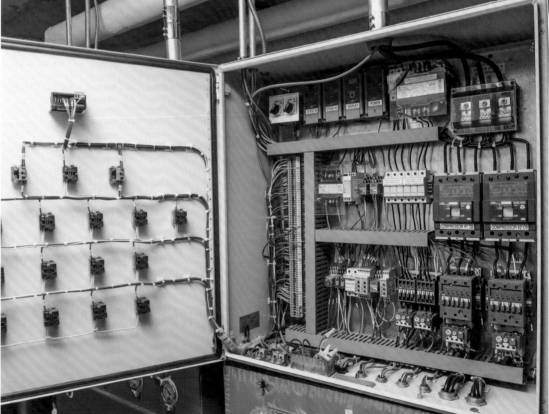

This is a control cabinet for a chiller, which is a machine that cools water to cool a building. It was installed in 2011. It was special-ordered with no computer for the sake of simplicity and ease of repair, and to eliminate problems with the software becoming obsolete. It was the first chiller in thirty years to come out of the factory without a built-in computer. It is still very complicated, but at least without a computer it is much simpler and easier to repair than a typical chiller.

Calculating peak cooling load is more complicated. The peak cooling load is the largest amount of heat and water vapor that needs to be removed from a room to keep it comfortable at any time of year. The peak cooling load in most rooms does not coincide with the hottest day of the year and often does not even coincide with the hottest time of day. This is because solar heat gain into windows dominates the cooling load in most rooms, and, depending on which direction windows face and where a building is located (as well as how well the glass is protected by shading), a room's cooling load can peak in the late spring, summer, or early fall, and might be in the morning, at midday, or in the afternoon. Calculating peak cooling load requires adding up all the heat and water vapor entering a room from many sources: solar gain; heat conducted from outdoors to indoors; heat contained in air entering from ventilation systems and air leaks; heat from lights, computers, and people; and water vapor from a range of sources, including cooking, ventilation systems, air leaks, and people sweating and breathing.

A person calculating a peak heating load assumes a room needs to be kept comfortable when no sunlight is shining into the windows, no people are in the room, and no equipment is adding heat to the room, which simplifies the task. And because heating systems generally don't add or remove water vapor from the room, heating load calculations do not consider humidity.

It is challenging to accurately calculate heating and cooling loads and accurately size the equipment, which is why most buildings today in most parts of the world still aren't being designed with accurate load calculations. Instead,

a rough estimate is made, which almost always includes generous oversizing. Oversized equipment does a poor job of keeping people comfortable and healthy, costs extra to buy and maintain, wastes space, makes more noise, and uses more energy. Many buildings today suffer from these problems due to oversized mechanical equipment.

Accurately sizing heating and cooling equipment is one of the cheapest ways to greatly improve the quality of a building. Paying for the calculations is not an extra cost because the reduced cost of correctly sized equipment will more than pay for the calculations.

The easiest and probably the only realistic way to predict how much energy a building will require is to look at the floor area of a building and the source energy input to the heating, cooling, and ventilation systems at peak loads. (For more on source energy, see the Appendix on Page 564). Dividing maximum energy input by floor area will produce the best prediction of the building's energy requirements (per floor area). In some parts of the world, this method is used as the basis for energy codes that are simple enough to be enforced.

These nine large rooftop HVAC units have a combined capacity that far exceeds the maximum possible heating, ventilating, and cooling needs of this building. Apparently nobody calculated the actual heating and cooling loads when the equipment was sized. That top floor built onto the building has no windows; therefore, it is probably not occupied by people. Perhaps it is just a giant duct cover (attic) for all the ducts for all that HVAC equipment. Smaller equipment would save money, space, and energy, while making the building quieter and more comfortable.

A ROOM WITHOUT A THERMOSTAT IS NOT A ROOM FOR PEOPLE

Ideally, every room in a building should have its own thermostat to control the temperature. Without a thermostat in each room, parts of a building will be overheated, overcooled, or both. The heating and cooling systems might be operating at the same time, using obscene amounts of energy while making the building uncomfortable.

What Is a Thermostat?

A thermostat is a device that has at least two information inputs and one output. One of the information inputs is the setpoint: the temperature a person would like the room to be. The other input is the sensed temperature: the temperature the thermostat's mechanism senses, or measures, in the surrounding air.

If the thermostat is controlling a heating system, and the sensed (room) temperature is lower than the setpoint, the thermostat will output a request for heat. The request for heat can be in the form of connecting two wires, similar to the way a light switch connects two wires. Or, with some types of thermostats, the demand moves a mechanical part to allow steam or hot water to flow into a heater.

Fancier thermostats make decisions based on additional information such as motion (which indicates the space is occupied) or time of day. Some even receive an electronic signal indicating that a person's cell phone is nearing the building, which can be used to switch the heating or cooling on before a person arrives.

Is a Thermostat in Every Room All It Takes?

In practice, though, certain types of heating and cooling systems are more difficult to control with thermostats in each room. Systems that deliver heating and cooling by moving air through ducts are difficult to control with a thermostat in each room because individual room controls would require large mechanical dampers to control the flow of air to each room, combined with some way of slowing the fan down when dampers close.

However, a thermostat in every room, or nearly every room, is necessary if energy efficiency and people's comfort are taken seriously. Systems that deliver heating and cooling with hot or cold water or refrigerant are easy to control this way by installing valves that slow or stop the flow of water or refrigerant to individual rooms. In Europe, almost every room has had its own thermostat for decades, but in other parts of the world this is not standard practice yet. The concept of a thermostat in each room is so young that the building industry does not yet have a unit of measure to describe the unevenness of temperature from one room to another or from one point in time to another. People who live in apartment buildings without thermostats in each room, or at least in each apartment, routinely control temperatures during the winter by opening windows. Many office workers keep coats or electric heaters at their desks, ready to use during the summer, when the cooling system is on full blast.

The cost to install a thermostat in every room can be thought of as an additional expense when installing a heating or cooling system. But since installing thermostats in every room allows a reduction in the size of the heating or cooling system (because they avoid the need to overheat or overcool some rooms to merely adequately heat or cool other rooms), the money saved by installing a smaller system can more than pay for the additional cost of the thermostats. Installing a system with a thermostat in each room would be less expensive overall.

The drawings on Pages 474 and 475 show the pitfalls of attempting to control the temperature of two rooms with a single thermostat. When more than two rooms—or all the rooms in one house—are controlled by one thermostat, the situation is even worse.

Thermostat Location

Many thermostats do not function well because they are not installed in appropriate locations. A design for a heating or cooling system is not complete unless it shows where the thermostats will be located.

Thermostats should be located where they will not be influenced by localized sources of cold air or heat. Locations to avoid include places near where sunlight enters a window, near a kitchen stove, or near a radiator or vent that delivers hot or cold air.

Thermostat Quizzes

Each of these photos shows a poorly designed thermostat installation.

Thermostat Quiz #1: What is wrong in this photo? Answer on Page 560.

Thermostat Quiz #2: What is wrong in this photo? Answer on Page 561.

Thermostat Quiz #3: What are some of the things wrong with the installation of the **four thermostats** in this photo? Clue: See the "Do Not Touch" signs in the close-up at right. Answer on Page 563.

Thermostat Quiz #4: What is wrong in this photo? Answer on Page 563.

Why One Thermostat Is Not Enough

The drawing at right shows a simple, two-room house with two radiators and just one thermostat.

The amount of heat the thermostat asks the heating system to deliver (to both rooms) depends on the temperature in the room with the thermostat.

On a day with no wind, the thermostat is keeping both rooms at a comfortable temperature.

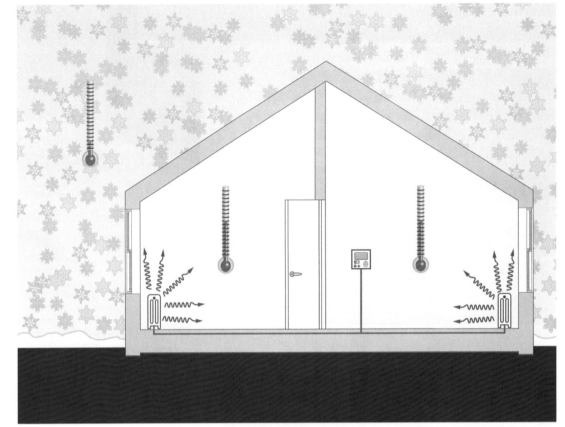

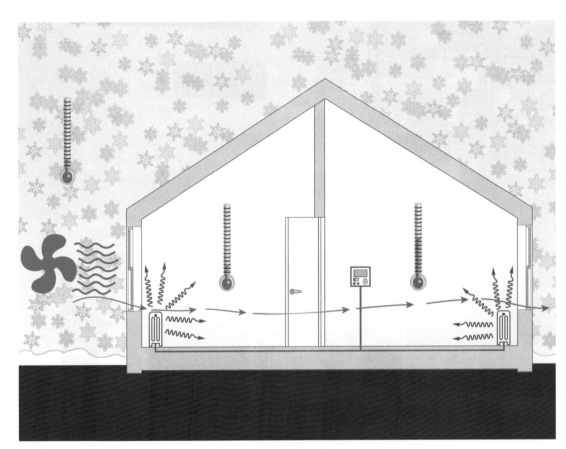

When wind blows from the left, cold outdoor air leaks into the room on the left, cooling that room. Because the thermostat is in the other room, it does not sense this lower temperature and won't send more heat to that room. The thermostat will eventually sense the cold air moving through the house and will tell the heating system to send more heat to both rooms, but when the room on the right is at a comfortable temperature, the heat will stop. The room on the left will still be cold.

Moving the thermostat to the room on the left solves the problem with the room on the left, but it creates a new problem. The cold air leaking into the room on the left is telling the thermostat to send a lot of heat to both rooms. The room on the right does not need as much heat because cold air is not leaking into that room—the air moving into that room has already been warmed by the radiator in the room on the left. There is no thermostat in the room on the right to sense the overheating and turn the heating system off.

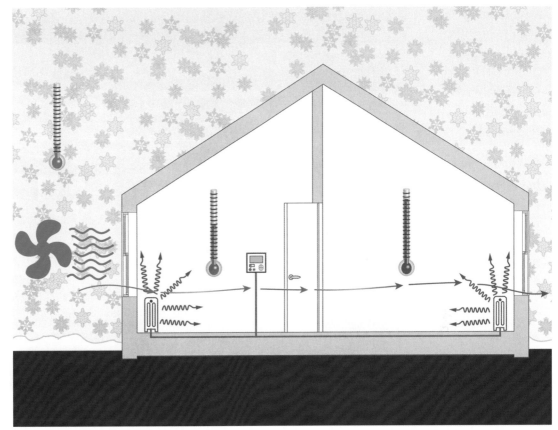

There is no single location for a thermostat that will solve this problem. Heat added by computers, refrigerators, people, and the sun further complicates the issue.

A good enclosure will help even out temperatures in different rooms but won't solve the problem completely. The only realistic way to stop overheating and underheating (or overcooling and undercooling by a cooling system) is to put a thermostat in every room and make sure they all work.

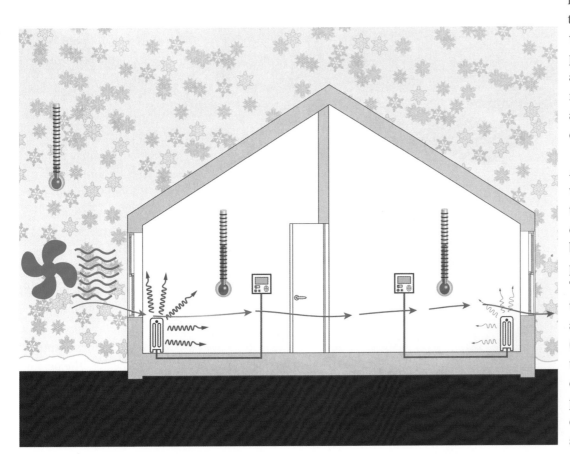

Each room in the apartment at right has its own individual **heater** controlled by its own individual thermostat.

Each room also has its own **air conditioner**, mounted in a removable panel in the casement window.

This makes the apartment very comfortable to live in while saving all the energy that would otherwise be wasted overheating or overcooling some rooms.

At left is a close-up of one of the heaters from the apartment above. The white thermostat knob contains a sealed capsule filled with heat-sensitive fluid. If the room is warm, the fluid expands and pushes on a valve that reduces or stops the flow of hot water to the heater. If the room is cold, the fluid shrinks, opening the valve and allowing hot water to flow through the heater. The person living in the apartment rotates the knob to select the desired temperature.

The photo at right shows the same type of thermostat controlling an old-fashioned cast iron radiator. The **thermostat** in the photo below left controls a bathroom heater that doubles as a towel warmer. The radiator valve in the photo below right is connected to a **wire** that communicates an open/close signal from a 24-volt electric thermostat (not shown) mounted on the wall.

Note that all the thermostats shown on these two pages are mounted low, where air from elsewhere in the room will pass over the thermostat as convection moves air up past the heater. This prevents heat from the heater from fooling the thermostat.

Arranging heating water piping so that each heater can be controlled individually, with each heater receiving about the same flow of heating water, can be very simple. One example of how to do this is shown on Pages 554 and 555.

HVAC SYSTEMS

As mentioned previously, HVAC is an acronym for heating, ventilation and air conditioning and typically refers to a system that moves air through ducts to accomplish these three tasks. Because air does not hold much heat (see Page 72), an HVAC system must move large amounts of air around a building to provide heating and cooling. Heating or cooling outdoor air and blowing it around a building would require too much energy, so HVAC systems typically heat or cool used indoor air and blow it around a building, which can spread germs. (See Pages 438 and 439.)

Because it is difficult to turn airflow on and off to individual rooms, many such systems are controlled by just one thermostat. Yes, whole apartments and houses with air-based systems usually operate on just one thermostat. In large houses, it is not unusual to install a separate air-based heating and cooling system for each section of the house. The additional equipment occupies space but makes the house much more comfortable than it would be if it had only one thermostat.

Sophisticated HVAC systems in office buildings can, in theory, provide heating, ventilation, and cooling with individual thermostats for each room or portion of the building. Sophisticated car-plane vehicles that can both drive on a road and fly through the air also exist—and perhaps some can even move through water like boats. But these vehicles are not popular—people prefer to buy separate vehicles, each optimized for one function.

Similarly, HVAC systems that provide all three functions in one system are a compromise, at best. And many systems described as HVAC systems only provide ventilation and cooling, while heating is provided with an easier-to-control "perimeter" heating system along the windows and walls that are exposed to outdoor air. Rooms located in the core of the building, which have no walls exposed to outdoors, never get any heat because they never need it. However, rooms in the core require cooling all year to remove heat added by lights, computers, copy machines, and people.

The perimeter heating system is usually a steam or water-based system, with valves controlling the flow of steam or water to heaters. The duct-based system sends cold air to all rooms, including rooms that need heat or don't need as much cooling. Sometimes heaters in the air grills on the ceiling reheat the cooling air; sometimes the perimeter heating system provides reheating (at the same time the cooling system is cooling those rooms). Sophisticated digital controls vary both the amount of cooling (to all rooms) to keep rooms in the core comfortable and the amount of reheating to keep perimeter rooms comfortable, while ideally also keeping the airflow high enough to provide sufficient fresh outdoor ventilation air. Because the same ducts supply air for ventilation as well as for cooling (and sometimes heating), the space is often either overcooled or underventilated. Frequent complaints of overcooling often lead to unhealthy underventilation because underventilation does not generate as many complaints as overcooling.

Even if all the spaces can be kept comfortable while providing required amounts of ventilation, a lot of energy is wasted cooling the air and then reheating it. Avoiding an HVAC system altogether is the best way to avoid this waste.

The box on the roof is an HVAC unit, which blows air throughout the office building for heating, ventilation, and cooling. The rooftop unit can only supply one temperature of air at a time. It sends the same temperature air to all areas of the building, including rooms in the core that need cooling during the winter, because they contain computers and other sources of heat. The cold air is also delivered to the perimeter, where it is reheated locally to keep people comfortable. Cooling air and then reheating it requires a lot of energy and also increases the difficulty of keeping people comfortable. Using the same ducts to also provide fresh outdoor ventilation air, ideally in the correct amount to each room, adds even more difficulty.

ADVANTAGES OF HVAC SYSTEMS

No Pipes to Freeze or Leak

An air-based heating and cooling system uses ducts to distribute heating and cooling air. The ducts do not contain any water-filled pipes that can freeze and break or that might leak when there is a problem with the pipes. However, the air handler or furnace that distributes the air might contain water-filled pipes that can freeze and break.

Cost

Air-based systems are often perceived as being inexpensive. But most such systems lack air return ducts, causing costly problems, which will be described later in this chapter. If an air-based system had both supply and return ducts, the cost would not be as attractive. An accurate cost comparison should also account for the cost of the space occupied by the air handling equipment and all the ducts. If every attic was thought of as a potential space for bedrooms, people might perceive the cost of ducts as being very high.

DISADVANTAGES OF HVAC SYSTEMS

Fire and Smoke Hazard

If a building catches fire, smoke and fire can easily spread through ducts. If the system is operating at the time of the fire, the fan will spread smoke throughout the building via the ducts even faster. Any time people are occupying the building, the system should be operating (for ventilation), so this hazard is always present when people are in the building. Heat-triggered fire dampers (see Page 325) in ducts will help, but they will not close if the smoke is not sufficiently hot. For this reason, codes generally require HVAC systems in large buildings to be equipped with complicated fire alarms, smoke alarms, and motorized dampers. This hazard and the cost of the additional required safety systems can be avoided by using individual HVAC systems in each fire zone, but this approach requires a lot of space. A better solution is individual ventilation-only systems in each fire zone, as shown in Chapter 20: Schools, Chapter 21: Apartment Buildings, and Chapter 22: Office Buildings.

Increased Airflow through Leaks

As mentioned earlier, most air-based systems have air supply ducts only. They lack ducts to return air to the air handler (or rooftop HVAC unit or furnace, etc.). This causes airflow problems, including increased airflow through leaks in the building enclosure, described on Pages 483-488. Even a system with return ducts will move air through leaks unless all its ducts are perfectly airtight and return the exact same amount of air they supply to each room, which is not easy to accomplish. Increasing airflow through leaks not only wastes energy, but causes indoor air to become dry during the winter.

Discomfort

Moving a lot of air around a building can reduce people's comfort during the winter.

Photo: Mary Hackie.

This **furnace** burns fuel oil to heat a house. **Ducts** send hot air to each room of the house. The oil burner is connected to an oil tank with two **copper tubes**. An **exhaust vent pipe** carries combustion exhaust to a chimney (not shown), which carries the combustion exhaust outdoors.

Occupying Valuable Space

The office and retail building shown on this page has an HVAC system that needs to move a large amount of air to provide heating and cooling to the building. Moving all that air requires fans so large they cannot fit in a single floor of the building. In this case, the mechanical "floor" that contains them, shown below left, is almost as tall as two normal floors.

The vast majority of the space is occupied by fans and ducts. The equipment floor also contains boilers, which heat water that is pumped to water-based heaters at the perimeter of each floor, and chillers, which cool water. The cooled water is used to cool air, which the fans push through the ducts to cool the entire building. Originally, the ducts also supplied hot air to the whole building for heating, but that portion of the system was abandoned, because the core never needed heat, and the perimeter had its own water-based heating system.

Large Fan Electricity Requirement

HVAC fans not only occupy a lot of valuable real estate, they also require a lot of electricity. When a modern office building's HVAC system is in full cooling mode on a hot day, the energy the fans require is generally over one-third of the energy the whole HVAC system requires.[1] Most of the remaining energy operates the chiller, the pumps that move water around the building, and the cooling tower, which is the device that sends heat outdoors.

The amount of electricity required to operate an office building HVAC system usually peaks on a hot summer afternoon when the sun is shining flat against the glass on

1   Steve Kavanaugh, "Three Air-Distribution Systems: Fan Demand and Energy," <u>ASHRAE Journal</u>, June 2000, Page 50; Australian Government Department of Environment and Energy, "Factsheet: HVAC Energy Breakdown," HVAC HESS, September 2013, Page 1; Detlef Westphalen and Scott Koszalinski, <u>Energy Consumption Characteristics of Commercial Building HVAC Systems, Vol. II: Thermal Distribution, Auxiliary Equipment, and Ventilation</u> (Cambridge, MA: Arthur D. Little, Inc., 1999), Page 5-25.

A man is standing on the HVAC equipment floor of the building at right. The green wall is part of a two-story-tall enclosure around one of the fans that moves air for the HVAC system. The ducts that move air through the building's HVAC system take up a lot of valuable space throughout all floors of the building.

The HVAC equipment floor is about as tall as two normal floors. It is mostly occupied by ducts and fans for the building's HVAC system (the system also serves a small two-story part of the building, not visible). The equipment floor occupies approximately 20 percent of the volume of the building. Large ducts occupy additional space.

the west side of the building. It is not a coincidence that the amount of electricity provided by North American grids peaks during summer weekday afternoons, not on weekends when home air conditioning systems run all day. Most electric-system blackouts occur during hot summer weekday afternoons when office HVAC systems are running at peak capacity. It is not a stretch to say that electricity-generating power plants are built to power the fans in HVAC systems—at least in North America. Eliminating HVAC system fans could reduce the number of power plants needed.

HVAC systems can be eliminated entirely by installing one or more separate ventilation systems. The fans in ventilation-only systems, as described in more detail in Chapter 17: Indoor Air Quality, can be much smaller because they only need to move enough air to ventilate— rather than enough to also provide heating or cooling. Heating and cooling can be distributed throughout the building by pumping hot or cold water or refrigerant through pipes, which requires only a small fraction of

the electricity required by HVAC fans. For example, the pump moving water to the heaters in all 24 apartments in the building on Page 476 requires only 90 watts (for all 24 apartments total). This is less energy than required to operate the lights in the same building's mechanical room.

With a water-based system, air does not need to be moved around a building to provide heating and cooling, but it still needs to be moved to provide ventilation. Individual ventilation systems on each floor of an office building, as described in Chapter 22: Ventilating, Heating, and Cooling an Office Building, require much less electricity than one large ventilation system for the whole building. One of the reasons is that the fans in individual ventilation systems don't need to move air long distances, just through short ducts on each floor only. (Because the ducts are smaller, they also save valuable space.)

The same principles hold true for any type of building: save energy and space with a ventilation-only system, and pump water or refrigerant to heat and cool the building.

A man is sitting on a spare electric motor for one of the HVAC system fans in the building shown on Page 480. The motor requires a large amount of electricity all year, including when electricity prices are at their peak: during hot summer afternoons.

The **equipment floor** of this fourteen-story building is taller than the other floors. It is occupied only by fans and pumps for the HVAC system. Eliminating the HVAC system and moving the pumps to the boiler room (in the basement) would free up this floor for more offices.

PROBLEMS RELATED TO DUCTING AIR AROUND BUILDINGS

Ducts Leak Air

The photo at right shows a duct on an attic floor. The duct transports air to heat the house.

Hot air escaping from connections between duct sections is heating the surfaces near the leaks, which show up as white (hot) in the infrared photo below.

The amount of air that typically leaks out of ducts is enough to have a significant impact on a building's comfort, durability, and energy use.

Fans Drive Air through Leaks

The drawing at right shows air leaking out of ducts in an attic. The + and - symbols show air pressure differences created by the fan.

Conditioned air is leaking out of the ducts. This causes the air pressure in the attic to increase and the air pressure in the living space to decrease (because the fan pushes air from the living space out through duct leaks into the attic). The air leaking into the attic escapes outdoors via the attic vent and is replaced by outdoor air the fan pulls in through leaks.

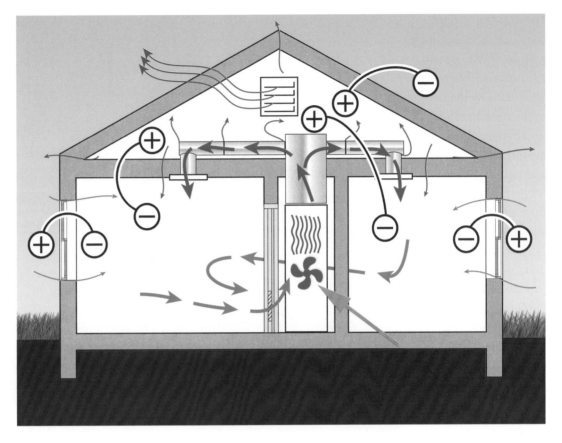

It is best to make the attic a fully indoor space. Or, ducts can be located in the indoor part of the house, as shown below. Now, when air escapes from the ducts, it leaks into the same indoor space that the fan is already pushing air into. The fan does not create any pressure difference between the house and the attic, or the house and outdoors. The fan is not pushing conditioned air outdoors or pulling outdoor air into the house. It is easier to fit heating/cooling ducts indoors if a building has a good enclosure because small heating and cooling loads allow the use of smaller ducts. Ventilation-only ducts would be even smaller.

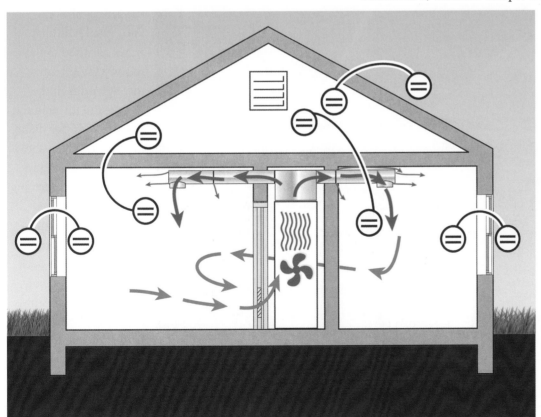

The drawing at right shows an office building with an HVAC system. Air pressure differences are caused by the fan in the rooftop HVAC unit blowing **heating air** through ducts and pulling **room temperature air** back through the space above the ceiling. The fan raises the air pressure in the office to a level higher than outdoors. This pushes air out through any leaks in the windows or walls. The air pressure in the space above the ceiling is lower than outdoors, which pulls outdoor air in through leaks near the roof, wasting energy.

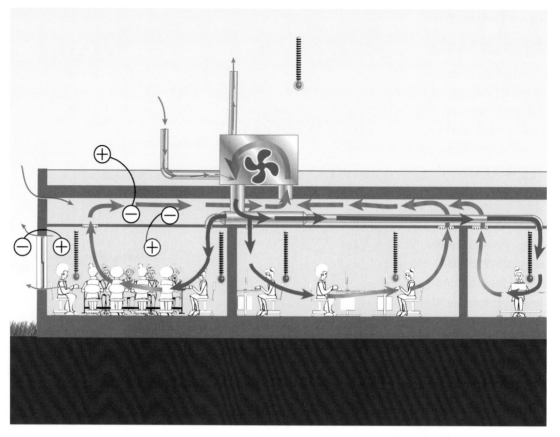

The photo at left shows air supply ducts that are normally hidden above the ceiling of a one-floor retail building. Air is returned to the rooftop HVAC unit through grills in the ceiling and through the space around the ducts, as in the drawing above. Using the space above the ceiling for returning air greatly increases air flow through any leaks at the connection between the **roof deck** and the wall assembly, which is prone to air leaks. (See Page 97.) A second set of ducts for returning air would solve this problem (but would also occupy additional space).

The photo at right shows an ordinary furnace in an apartment closet. The furnace heats air, and its fan blows it through ducts to heat the apartment. The fan in the furnace pulls return air from the apartment through a grill in the closet wall, then through a **box** the furnace rests on, and then up into the furnace. A gas fire inside the furnace heats the air. The same fan in the furnace pushes the hot air through a **main duct**, which branches out to other ducts that supply hot air to each room of the apartment.

The gas fire in the furnace needs air to supply oxygen for combustion, and the combustion exhaust (nitrogen, carbon dioxide, water vapor, soot, etc.) needs to be exhausted outdoors. Air enters the apartment through leaks and then enters the closet through **louvers** in the closet door. Products of combustion are exhausted from the furnace by convection via an **exhaust vent pipe**, which is routed to a **tee connection**, which connects to the **vent pipe** that comes from the furnace in the apartment downstairs and continues up to a connection to the furnace upstairs, then through the roof to outdoors.

This arrangement will work if there are no leaks in any ducts or vent pipes and if the draft in the chimney pulls all the products of combustion from all of the furnaces out of the building. It also depends on the apartment walls leaking enough air to supply combustion air to the furnaces (and to replace any air that leaks from leaky ducts to outdoors).

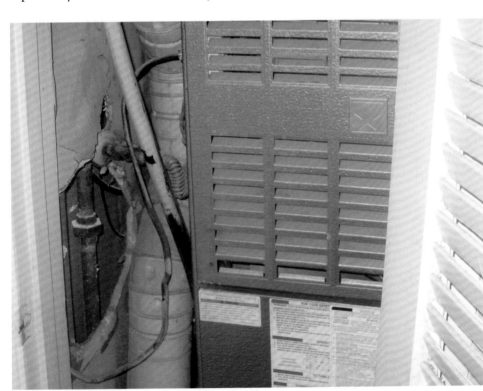

If anything disturbs the supply of combustion air, or if a strong wind or anything else disturbs the flow of exhaust to outdoors, the furnace can produce deadly carbon monoxide, which the fan and ducts will quickly spread throughout the apartment. The photo at left shows a hole in the wall of the closet, probably made to service the gas pipe years ago, which was never repaired. Airflow through the hole driven by the stack effect, wind, and the furnace fans can easily disturb the supply of combustion air or the flow of combustion exhaust out of the chimney. This installation would be much safer if the hole were patched and if the furnaces in the building were the sealed combustion type. (Sealed combustion will be explained later in this chapter.)

Closing Doors Forces Air through Leaks in the Walls

The drawing at right shows **ducts** supplying air to each room of the house. The air comes out of a grill on the ceiling of each room and then moves through the room, through each doorway (all the doors are open), through the hallways, and then back to the **furnace**, which heats the air and sends it back into the ducts. The drawing shows all the air going where intended, as if no ducts leak.

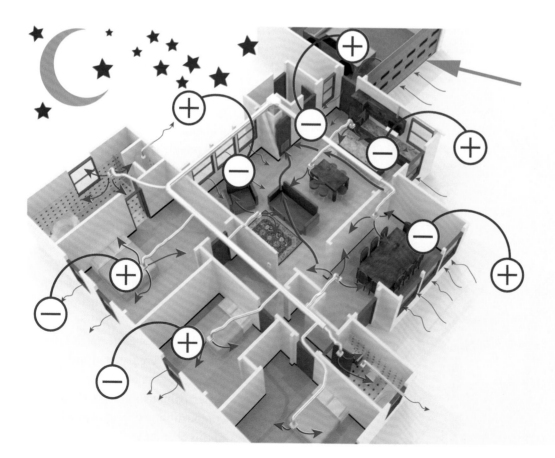

At night, however, people tend to close bedroom doors. The bedroom doorways are part of the return path for the air to get back to the furnace. Closing the doors keeps air from circulating. This causes the pressure differences shown by the + and - symbols. The pressure differences move air through leaks in the building's enclosure, as shown, which wastes energy. Because the garage is connected to the house, some of the air pulled in comes in through the **garage**, which is not a healthy place to get air from.

The drawings on this page show the same house with one important difference: the garage is a separate building. Now, when bedroom doors are closed (drawing below), pressure differences still move air into and out of the house. The air still leaks from indoors to out through leaks in bedrooms because the fan is pushing air into the bedrooms; the air also leaks from outdoors to indoors through leaks in other rooms, because the fan is pulling on those rooms. But now, at least, incoming air won't be pulled through the garage.

Gaps under bedroom doors can solve the problem of closed doors restricting the path of air returning to the furnace—but at the cost of greatly increased sound transmission between the bedrooms and the rest of the house. Transfer grills, as shown on the next page, can help by allowing air to move while reducing sound transmission.

Reducing the Problem: Transfer Grills Provide the Air with an Easy Return Route

The drawing at right shows a transfer grill mounted at the bottom of a door. Grills are sold specifically for this purpose and are designed to minimize the transfer of light and sound through the door. They reduce light transmission by creating a zigzag pathway light cannot pass straight through, and they reduce sound transmission by eliminating openings big enough for a large sound wave to pass through. The drawing below shows a method that transmits even less light and sound.

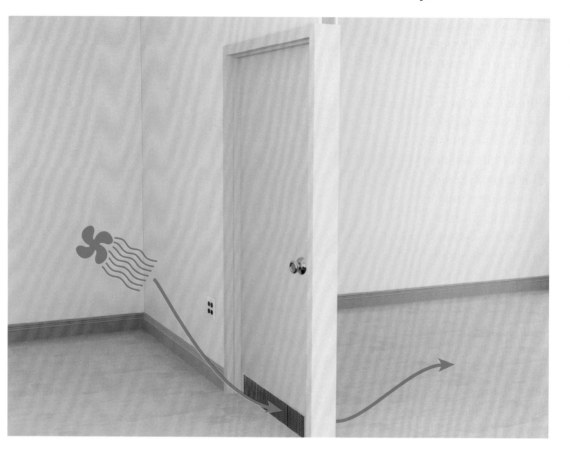

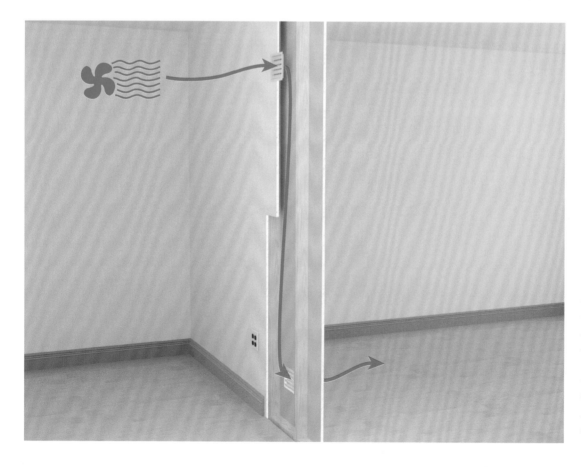

The drawing at left shows a wall with a grill mounted high up on one side and another grill mounted down low on the other side. Both grills are mounted within the same wall cavity, so air can easily flow from one grill to the other. This gives air a pathway to return to the furnace without having to go through the doorway. The long vertical separation between the grills greatly reduces the amount of light and sound that passes through the wall.

BEST SOLUTION: COOLING AND HEATING WITHOUT DUCTS

People think ducts are necessary for cooling, and a good idea for heating, but nothing could be further from the truth. Many types of cooling systems do not use ducts. One is the ductless split system, as shown here and on the following pages. During the summer, each indoor unit cools the room it is in and is connected via small copper tubes to an outdoor unit that rejects heat outdoors. During the winter, the same unit can heat the room.

Valences, which don't use ducts either, have the additional advantage of being completely silent. (See Pages 501-503.) Another silent system that does not use ducts is a radiant ceiling, shown on Pages 505-506.

Heating and cooling with a radiant floor is possible, too. Radiant heating floors are discussed on Page 504. Radiant cooling floors have several major limitations. Condensation easily forms on a cold floor, such as the uninsulated floor in the photo on Page 154. Convection causes cold air to blanket a cold floor in a layer, worsening the problem. The insulating value of furniture will keep the floor even colder, creating even more condensation. Condensation on a floor not only creates a slip-and-fall hazard, but also can cause mold. Therefore, the use of radiant cooling floors should be limited to rooms that have good humidity control and no furniture. Few rooms (other than a lobby or an art gallery) fit this criteria.

A deciduous tree is also an effective form of cooling, although it can take years for it to grow tall enough to shade a two-story house. Vines clinging to fishing line strung across a window can provide shade while preserving most of the view outward. (See Page 68.)

All of the systems described above (except the trees and vines) are easily controlled by a thermostat in each room. All of them, including deciduous trees, can also be used to heat a building. (Deciduous trees lose their leaves during the winter, allowing the sun to heat the building.)

Installing a Ductless Split Indoor Unit

The photo at right shows installation preparations for a ductless split indoor cooling and heating unit. (A "split" system has one piece of equipment indoors and another outdoors.)

The **two copper tubes** will carry refrigerant between the indoor and outdoor parts of the system. The **drain tube** will carry condensation to a drain. The **wires** will carry both the thermostat signal and the electricity (about 100 watts) to operate a small fan.

The square **hole in the ceiling** (see photo above) is for a ventilation duct that will supply a constant flow of fresh outdoor air to the room from an ERV ventilation system. Because the ventilation duct is small enough to fit between roof joists, the bedroom ceiling can be mounted directly on the roof joists, eliminating the need for an attic to contain ducts.

At left is the **indoor unit** installed above the doorway.

Ceiling Cassette Units

The photo at right shows **ductless split ceiling cassettes**. These units cool (and probably also heat) a fancy steakhouse. During the summer they pull warm room air in through the grill in the center and blow cool air out through the slots around the edges.

The **smaller ceiling grills** are for a separate ventilation-only system.

The mezzanine floor in the photo at left is above the counter at a busy delicatessen. Mounted within the floor are two ductless split ceiling cassettes, which cool people below—on both sides of the counter. The supporting structure within the floor doesn't leave a lot of room for ducts but does have space for ductless splits, which eliminated any temptation to lower the ceiling to make room for ducts.

The photo at right shows the same kind of ductless split ceiling cassette in the lobby of an apartment building, where it provides cooling during the summer and heating during the winter.

Ductless split indoor units are available in many sizes to handle different loads. In a very large room, such as the steakhouse on the top of Page 491, multiple smaller units are used to avoid hot and cold spots within the room.

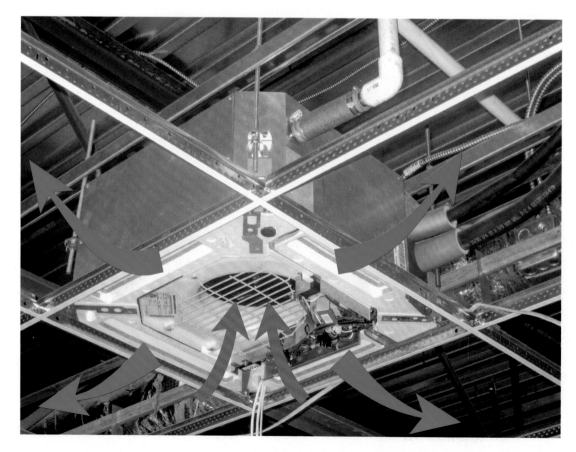

At left is a close-up of a ceiling cassette with the ceiling around it removed. A small fan built into the cassette pulls **room-temperature air** into the center of the unit and blows **cold air** out slots around the sides, from where it skims along the ceiling.

The unit also contains a small pump to move condensate to a drain and has connections to refrigerant tubes and wires like other ductless splits do.

Ceiling-Mounted Ductless Splits

The large ceiling-mounted ductless split indoor units shown on this page are much larger than ceiling cassettes. They can cool rooms with very large cooling loads.

At right is a conference room that sometimes fills up with a lot of people. The room has a lot of single-pane, unshaded glass that gets sun during both the middle of the day and the afternoon, when the sun is setting in the west. This ductless split can handle the large cooling load.

The grill on the ceiling is a remnant of an old duct-based system that has been abandoned. (That system should be removed, or at least its ducts should be closed off, as it is now just a series of large holes.)

The high-capacity ceiling-mounted indoor unit in the photo below cools part of a restaurant that gets crowded with people. Also contributing to the cooling load are lights, warm humid air coming in the front door, and countless plates of food that give off both heat and water vapor. The unit removes both heat and water vapor, just as most cooling systems do.

Hiding Ductless Splits

Some people want to hide their ductless splits; other people show them off.

Barbara Carmody, the owner of a house cooled by ductless splits, is one of those people who thinks they are cool. (Her kitchen is shown on the bottom of page 489.) "It's not unlike radiators in older homes—you get used to them in the room," says Carmody. "They remind you that you made a good choice."

She also likes it when friends notice the ductless split indoor units. "It gives me a chance to brag about our energy efficiency," she says.

For those who don't like to brag, there are other options. The photo on the right shows a wall-mounted unit with a wood box built around it, carefully built to hopefully not block airflow into or out of the unit. The photo below shows a wall-mounted unit partly hidden by a built-in bookcase. Neither of these units will have perfect air circulation around them. Poor air circulation could hinder performance, so any efforts to hide indoor units should be done with care to avoid blocking airflow.

In both of these cases, it might be better to buy another type of ductless split indoor unit, which can be completely hidden above a ceiling, as shown on the next page.

Ceiling-Concealed Units

Ductless split indoor units can also be hidden inside ceilings. This type is called a "ceiling-concealed" unit, or a "slim-ducted" unit. Strictly speaking, this type is not ductless, but because the ducts are so short, they are relatively problem-free (and don't occupy much space).

The arrows in the photo at right show the airflow path. The fan in the ceiling-concealed unit pulls **room-temperature air** under a closet door and through a grill on the closet ceiling. It then pushes the air through the coil filled with refrigerant, which cools the air, and then the **cold air** comes out a grill on the wall above the closet door.

Because the ducts that connect the grills to the indoor unit are all within the same room, the fan moving air through those ducts does not create air pressure differences between rooms or between indoors and outdoors.

If ducts are run from a ceiling-concealed unit to a few nearby rooms, the unit can cool (or heat) a whole apartment or a few rooms of a house. As soon as the doors between those rooms are closed, however, significant pressure differences will be created, which will cause the problems common to conventional air-based systems mentioned earlier (more air moving through leaks). If budget allows, it is better to install a separate ceiling-concealed unit for each room, unless the apartment or house has very small rooms.

The photo at right shows a ductless split unit built into a ceiling. It is connected to two air ducts. One **duct** will move cold air into the room where the unit is located; the **other duct** will move cold air to the adjacent room.

The **blue tape** covering the return-air intake is there to keep dust out of the unit during construction. The tape will be removed before the unit is turned on. (The open ends of the supply ducts should also be covered.)

The photo at right shows gypsum board covering the same unit shown on the bottom of Page 495. The **opening** at the top of the photo will be covered with a grill (also called a "register") which will supply cold air (or hot air during the winter). The **opening** at the bottom of the photo will be covered with a grill through which room air will return to the unit.

The photo at left shows where the unit in the photo above will deliver cold (or hot) air to each room. In the room the unit is located in, air will be discharged from **a grill** on the side of the box (soffit) built into the ceiling. Air for the adjacent room (at left) will be discharged from **a grill** in the brick wall. The doorway between rooms will not have a door. It will remain open, which will allow air to move freely back to the indoor unit.

Sequence of construction for hiding a ceiling-concealed unit above a closet ceiling: ① The ceiling-concealed unit gets mounted to the floor/ceiling structure above—wood joists in this example. ② The wood studs for the closet walls get installed. ③ Short ducts get installed: a **return duct** will bring air from the ceiling to the unit, and a supply duct will move air from the unit to the room. ④ Gypsum board goes up, and then finally return and supply grills get installed. Because the supply grill is located on the wall near the ceiling, the air coming out of it will skim along the ceiling, reducing discomfort caused by heating with hot air. (See Pages 460-461 for an explanation of how this improves comfort.)

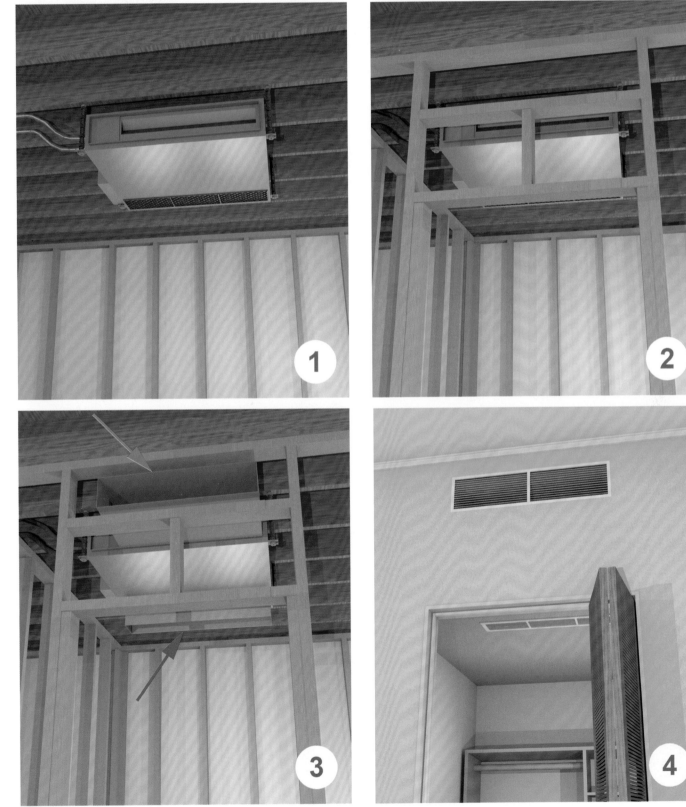

Drawings by Tiffany Benavides.

The photo at right shows a **ceiling-concealed unit** mounted in a ceiling with no closet to hide it. The ceiling was partly closed up when the photo was taken. The blue tape covers the air intake to keep dust out during construction. After the air gets cooled, the **short duct** moves air a short distance away, where it will exit through a grill (not installed yet) that will be connected to **the end of the supply duct**.

The photo at left shows the same installation with all the gypsum board installed and painted. The next step will be to remove the blue tape and install the grills.

Ductless Split Outdoor Units

When ductless splits are cooling (or heating) a building, the circulating refrigerant moves the heat to (or from) the outdoor unit, which conducts and radiates the heat to (or from) outdoors, just as other cooling or heat pump systems do. (See Page 511.)

The photo at right shows an outdoor unit that is connected to four indoor units. Each of the four **pairs of copper tubing** circulates refrigerant in a loop between the outdoor unit and one of the four indoor units.

The photo at left shows a mounting bracket that will be used to hold an outdoor unit. The wires will supply electricity to the outdoor unit and carry control signals between the indoor and outdoor units.

Ductless split outdoor units can also sit on a small piece of concrete resting directly on the soil. If they will be used for heat during the winter, it is better to mount them above the ground to keep them clear of snow.

Each ductless split outdoor unit in the photo at right provides heating and cooling to an individual apartment in a nine-story apartment building. The refrigerant tubes are routed through **sheet metal goosenecks**, which keep rain from penetrating the roof.

Note that there are no ventilation fans or ducts on the roof. In this building, each apartment has its own individual ventilation system, which moves air in and out through each apartment's exterior wall.

Each ductless split in the building above is connected to it's apartment's electric meter, which gives the occupants an incentive to conserve both heating and cooling energy.

The photo at left shows an office building with a **row of ductless split outdoor units** on the roof. The building has no HVAC system, which means no space is occupied by HVAC system ducts. The building gets all its heating and cooling from ductless split indoor units throughout the building.

Valences for Heating and Cooling

Valences are another way to provide heating and cooling without ducts or fans. The photo at right shows a **valence** that provides heating and cooling in a retirement home. Valences have many advantages: they require no fan, make no noise, have no filters to clean or change, can be controlled by individual thermostats, and require little or no maintenance. The energy saved by not having fans is another advantage. The main disadvantage is that they can't easily be hidden behind a ceiling the way ductless split ceiling-concealed units can.

The photo below shows the inside of a valence. An **electric valve** opens or closes in response to a signal from a thermostat, controlling the flow of hot or cold water through a **coil**. Hot water comes from either a boiler or a solar thermal system, and cold water comes from a chiller. The hot or cold water flows as long as the thermostat asks for heating or cooling and stops flowing when the thermostat is satisfied and closes the valve.

The coil is a row of copper tubes with fins on them, similar to a car radiator. Water flows through the copper tubes. The large surface area of the fins transfers heat to or from the surrounding air by conduction and to or from nearby objects by radiation. The difference in temperature between the air around the coil and the air in the room drives convective air currents, which move air through the coil. (See illustrations on the next page.)

During the summer, the coil usually cools air to a temperature lower than its dewpoint temperature, condensing water out of the air. Each valence has a **foam insulating layer**, which keeps the outside surface of the valence warm enough to prevent the formation of condensation there and muffles the sound of water dripping off the coil. Each valence has a **condensate drain pipe**, which is connected to the building's plumbing drains. Condensate drips off the coil, runs down the foam, and then goes down the drain.

Because a valence has no fan, it is completely silent. Complete silence is a big advantage in many types of buildings, especially schools and libraries.

The drawing at right shows a **valence** heating a classroom on a cold day. Hot water in the coil heats the air around the coil, which drives a convective air current that pulls room air into the bottom of the valence and pushes hot air out the top of the valence.

The drawing at left shows a valence operating in cooling mode during the summer. Cold water in the coil cools air, which falls by convection out the bottom of the valence, pulling hot air into the top of the valence. Because convection moves air through the coil slowly, the air gets cooled close to the temperature of the water in the coil (normally below the air's dewpoint temperature), which makes valences very effective at dehumidifying summer air.

The valence at right cools and heats a research scientist's office.

The valence in the photo below right cools and heats a hallway in the basement of a hotel. Low maintenance requirements make valences popular in dormitories, too.

The valence below left has a long fluorescent light mounted behind it, making it double as a cove-type light fixture, supplying the room with indirect light.

Radiant Floors

The photo at right shows a radiant floor that heats the room with hot water circulated through tubing hidden underneath it. The infrared photo below gives an idea of what is happening beneath the floor. One advantage of a radiant floor (or ceiling) is that it takes up zero floor space.

Radiant floors can be problematic in energy-efficient buildings because it takes so long to warm up and cool down the thermal mass (see Page 13) of a floor and its supporting structure. A common problem with radiant floors in any type of building occurs when sunlight shining in a window meets much or all of the room's heating load, yet the floor, though turned off, is still emitting heat. Regardless of how quickly the thermostat turns off the heat, the heat stored in the thermal mass of the floor will continue to heat the room for some time, causing overheating. Later, when the sun suddenly disappears behind a building across the street, the room will be underheated until the floor warms up. Solving the underheating problem by operating the floor at a higher water temperature can increase the overheating problem.

Comparing two buildings with floors that have identical thermal masses but with higher and lower heating loads, the building with the lower heating load will have more of a problem. Described another way, Stage Three buildings are more vulnerable to this problem than Stage Two buildings, which are more vulnerable than Stage One buildings. Comparing two buildings with identical heating loads but floors with higher and lower thermal mass, the building that has floors with a higher thermal mass will have more of a problem because those floors will respond more slowly.

Much of the comfort that radiant floors are credited with is actually deserved by other things usually installed at the

same time as radiant floors: insulation that keeps a floor warm, a thermostat in each room, an "outdoor reset" control which makes the heating system water warmer in colder weather, and a sealed combustion boiler (which does not pull cold air through the building—described later in this chapter). These same comfort improvements can be combined with low thermal mass heaters such as the one shown on Page 530, which can respond fast enough to prevent problems.

A radiant floor can also provide cooling if cool water is circulated through the tubing. Unfortunately, during the summer, people are generally comfortable with a cool upper body but not with cool feet. This problem and problems with condensation limit the use of radiant cooling floors.

Radiant Cooling Ceilings

A radiant cooling ceiling can provide people with the comfort of a cool upper body during the summer—without the discomfort of cold feet.

The photo at right shows the back (upper) side of a radiant cooling ceiling. Heat moves from the room to the metal panels by conduction and by infrared radiation. Cool water pumped through the tubing absorbs heat from the panels. To prevent condensation, the temperature of the panels must be above the dewpoint temperature of the air in the room. This is easiest to do in a Stage Three building.

Half the new office space in Europe is cooled by radiant cooling ceilings according to one manufacturer. The panels and controls are easily reconfigured when tenants move out and in.

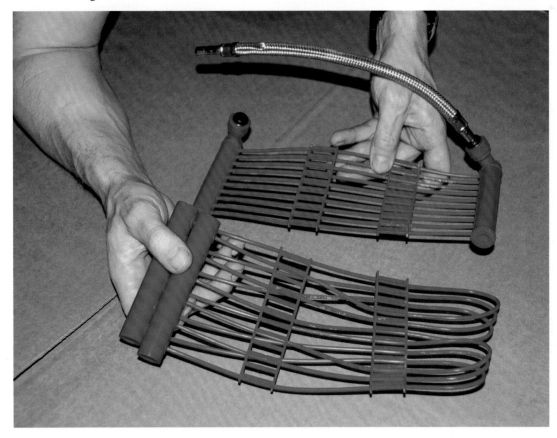

The photo at left shows small-diameter plastic tubing that can be embedded in the plaster of a ceiling. (The actual tubing used is much longer. These are just samples.) Cool water circulated through the tubing can cool the room. Many small-diameter tubes are necessary to keep the ceiling's surface temperature even, which helps prevent condensation. Radiant ceilings save energy because they require no fan and make it easy to control each room with its own thermostat.

Radiant Gypsum Board Ceiling Panels

Another type of radiant ceiling, shown below, is a radiant gypsum board panel. The gypsum board surface makes it appropriate for use in homes and many other types of buildings. The **back layer**, furthest from the finished surface, is foam insulation. Large **main water-supply pipes** and a network of smaller **tubes** move cold water through grooves in the foam. A layer of aluminum conducts heat to the network of small tubes. The outer face of the panel, which will be exposed, is a **layer of gypsum board**. Special connectors join the pipes from one panel to another. The face of the gypsum board is marked to show the locations of tubing within the panel. This makes it easy to cut the panels and make holes in them for lights or sprinkler heads without damaging the tubing.

Note that a house with radiant cooling can have high ceilings because it has no need for cooling ducts.

People are generally comfortable with a heating system that makes their feet warmer than their heads but not comfortable with a heating system that makes their heads warmer than their feet. This limits the use of radiant heating ceilings to buildings that require only a little heat during the winter, such as some of the very well-insulated Stage Three buildings being built now.

Because ceilings generally have lower thermal mass than floors, radiant ceilings respond to changes in load (cool down and heat up) much faster than radiant floors, which of course makes it easier to control room temperature.

Any building with radiant cooling ceilings needs an effective air barrier in the enclosure to prevent humid outdoor air from leaking into the building and causing condensation on the ceiling. A building with an air barrier, radiant cooling ceilings, and a separate dehumidification system will be comfortable, healthy quiet, spacious, and energy efficient.

Window Air Conditioners

A window air conditioner is a unitary type of cooling system: all the parts are in one place. Unitary systems are assembled, filled with refrigerant, adjusted, and tested under controlled conditions at the factory, which improves their reliability.

Window air conditioners each have their own thermostats, too (sometimes with remote controls), which automatically provides room-by-room thermostatic control.

On the downside, window air conditioners are noisier than some other types of cooling systems, though the constant hum can serve as a form of white noise, which can be useful in cities. Window air conditioners also block part of the view. Also, if they are left in place during the winter, as in the photo at right (note the **snow** on the ground) they allow cold, dry outdoor air to leak in, which decreases comfort while increasing energy use. Ideally, window units should be removed during the winter and re-installed in the spring. This keeps cold air from leaking in.

The photo at right shows a storage room in an apartment building's basement. This is where window air conditioners should go to sleep during the winter. Not only will people who live in these apartments be healthier because of reduced leakage of cold, dry outdoor air, but also their heating bills will be lower.

Another approach is to leave the window unit installed and cover the indoor side of it with a foam cover like the one on the top of Page 476 (the room on the right). The cover reduces air leakage while also providing a little insulation.

Creative AC Installations

The window air conditioners in the photo at right are mounted through the wall of the building. The building is in a hot climate where the AC units are used year round, thus they never need to be removed. This keeps windows functional and unobstructed all year.

The unit in the photo below is mounted in a window with a small fixed opening. When the air conditioner is removed during the winter, it can be replaced with a piece of glass.

The decorative covers above and the stainless steel mesh cover at left do a nice job of hiding the air conditioning units. However, they reduce air circulation around them, too, which increases energy use, reduces cooling capacity, and shortens the life of each air conditioning unit (because it is surrounded by hotter air, which can contribute to overheating the motors and circuit boards in the unit).

Sleeve Air Conditioners

The air conditioner at right is a sleeve unit, which is similar to a window unit, with one key difference. Sleeve units reject heat to outdoors by moving outdoor air in and then back outdoors through the part of the unit that faces outdoors. Window units work a little differently: they pull outdoor air in the sides of the unit and push it back out the part facing outdoors. Because a window unit pulls air in through its sides, the sides need to be exposed to outdoor air. Sleeve units do not need to be exposed to air on their sides.

Because sleeve units have a smaller surface area to move air through (the part that faces outdoors only, not the sides), they need a proportionally larger fan to move the same amount of air a window unit would need for the same cooling capacity. A larger fan requires more electricity and makes more noise. Designing a unit with a smaller fan is possible but only by compromising some other aspect of the design, which can result in lower efficiency or lower cooling capacity than that of an equivalent window unit.

The photo at top right shows a sleeve unit used to cool a small security guard building. The AC unit looks grossly oversized for such a tiny building.

The photo at right shows a relatively attractive way to cool a building: with sleeve units mounted in windows. The sleeve units are mounted flush with the facade. Window units would have to protrude from the facade, which would create a different look.

PTACs

"Package terminal air conditioners," also called PTACs, are used to provide heating and cooling in one room, typically in a motel, hotel, or apartment. The photo at right shows a typical PTAC unit in a motel room.

There are many types of PTACs. Some reject summer heat to outdoors through a grill in the wall (see bottom of Page 33); some reject heat to a loop of water pumped around the building. Another type, usually considered the indoor part of a ductless split system, rejects heat to refrigerant piped around the building. A "fan coil" (see Page 557)—which cools or heats a room by blowing air over a coil containing cold or hot water—is sometimes also considered a type of PTAC.

There are still other types of PTACs. Some are heat pumps that get heat from outdoor air, others get heat from steam piped around the building, and still others burn gas that is piped to each PTAC.

Exactly what qualifies a device for the name PTAC depends on who you ask. But it generally is a device that does both heating and cooling, is mounted on an outdoor wall below a window, and is so easy to remove and replace that repairs are usually done off-site in a repair shop, while a "loaner" unit is installed temporarily.

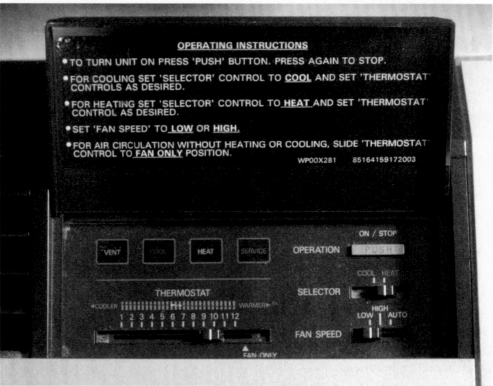

Any equipment complicated enough to require instructions, such as this PTAC temperature control panel, is inherently flawed. Poor controls have caused many hotel and motel guests much suffering over the years and have cut into the profits of the hospitality industry by increasing energy costs. This control is located within the PTAC, where outdoor air leaking through the unit distorts the sensed temperature. A much better approach would be a wall-mounted thermostat with a simple temperature setting and automatic controls for fan speed (high when the sensed temperature is very different from the setpoint, low or off at other times). Ideally, the thermostat should be mounted some distance away from the PTAC, where it can accurately sense room temperature. Wall-mounted thermostats for PTACs have been available for many years but are rarely used because they cost a little extra, and they require running wires to a box on the wall. (Wireless options are now available for people who think going wireless is a good idea.)

How Does an Air Conditioner Work? Everyone is familiar with air conditioners, but how do they actually work? A **compressor powered by electricity** compresses a refrigerant (Freon® or a modern equivalent). Squeezing a gas (the refrigerant is a gas at this point in the cycle) to a smaller volume causes the temperature of the gas to increase. The pressure difference created by the compressor moves the hot refrigerant to the outdoor heat exchange tubes. A **fan** blows outdoor air across the tubes, transferring heat from the hot refrigerant to the tubes and then to the outdoor air (making the outdoor air hotter). From there, the refrigerant flows to the indoor part of the system and passes through the expansion device—which uses a small hole to control the flow of refrigerant—to the low-pressure side of the system, where it expands to a larger volume. Expansion chills the refrigerant, because expanding a gas decreases its temperature. The cold refrigerant flows through the **indoor heat exchange tubes**, where another fan blows indoor air across the cold tubes, heating the refrigerant while cooling the indoor air. After the refrigerant absorbs heat from the indoor air, it continues its journey back to the compressor, which compresses it again and sends it around again.

Even though Freon®, carbon dioxide, air, ammonia, and propane have all been used as refrigerants, none of them is ideal. A refrigerant should condense into a liquid on the hot side of the system and then change phase back into a gas on the cold side of the system. The latent heat given off or absorbed by the refrigerant as it changes phase greatly increases the capacity and efficiency of the system. Air's disadvantage is that it doesn't change phase; ammonia is toxic; propane can explode; and Freon® damages the atmosphere's ozone layer. Carbon dioxide requires relatively high pressure to change phase, but it is becoming more popular, as are sophisticated, less environmentally damaging replacements for Freon®.

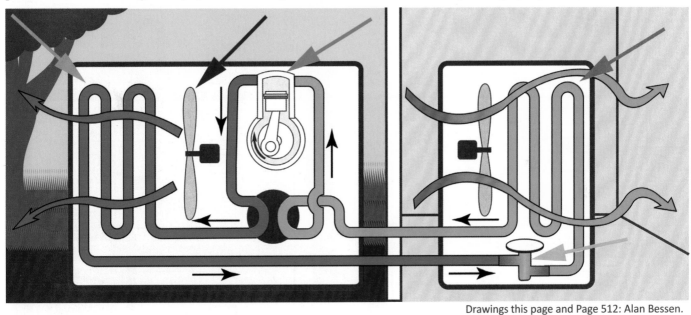

Drawings this page and Page 512: Alan Bessen.

How Does a Heat Pump Work?

A physicist would call any machine that moves heat from a cold substance to a warm substance, including an air conditioner or an ordinary kitchen refrigerator, a heat pump. In the building industry, "heat pump" refers to an air conditioner that heats a building by working backwards.

In the drawing at right, a reversing valve reroutes the hot refrigerant from the **compressor** to the **indoor heat exchanger**, where it heats the indoor air. Then the refrigerant goes through the expansion device and gets cold—so cold that it can absorb heat from cold outdoor air. Then the refrigerant goes back to the compressor, which compresses it, which makes it hot again, and sends it around again.

Water-Source Heat Pumps

The apartment building below is heated and cooled by heat pumps. During the winter, they take heat from water pumped around the building, and, during the summer, they reject heat to water (unlike the "air source" heat pump on Page 511).

During the winter, as shown at bottom left, a boiler heats water, which is pumped through pipes to heat pumps in each apartment. When a thermostat senses that an apartment needs heat, it turns on the heat pump, which takes heat from the water and sends hot air into the apartment.

During the summer (see bottom right), heat from outdoors heats the indoor air. Each apartment's thermostat calls for cooling, which moves the reversing valve to cooling mode. The fan moves indoor air over one of the heat pumps's heat exchangers, which transfers heat from the indoor air to the cold refrigerant, cooling the indoor air. The refrigerant transfers its heat to the water being pumped around the building, which moves the heat to a cooling tower (basically a large waterfall with a fan), which cools the water while transferring the heat to outdoor air.

Information flows through the system as follows: the thermostat senses that the apartment is hot (or cold) and turns the heat pump on. The heat pump sends cold (or hot) air into the apartment, the thermostat senses the lower (or higher) air temperature, and it turns the heat pump off. Water temperature sensors turn the cooling tower (or boiler) on.

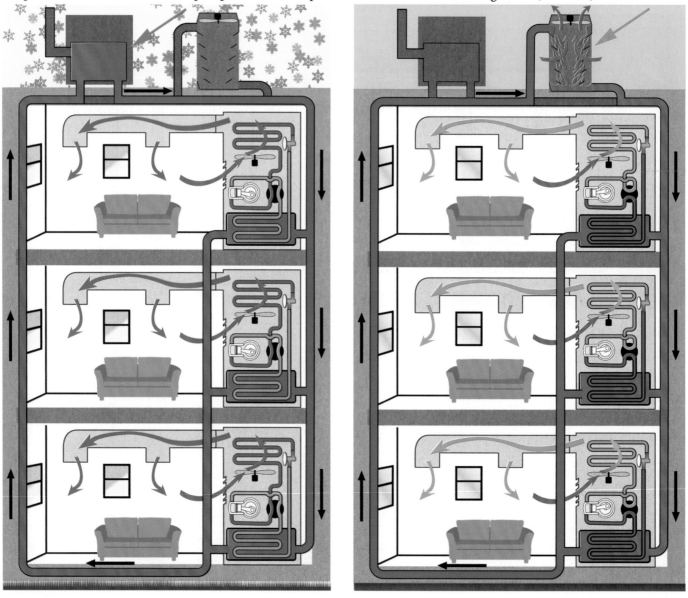

LOCATE HEATERS NEAR WINDOWS

The drawing at right shows a room with a heater located far from the window.

The man is receiving a lot of infrared heat radiation from the heater and the warm wall near it but very little heat from the window and wall on the other side.

Warm air rising up from the heater and cold air falling down near the window move in a nonstop convective current of cold air from the window past the man.

Locating the heater next to the window causes hot air currents rising up from the heater to meet cold air currents falling down along the window, greatly reducing convective air currents in the room. This location also evens out the amount of infrared heat radiation reaching each side of the man's body, making him more comfortable.

Smart heater location improves comfort in any room but is less important in a well-insulated, Stage Three building.

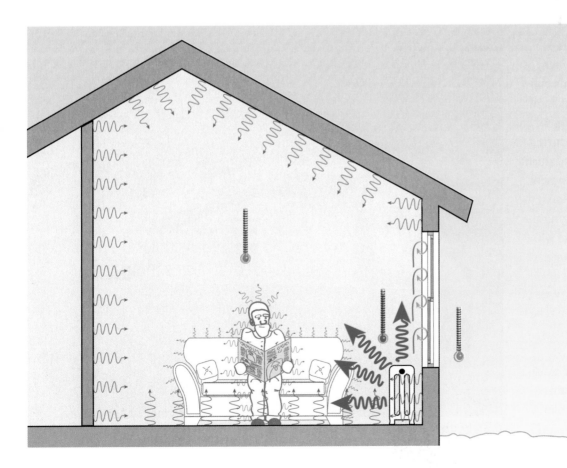

SOLAR THERMAL

There are two types of solar panels. Photovoltaic panels, also known as PV, make electricity. If the electricity is not used at the time it is produced, it can be stored in a battery. But batteries are expensive, so the electricity is usually sent to other buildings through the electric grid.

The other type of solar panel, known as solar thermal, heats water, which can be used for faucet water or for heating a building. Heating a building with solar thermal panels is challenging because buildings need more heat during the night than during the day, and the sun does not shine during the night. Buildings also primarily need heat during the winter, when the sun does not shine as long as it does during the summer and cold outdoor air cools the panels, reducing the amount of heat they send to the building. This reduces the financial payback for solar thermal panels used for heating a building.

Solar thermal is generally a better match for heating faucet water because most buildings need about the same amount of hot water for faucets all year long, and because heat captured in hot water during the day can be used at night. Therefore, equipment dedicated to heating faucet water will function all year long, even during the winter.

A solar thermal system large enough to provide 100 percent of a building's hot water needs will be underutilized on all but a few cloudy winter days. A system sized to heat most of the water during the winter will be oversized during the summer, wasting equipment. The solution is to size a system to heat most of the water during the summer. A system this size will have a load on it all year long.

There are several popular types of solar thermal systems. One type requires anti-freeze chemicals to protect the panels against freezing during the winter. Anti-freeze is difficult to maintain at the high temperatures solar thermal systems operate at, yet one cold night without protection will destroy the panels. A "drainback" system is easier to maintain because it does not require anti-freeze. A drainback system avoids freezing during the winter and overheating during the summer by periodically allowing gravity to drain water into an indoor tank located near the panels.

Even if there are no immediate plans to install solar panels, the possibility of installing them in the future should be considered. Reserving space for a drainback tank can make a future installation easier. A sloping roof facing the equator should be kept clear of utility wires, ventilation exhausts, and plumbing vents. Plumbing vents can be combined (see Page 425) and located on the shady side of the roof. Some people even install pipes or wires in the wall to facilitate installing a solar thermal system later without needing to open walls.

A solar thermal system sized to heat most of a building's hot water will also need a back-up source of hot water. The same source may be a boiler that also heats water for heating the building (with radiators). In many cases, the back-up boiler or water heater burns oil or gas.

This solar thermal system provides some of the apartment building's hot faucet water. It is unshaded, tilted away from horizontal at an angle equal to the location's latitude, and faces the earth's equator.

ENERGY WASTED UP THE CHIMNEY

Though all boilers (and furnaces and water heaters) sold today have good efficiency ratings, many still have a serious problem: heat escaping up the chimney when the boiler is hot but not firing. The amount of heat escaping is not included in most ratings, and is hard to measure, but can be enormous.

A normal chimney that uses convection to pull exhaust out of a combustion appliance continues to pull room-temperature air through the appliance when the fire turns off. This air absorbs heat from the appliance and carries that heat with it up the chimney to outdoors, wasting it. Another problem is that the outdoor air pulled through leaks in the building causes high summer humidity, low winter humidity, and the resulting discomfort.

Several factors determine how much heat gets wasted via a chimney when the fire is off. One factor is chimney height: the taller a chimney is, the stronger the draft it pulls. Another factor is the material the chimney is made of: is it a layer of bricks that will stay warm for days? Or is it a piece of sheet metal that will cool off soon after the fire turns off? Another factor is how easily air can flow through the building and then the appliance, which depends on the construction of the building and the type of appliance.

An Elegy for the Chimney

Chimneys are obsolete because they depend on a generous supply of outdoor air leaking through the building, which wastes energy. And many modern buildings do not leak enough air for a chimney to operate safely. If or when a chimney stops working, products of combustion, including poisons such as carbon monoxide, can spill back into the living space. A chimney is also expensive and occupies a lot of valuable space. For example, the chimney in the photo at right needs to be taller than the apartment building it serves and has to be welded together at every connection.

One partial solution is a motorized flue damper, which partly closes the chimney when the fire is off. For safety reasons, the flue does not close 100 percent (dampers could stick closed, allowing exhaust to build up in the building), but they close enough to significantly reduce the amount of outdoor air the chimney pulls through the building and the appliance when the fire is off. A more complete solution is a type of combustion appliance that does not use a conventional chimney: a sealed combustion appliance.

What would this house look like without its chimney? Would it still look cute, or would it look like something was missing? Removing the chimney would allow space for more windows, but it would detract from the "old-fashioned" look. The "old-fashioned" description is key because a chimney is an obsolete technology.

The Solution: Sealed Combustion

The majority of the heat lost up a chimney while an appliance is hot but not firing can be saved by using a sealed combustion appliance. The term "sealed combustion" (as used in this book) means the appliance has two pipes connecting it to outdoors: one to supply outdoor air to the appliance for combustion and one to eject exhaust outdoors. The exhaust can be piped out either a side wall of the building or the roof.

Some appliances are similar to sealed combustion but are not truly sealed combustion because they do not use a dedicated pipe to bring outdoor air to the appliance. One example is the water heater in the photo on the top of Page 521; it uses a fan in the exhaust pipe to pull air into the building and to move the exhaust out of the building. This type of appliance should be avoided not only because the life of a fan located in an exhaust pipe is nasty, brutish, and short, but also because the fan pulls outdoor air into the building through leaks in the enclosure.

A true sealed combustion appliance uses a fan in the fresh air intake to pull air in through a pipe from outdoors and push exhaust out another pipe. For large boilers that require a conventional chimney, the best strategy is to minimize the length of the chimney by putting the boiler room on the roof, as shown on Pages 523 and 524.

Using outdoor air for combustion is not a new idea. Hundreds of years ago, Native Americans used underground pipes to supply outdoor air to fires they lit in their tepees. People in more "civilized" parts of the world caught on to this idea much later. In 1715, French energy-efficiency expert Monsieur Gauger advocated the use of outdoor air for combustion in his book on saving fuel:

> *In the middle of the hearth, at about 10 or 12 inches distance from the bottom plate, must be made a trap-door that may easily open and shut, and under it a little hollow passage communicating with the outward air; when this trap-door is lifted up a little way, the air from without will go out thro' the passage of the bellows or vent-hole; for there will always be a greater pressure of air from without,*

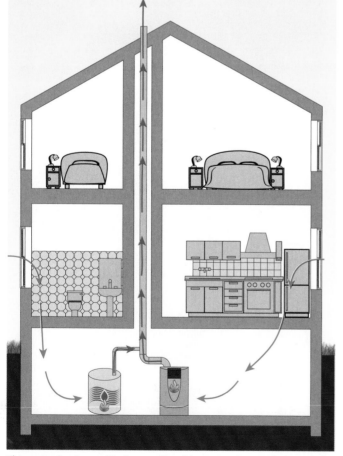

This water heater and boiler are the older types that use indoor air for combustion and a tall, gravity-driven chimney for exhaust.

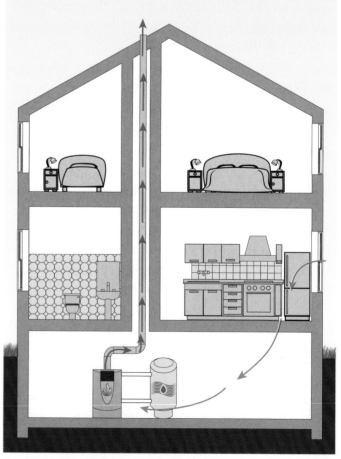

One combustion appliance is better than two. This boiler heats both the house and the faucet water, but still uses indoor air, which is not ideal.

than from within the room, whether the wind blows, or the weather be calm, if there be a fire in the hearth, because the heat of the fire rarifying the air, and driving part of it up the chimney with the smoak, there will be a kind of vacuum, or at least, the air will be made so thin over the vent-hole, as to press less than that which is coming in from without; the external air therefore will rush in violently, and not only light the fire, but cause it to flame even tho' the wood should be green...[1]

Should the doors and windows of a room be closed with so much nicety as to leave no crevices by which a supply of air can enter sufficient for maintaining the fire, after the current of air up the Chimney has been diminished as much as possible by diminishing the throat of the Fireplace; in that case there would be no other way of preventing the Chimney from smoking but by opening a passage for the admission of fresh air from without;--but this, I believe, will very seldom be found to be the case.[2]

Gauger knew that the stack effect would make air pressure higher outdoors than in the fireplace, despite the lack of air barriers in the Stage One enclosures of the 1700s. Not much later, in 1798, the American scientist Count Rumford discussed buildings that don't leak enough air to supply combustion air to a fire when he wrote about the need for "fresh air from without to maintain a fire":

Now that, ideally, buildings are being built more airtight than they were in the 1700s, there is even more reason to heed this advice and "admit fresh air from without." Every boiler, furnace, water heater, woodburning stove, fireplace, and any other combustion appliance, with few exceptions, should be sealed combustion. Appliances that are not sealed combustion should be located outdoors or in rooftop boiler rooms, which minimize energy losses by keeping the chimney short (which minimizes draft).

1   Nicolas Gauger, <u>Fires Improv'd: Being a New Method Of Building Chimneys So as to prevent their Smoaking: in which A Small Fire, shall warm a Room better than a much _Larger_ made the _Common Way_</u>, trans. J.T. Desaguliers (London: J. Senex and E. Curll, 1715), Pages 16-17. This was probably the first book ever written about heating buildings.

2   Count Benjamin Rumford, <u>Rumford's Essays</u>, Vol. 1 (Boston: David West, 1798), Page 369.

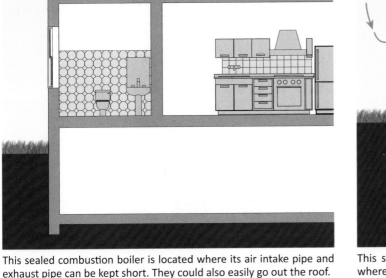

This sealed combustion boiler is located where its air intake pipe and exhaust pipe can be kept short. They could also easily go out the roof.

This sealed combustion boiler is occupying space in the basement, where it is not too valuable. It is vented out the side wall of the house.

Replacing a chimney-vented combustion appliance with a sealed combustion appliance can improve comfort by avoiding the drafts and low humidity associated with too much winter air moving through a building.

The photo at right shows a sealed combustion furnace in an apartment closet, with the combustion air intake pipe and exhaust pipe both labeled.

The boiler at bottom left provides both heat and hot faucet water to a house. It heats faucet water without any storage tank, while also heating water that is pumped to radiators to provide space heat. The boiler has two **pipes** connecting it to outdoors: one to bring combustion air in and one to carry combustion exhaust outdoors. The boiler is located in a small closet on the top floor of the house, which made it easy to run both pipes through the roof.

The photo at bottom right shows the outdoor ends of two sealed combustion exhaust pipes. Combustion air is pulled in around the edges of the grey boxes, along the building's wall, then through an air intake pipe.

Model: Amaury Castillo.

The photo at right shows air intake pipes and **exhaust pipes** that are connected to two sealed combustion boilers located in a rooftop boiler room. If the exhaust is located above a walkway, it is potentially hazardous because modern sealed combustion appliances are so efficient that their exhaust is not very hot. As a result, instead of all the water vapor in the exhaust leaving as a hot gas, some of it condenses in or near the exhaust pipe. Just how much depends on outdoor temperature and humidity, the firing rate of the boiler, and the temperature of the water in the boiler. But there will be times when enough water condenses to form a puddle on the ground under the exhaust pipes. While a puddle itself is not dangerous, of course, during cold enough weather, it will freeze, as it has in the photo at right. Because people could slip and fall on the ice, sealed combustion exhaust outlets should always be located away from walkways.

The photo at bottom right shows a fireplace in an 1890s brownstone. To the right of the fireplace is a fresh-air grill. While the intake does not provide fresh air directly to the fireplace, at least it provides it close by.

Wingback chairs were invented to shield people sitting in front of a fire from the cold air the chimney pulls through leaks in the house. With a fresh-air intake like this one, though, people will not need wingback chairs because cold air will go directly from the intake to the fireplace. Unfortunately, the fresh-air intake will also let cold air into the house even when there is no fire in the fireplace. Using a sealed combustion fireplace, as shown on the next page, solves this problem.

Sealed Combustion Woodburning Stoves and Fireplaces

Long gone are the days when people had enough firewood to keep a fire burning in an open fireplace. An open fireplace also pulls outdoor air in through leaks in other rooms, making other rooms in the house cold.

The situation gets worse late at night. As the fire starts to die down, it no longer provides much heat. But long before the fire goes out, it is still hot enough to generate a strong draft up the chimney, which continues pulling cold air into the house through leaks in the enclosure. As the fire dies down, the cold air pulled through the house by the chimney can remove more heat than the fire provides. Described another way, the energy efficiency of an open fireplace is a negative number at times: it removes more heat from the house than it adds.

A far better idea is to use a woodburning appliance that has a pipe from outdoors to provide combustion air. Manufacturers make upgrade kits for connecting an outdoor-air intake pipe to a regular wood stove. The photo above right shows a woodburning stove with a **pipe** that brings fresh outdoor air for combustion directly to the stove. The photo below shows a fireplace insert (a factory-made enclosure that avoids the need to build a brick fireplace) with a **duct** bringing fresh outdoor air for combustion directly to the insert. Both the woodburning stove and the fireplace insert still use a conventional chimney to the roof to remove the combustion exhaust. But neither of these woodburning appliances will cool the house by pulling cold outdoor air through the house, regardless of how small the fire gets.

Today, supplying outdoor combustion air directly to a wood stove is required by code in many areas.

Not Quite Sealed Combustion

The water heater in the photo at right is not the best choice of equipment. It does not have a dedicated air intake pipe but has a **fan** located in the exhaust pipe. The fan pulls fresh outdoor air in through holes in the building, then through other rooms in the building, and then directly into the water heater. Finally, it pushes exhaust out the **exhaust pipe** to outdoors.

Because this water heater does not have a dedicated pipe to supply it with combustion air from outdoors, it might be called "power vented," "sidewall vented," or "direct vented." But it should not be called a sealed combustion appliance. When the fire is off, the chimney acts as a hole in the building, regardless of whether or not it goes out the side wall of the building or up to the roof. If the fan breaks, combustion exhaust that is normally blown out the exhaust pipe could leak back into the building, which is dangerous. It is better to avoid this type of appliance altogether.

Some combustion appliances can be optionally installed with or without an air intake pipe. These appliances are only sealed combustion if the air intake pipe is installed, which it should be. Air intake pipes should be located near the exhaust, to minimize stack-effect-driven or wind-driven outdoor air flow through the appliance.

The photo at right shows an oil-fired boiler upgraded with an **air intake pipe**. This boiler still uses a conventional chimney to the roof for exhaust, which pulls a lot of heat out of the boiler when it is hot but not firing. But the fresh air intake pipe is a big improvement over the old arrangement of having the chimney and the boiler's fan pull cold outdoor air through the building.

Boilers Belong on Roofs

Basements are the first place water goes in a flood, and getting fresh combustion air and ventilation air into a basement boiler room can be difficult. But despite these disadvantages, there was a time when it made sense for boilers to go in basements.

One good reason was so coal could slide down the delivery chute (see photo at right). Another reason was that when steam condensed in the radiators, the water could drain back down through the pipes to the boiler by gravity. Finally, putting the boiler in a basement meant the chimney would be tall enough for convection to generate enough draft to supply combustion air if a fan couldn't be used because the area was not yet wired for electricity.

But almost nobody burns coal or installs steam heating systems anymore. These days, boilers burn oil or gas to heat water for radiators or radiant floors. And most places have electricity which can run a boiler's fan. There is little reason to put a boiler in a basement any more.

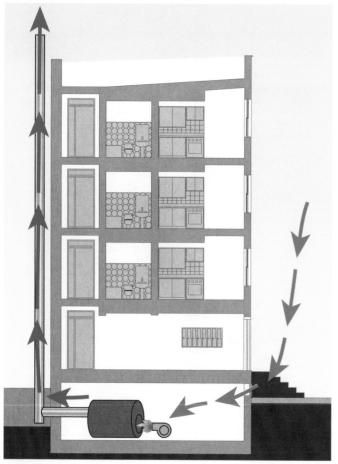

The fire is burning in the non-sealed combustion boiler in the basement. The hot exhaust gases generate a strong draft in the chimney.

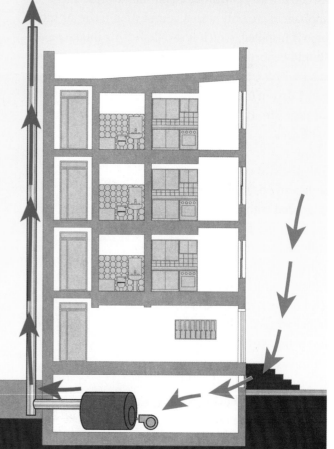

With the fire off, the tall chimney is still pulling a lot of cold air through the boiler. The hot boiler heats the air, which escapes out the chimney.

The amount of energy a chimney wastes by pulling cold air through a combustion appliance that is not firing but is still hot depends on the type of chimney, length of the chimney, type of combustion appliance, climate, wind, and many other factors. Because it is so difficult to determine how much fuel is wasted, this way of saving energy is often overlooked. However, a building could waste as much as one-third or more of its annual fuel use this way. Suffice it to say that the amount is large enough that no new building should be built with a tall chimney.

Note that a rooftop boiler room is not a good place to locate the type of combustion appliance with no fan that depends on the draft from a tall chimney to remove exhaust.

A rooftop boiler room should have a waterproof membrane under the floor, which extends up the wall higher than the door sill and wraps around all the pipes that penetrate the floor. That way, if the boiler leaks water and the floor drain clogs, water will drain out to the roof instead of into the building.

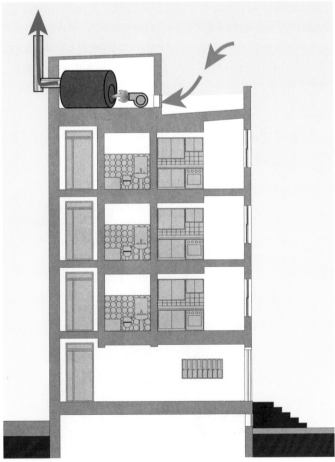

The boiler is now on the roof. When the fire is on, the boiler's fan pushes cold air into the boiler and pushes exhaust out the chimney.

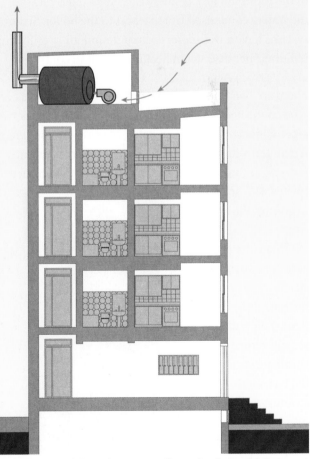

With the fire off, the short chimney is pulling only a little cold air through the boiler. This wastes much less energy than a tall chimney wastes.

This rooftop boiler room contains a boiler that is not sealed combustion. Because the boiler room is on the roof, the chimney is very short, which drastically reduces heat loss from the boiler while also saving money on the cost of the chimney. The louver in the wall is an easy way to provide fresh air for combustion and ventilation. The chimney penetrates the wall, not the roof, to avoid a roof leak.

STEAM HEAT

A steam heating system uses a boiler to boil water, pipes to distribute steam throughout the building, and radiators to transfer the latent heat of vaporization from the steam to the room. Finally, condensate return pipes return the water (condensed from steam) to the boiler. Steam systems have a well-deserved reputation for overheating buildings because steam heat is difficult to control.

There are two types of steam systems: "one-pipe" has one pipe connected to each radiator, and "two-pipe" has two pipes connected to each radiator. If a two-pipe system is retrofitted with individual thermostats to control each radiator, it can work fairly well. "Radiator inlet orifices" (plates with small holes) to control the flow of steam into radiators can eliminate the need for constantly maintaining steam traps (valves used to control the flow of steam) on radiators. A second return pipe can eliminate steam traps in the basement. One-pipe steam systems cannot be retrofitted this way, and are best replaced with hot water heat.

SUMMARY

Heating and cooling systems should be as simple as possible, and equipment should be sized to deliver the peak amount of heating or cooling each room needs, but no more.

Any serious attempt at keeping people comfortable and creating an energy-efficient building includes a thermostat in every room, or almost every room. Thermostats should be carefully located and should be capable of actually controlling the temperature in the room.

Heat is best delivered to or removed from a room by moving hot or cold water or refrigerant to and from the room. Heating or cooling a room by blowing hot or cold air into a room has many disadvantages. These disadvantages include lost space used by the fan and the air ducts, noise, difficulty controlling temperature in individual rooms, unnecessary energy use, and increased air flow through leaks in the building.

Chimneys, especially tall chimneys, are not a good idea. Combustion appliances should be sealed combustion, meaning they have a dedicated combustion air supply pipe and a separate dedicated exhaust pipe. If a boiler can't be sealed combustion, it should be installed in a rooftop boiler room with a short chimney and a fresh air louver.

Heating and Cooling Quiz: What is noteworthy about the sizes of the outdoor parts of the air conditioning systems in this photo? Answer on Page 562.

Chapter 19 **HOUSES**

VENTILATING, HEATING, AND COOLING A HOUSE

The challenge of keeping a house comfortable is dominated by the fact that a house has a larger enclosure surface area than any other type of building. Described another way, the ratio of enclosure area to floor area is higher for a house than for any other type of building.

If someone were to take a giant saw and cut an apartment building into many individual houses, the cuts would add surface area, or enclosure area, that would be exposed to outdoor temperatures, increasing the heating and cooling needs of each living space. Described yet another way, the space inside of a house is surrounded by outdoor space on many more sides than an apartment is, and it is therefore especially important that it have a well-designed and well-built enclosure to keep it comfortable. The large enclosure surface area also makes the quality of the enclosure especially important to a house's energy use.

Houses can also be especially challenging to heat or cool because they are usually the only type of building with spaces that are partly indoors and partly outdoors: attics and crawl spaces.

Designing and building a good enclosure is the primary way to keep a house comfortable, safe, and healthy, as well as durable and energy efficient. Carefully following the applied science chapters in this book, especially Chapter 16: Building Enclosures, will help create a good enclosure. Once a house has a good enclosure, the next step is to ensure that it is properly ventilated, heated, and cooled.

VENTILATING A HOUSE

In a climate where a house does not need a significant amount of heating, cooling, or dehumidification, supply fresh air with trickle vents (see Pages 441-442), and exhaust stale air with an exhaust-only system, perhaps running nonstop.

In any climate where a house needs a significant amount of heating, cooling, or dehumidification, the best way to ventilate it is to include an air barrier in the enclosure and supply and remove air with an ERV system. Ventilation ducts can be hidden within walls and ceilings. (The photos on Pages 528 and 529 show one way to hide them.)

Exhausting Stale Air and Supplying Fresh Air

In a house, the rooms that most need air exhausted from them are the kitchen and the bathroom(s). The exhaust vent in the bathroom should not be in the shower enclosure but on the ceiling elsewhere in the room. In the kitchen, cooking exhaust should be removed from near the stove with an exhaust-only system with a damper that closes when not in use. There should also be a general exhaust outlet on the ceiling but not near the stove, because cooking grease will quickly clog an ERV. Additional exhaust vents can be located wherever kitchen garbage or a cat litter box will generate smells. Fresh outdoor air is best delivered to bedrooms because people spend most of their time in bedrooms. Air pressure differences will then move fresh air to the rest of the rooms.

A house should have an ERV ventilation system and a separate kitchen exhaust fan with a duct to outdoors.

DON'T LET DUCTS STEAL VALUABLE LIVING SPACE

Too many people are stuck living in the space left over after air-based cooling and heating system ducts selfishly occupy too much of their house. Cooling and heating ducts cause other problems: they transmit noise between rooms, make it difficult or impractical to control temperatures in each room, require a fan that uses a lot of electricity and makes noise, and increase airflow through leaks, as explained on Pages 482-487. Heating and cooling without ducts, as described in Chapter 18: Heating and Cooling, can avoid these problems

Think about how much space will be left for people in the brownstone at right after the cooling and heating ducts being carried up the stairs are installed. The photo below shows an air handler and ductwork taking up space in the house that could have accommodated a larger basement play room. In expensive homes such as this one, cooling and heating systems tend to be especially oversized. If the owner of the house had calculated how much the space occupied by ducts and fans was worth, she might have asked to see a cooling and heating load calculation.

The photo above shows a large **duct** dominating the ceiling of the living room/kitchen area. The box being built around the duct will hide it, but will forever make the room smaller than it needs to.

The photo at left shows an absurd amount of oversized and noisy **equipment** on the rooftop. A cooling and heating load calculation (which someone was presumably paid to do) would have shown that the house could have been cooled and heated with equipment much smaller than what was installed. This would have saved the owner money while leaving more space outdoors for a nice rooftop garden and more space indoors for living. If the heating and cooling load reduction strategies described in this book were used, the equipment could have been even smaller (and quieter, and less expensive).

Concealing Ventilation Ducts

The ventilation ducts in the photo at right will be hidden above a false ceiling in a master bedroom. The cavity above the false ceiling is a fully indoor space. The ducts perpendicular to the roof joists run within the ceiling cavity, and the ducts parallel to the roof joists run between the joists. All the ducts perpendicular to the joists are located on the right side of the room, therefore there is no need for a false ceiling on the left side.

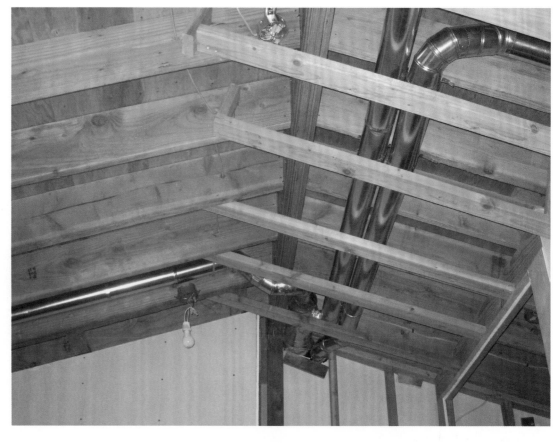

The photo at left shows the installed ceiling. There is no way to know that there are ducts hidden behind the ceiling, and it is hard to notice that the ceiling is slightly lower on one side.

Ventilation-only ducts are so small and easy to hide that they allow for high ceilings, as shown on the next page.

At right is a light-filled office on the top floor of a house. The lack of heating or cooling ducts eliminates the need for an attic. As a result, there is room for this office and other rooms (not shown).

Not using ducts to heat and cool a house makes room either for an extra room like this, or for higher ceilings, such as those in the photos below.

Anyone who doesn't like high ceilings can still skip heating and cooling ducts and have a fully indoor, conditioned attic for storage.

Photo: Phebe Horschel.

COOLING A HOUSE

Houses in most climates can be cooled with a good enclosure that includes multi-pane windows with low-e coatings, deciduous trees or other shading that protects the windows from direct sunlight, energy-efficient lighting, an induction stove (produces less heat than other types), and a cooling dehumidifier (see Pages 466 and 467). A ceiling fan can keep people comfortable by making a house feel cooler than it is. Houses not designed and built this well can be cooled with ductless splits or radiant cooling ceilings (see Pages 505 and 506).

HEATING A HOUSE

Most ductless split cooling systems can operate as heat pump heating systems during the winter. However, if too many houses are heated with ductless splits, together they will create a winter nighttime peak electric load. If this peak ever becomes the highest peak in that area, new power plants or transmission lines will have to be built to satisfy this new peak load. Unlike the air-conditioning-driven summer afternoon peak, which is the highest in many areas, a nighttime peak can never be eliminated or even reduced by solar electricity (because sun doesn't shine at night). This is a good reason to not use electricity for heating, which means not using a heat pump for heat.

In parts of the world that are warm enough year round to not need much heat, many buildings have no boiler and instead use electric resistance space heat. These areas have a winter morning peak caused by electric space heat and electric water heaters. Ironically, even though these areas are generally sunny, solar panels cannot reduce this peak because the peak occurs early in the morning when there is not enough sun. This peaking problem can be avoided by burning fossil fuel to heat faucet water and houses. This generally uses less fossil fuel then burning the fuel in a power plant and heating the house with the resulting electricity (see the Appendix on Page 564).

In any climate where a house needs heat, heat from a boiler can be distributed by pumping hot water to heaters in each room, each with its own thermostat. (The lower the thermal mass of the heaters the easier it is to control temperature.) In houses with very low heating loads, heaters can be eliminated by distributing heat by heating only the air already necessary for ventilation. In cold climates this requires the best enclosures being built today.

This wall-mounted panel radiator is heated by hot water from a boiler and controlled by its own thermostatic radiator valve.

SUMMARY

A house is more challenging to heat and cool than an apartment because it has more surface area exposed to outdoor temperatures. A house's heating, cooling, and dehumidifying loads are greatly reduced when the enclosure includes an air barrier.

The choice of ventilation system for a house depends on climate. In very mild climates, exhaust-only ventilation systems are a good choice. In any climate that requires a significant amount of heating, cooling, or dehumidifying (most climates), ERV systems are a better choice. The kitchen should be ventilated with a separate exhaust-only system with a damper that closes when the fan is turned off.

Cooling a house requires, first, shading the windows, using good windows, and installing energy-efficient lights and appliances. Dehumidifying can make the house comfortable at a higher summer temperature. If more cooling is still necessary, a cooling dehumidifier or a ductless split will work. Faucet water and the house should be heated with a sealed combustion boiler. In cold climates, heat can be distributed by pumping hot water to heaters in each room, each with its own thermostat. For houses with very low heating loads, heat can be distributed by heating the ventilation air.

Chapter 20 **SCHOOLS**

VENTILATING, HEATING, AND COOLING A SCHOOL

The challenge of keeping a school comfortable is dominated by the need to heat, cool, dehumidify, and move a large amount of ventilation air to meet the needs of a large number of people, because a large number of people occupy classrooms, the cafeteria, and the gym at any one time.

Energy improvements in schools can be a good idea, but can have a long payback because schools are occupied fewer hours per year than other types of buildings. They are not occupied in the middle of the night, when the heating load peaks, and they tend to be empty or lightly occupied during the summer. During a typical school day, many people leave during the afternoon. This is why the economics of energy-saving improvements in a school is poor compared to, say, an apartment building, which is occupied 24 hours per day all year. Described another way, better windows or additional insulation or airtightening will have a faster payback in an apartment building than in a school.

One way to avoid surprises when designing a new school building is to set up and operate a room with a sample of the proposed mechanical equipment in it. The sample room should include whatever heating, cooling, and ventilation systems, as well as light shelves, lights, and lighting controls, are being considered for the new school. The equipment can be set up in an existing classroom during the summer or in a garage at any time of year. The equipment should be powered up and actually operated. Then the equipment design should be critiqued by the people who will manage the building, clean the building, maintain the building, and, most importantly, teach in the building.

Noise should be a major consideration when designing ventilating, heating, and cooling systems for schools because teachers already have enough noise to compete with. Noisy equipment reduces the ability of students to hear what the teacher is saying. A good air barrier around every classroom not only reduces heating and cooling loads and helps ventilation systems work more effectively but also reduces sound transmission between rooms.

Because schools have large ventilation systems compared to most other buildings, it is worth installing switches that sense when windows are open and can then immediately turn off all heating, cooling, and ventilation systems.

Schools have other unique challenges. They are the only type of buildings that typically have blackboards mounted on the walls. Old-style slate blackboards are resistant to the transmission of water vapor. The new plastic blackboards or whiteboards are complete barriers to water vapor. Adding a vapor barrier to a wall facing outdoors can cause problems by preventing the wall from drying. It is safer to mount the board on a wall backed up by another room. If the layout of the school demands that a blackboard be mounted on an outdoor wall, the blackboard (of any type) should be mounted on spacers to leave an air gap between the blackboard and the wall.

The best way to ventilate a school is with ERVs.

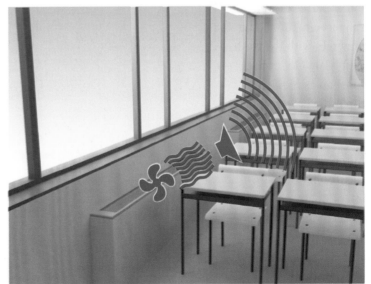

Some schools are heated, and sometimes cooled, with one or more PTACs (package terminal air conditioners) in each room. PTACs tend to be noisy, and as they age they tend to get noisier. This makes them a poor choice for classrooms.

VENTILATING A SCHOOL WITH ERVS

Central ERVs

The school at right has one enormous ERV for many classrooms. It is mounted outdoors on the school's roof. Using one or more large ERVs instead of multiple small ERVs means fewer filters to clean but requires larger ducts and therefore maybe lower ceilings. Because ducts cross demising partitions, fire dampers are required.

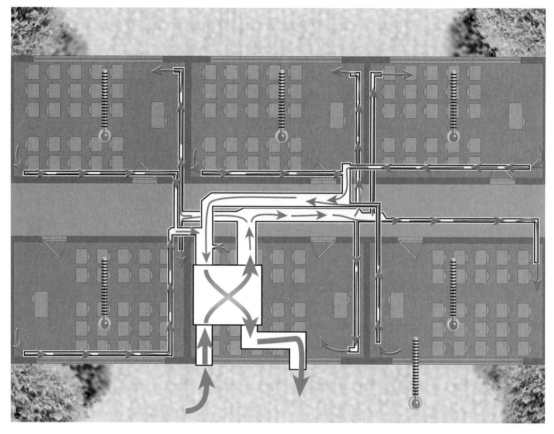

Individual ERVs

Individual ERVs can be much simpler. As shown at below right, **air inlets** that bring fresh outdoor air into the building should be located some distance away from **exhaust outlets**. This prevents exhaust air from being drawn in with the fresh supply air. Codes in some areas require a three-meter (ten-foot) separation.

In the school at right, classroom doors are intentionally not adjacent to each other, nor are they directly across the hall from each other. This helps reduce sound transmission from one classroom to another.

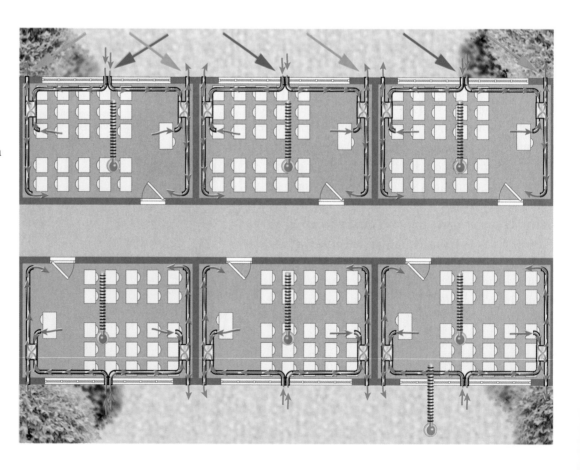

One or Two ERVs per Classroom?

The drawing at right shows ventilation ducts and a single ERV in a classroom. The ERV is mounted inside the ceiling at the front of the room. If the classroom had a closet, the ERV could have gone on the ceiling of the closet.

At least some portion of the ducts between the ERV and the classroom should be flexible ducts, which will help reduce noise, as described on Page 457.

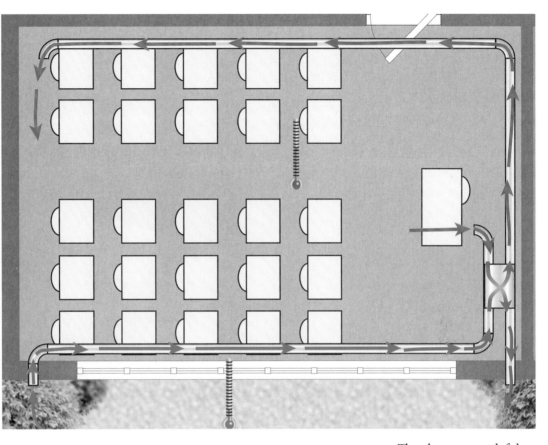

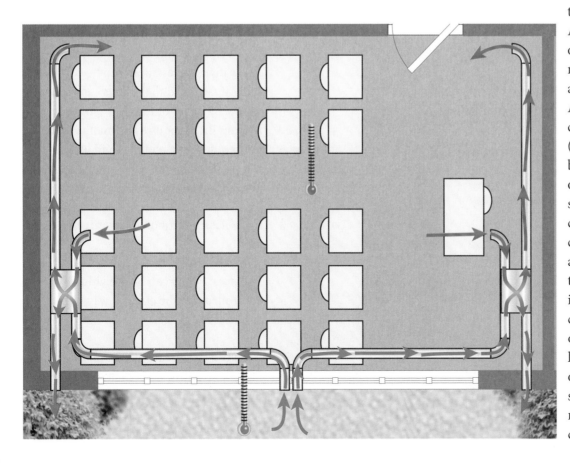

The classroom at left has two small, quiet ERVs. A timer can switch on one ERV early in the morning to freshen the air before people arrive. A motion sensor or carbon dioxide sensor (senses CO_2 exhaled by people) can turn the other ERV on when students arrive. After class is over, the timer can turn off one ERV, and the sensor can keep the other one running if people are still in the classroom. Another option is to use one large ERV that can be operated at multiple speeds, but that requires more complicated controls.

HEATING AND COOLING A SCHOOL

Valences, described on Pages 501-503, are a good choice for heating and cooling schools because they are completely silent, can be controlled individually in each room, and require almost no maintenance.

If a classroom only needs heat, not cooling, then heat can be provided by pumping hot water to radiators under the windows. In addition to being silent, these can be controlled individually in each room and require no maintenance.

Ductless splits are also a possibility for both heating and cooling, but they can increase the peak electric load, have filters that require maintenance, and have fans that make some noise.

Many schools have problems with mold during the summer when the air conditioning system is turned off to save energy. Ducted dehumidifiers or in-wall dehumidifiers (see Pages 465 and 468) can solve this problem. They are more effective at dehumidification than an AC system and require less energy.

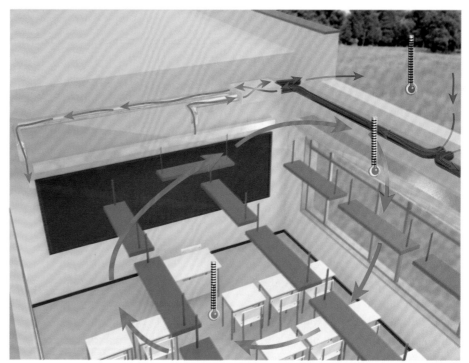

This classroom is ventilated with an ERV and cooled with a valence.

SUMMARY

Schools require more ventilation than most buildings—and it is important that their ventilation systems be quiet. Follow the advice about ducts and noise on Page 457. Ventilate with ERVs. One or two ERVs in each classroom can be controlled individually, and their ducts can't spread smoke or fire to other rooms. Large rooftop ERVs require less maintenance but require lower ceilings and longer ducts, which might move smoke or fire across demising partitions.

Each classroom should have an air barrier around it.

Valences, which can be individually controlled, are the quietest way to heat and cool a school.

Designing a school without input from teachers is a mistake. Teachers and maintenance people should hear and see proposed equipment operating and evaluate it before a final decision is made.

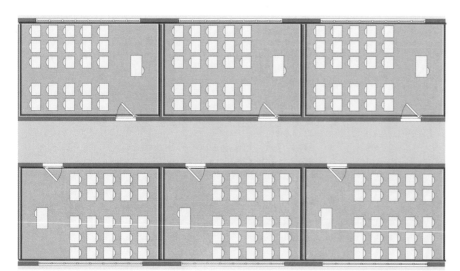

Each classroom should be surrounded by an air barrier to improve fire safety, indoor air quality, and comfort; to isolate classrooms from sound and insect infestation; and to reduce energy use.

Chapter 21 **APARTMENT BUILDINGS**

VENTILATING, HEATING, AND COOLING AN APARTMENT BUILDING

The major challenges of keeping an apartment building ventilated, heated, and cooled are delivering the correct amounts of ventilation air, heating, and cooling to many small rooms; finding space for the equipment; and accurately allocating energy costs to each apartment so occupants can pay their fair share.

Because an apartment building has a low enclosure-area to floor-area ratio, the quality of the building enclosure is less important than it is for a house. An apartment building can be thought of as a number of houses glued to the sides and tops of each other, with all the glued surfaces no longer exposed to outdoors. This eliminates the heating and cooling loads that would be created if an apartment building were divided up into separate stand-alone houses. Because of this, in general, the mechanical systems of an apartment building are more important to its energy profile than the enclosure, and the larger a building gets, the more true this is.

The least expensive and most reliable way to heat and cool an apartment building is an air barrier that stops air from leaking between apartments and outdoors, between different apartments themselves, and between apartments and common areas such as hallways, stairways, and elevator shafts.

Maintaining an air barrier between the common areas of an apartment building and outdoors is more difficult. This is because apartment building enclosures have many air leak vulnerabilities such as vents to outdoors from stairways, elevator shafts, gas meter rooms, garbage chutes, and laundry rooms, plus entrance doors that open and close frequently.

Air leakage through entrance doors can be reduced with weatherstripping and with a vestibule long enough so that the first door will close before a person opens the second door. Codes in many areas permit closing or partly closing vents in stairways and elevator shafts when they are not needed. Gas meter rooms should stay vented to outdoors, but good airtightening between the gas meter room and the rest of the building can prevent air leaking through the rest of the building. Air leaking through garbage chutes and clothing dryer vents can be reduced with a good air barrier in the walls separating the garbage room and the laundry room from the rest of the building.

After the building is made as airtight as is practical, each apartment should get its own separate ventilation system. Individual ventilation systems have many advantages. They do not have to move air long distances, they don't transmit sound or fire from one apartment to another, and the ducts do not occupy valuable floor area (but must be squeezed into apartment ceilings or walls). Individual ventilation systems are not tall enough to be significantly influenced by the stack effect, therefore they have a much better chance of working properly than central systems with long vertical ducts. To avoid compromising the integrity of fireproof assemblies, ducts should not be located within them. The following pages show examples of apartment ventilation systems.

Each apartment should be surrounded by its own air barrier, as if it were an individual house.

VENTILATING AN APARTMENT BUILDING

An individual exhaust-only ventilation system in each apartment (or hotel room) is different from an exhaust-only ventilation system that uses a large fan to exhaust air from multiple apartments as shown on Page 443 and the top of Page 538. Individual exhaust-only systems are simple, are inexpensive to install, and require no floor space for vertical ducts.

The photo at right shows some parts of individual exhaust-only ventilation systems. A fan (not shown) is pulling fresh outdoor air in through **trickle vents** and pushing it outdoors through **exhaust hoods**. The drawing below shows an exhaust-only ventilation system for an individual apartment. An exhaust fan in a bathroom ceiling pulls air through a trickle vent in the window of the adjoining room, moves the air through the apartment, and then pushes the air through a duct above the bathroom ceiling, which moves the air outdoors.

Exhaust-only systems are not the best choice for schools and office buildings, which require higher ventilation rates (per floor area) than trickle vents can provide.

Trickle vents are often not necessary in single-family houses because, unless a house's enclosure is built with one of the very best air barriers being built today, a house's large surface area will generally leak enough air to satisfy the required ventilation rate. Apartments that do not have a good air barrier around them (Stage One or Stage Two enclosures) also leak enough air to make trickle vents unnecessary. Because apartments have a relatively small enclosure area, Stage Three apartments with good air barriers usually can benefit from trickle vents.

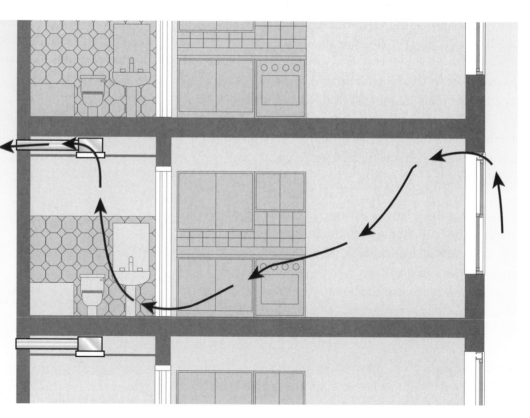

The photo at right shows an apartment building that has a separate ERV ventilation system in each apartment. The air intake and exhaust vents on the outdoor wall connect to ducts that supply and remove air.

The photos below show apartment buildings that have individual exhaust-only ventilation systems in each apartment. The air exhaust vents are visible on the outdoor walls.

Roof Penetrations

The photo at right shows **exhaust fans** on the roof of an apartment building. They are exhausting air from vertical ducts that connect all the bathrooms and kitchens in a vertical line of apartments.

Installing these fans requires coordination between the roofer, the duct installers, the electricians, and the carpenters who build the supports for the fans. Each fan represents a roof penetration that might leak someday.

The photo at left shows the roof of an apartment building that has individual ventilation systems in each apartment. Rather than venting air out the roof, they vent it out the wall of the building. Because of this, the roofer never needed to talk to the duct installers, electricians, or carpenters. This greatly simplified construction.

Individual ERVs

The drawing at right shows an apartment building with an individual **ERV** ventilating each apartment. Each duct runs only within the apartment it serves, therefore there is no possibility of smoke or noise traveling through a duct from one apartment to another.

ERVs save energy compared to an exhaust-only system by heating (or, as shown below, cooling) the incoming ventilation air before it is delivered to each room.

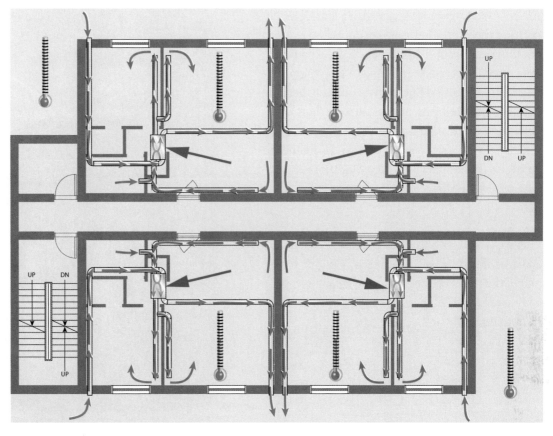

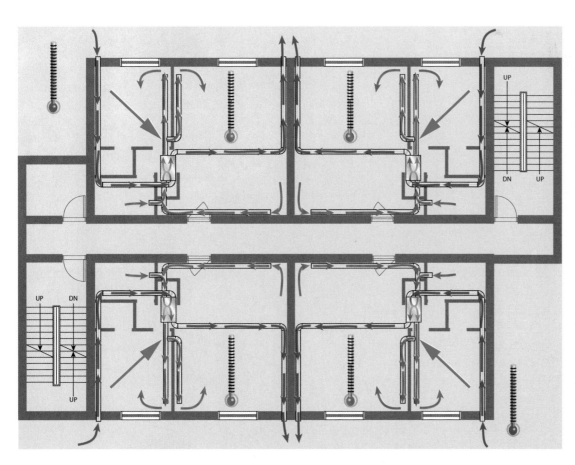

The supply ducts to the bedrooms **tee off from each other** some distance before they end. This reduces sound transmission from one bedroom to another.

ERV systems in adjacent apartments are mirror images of each other. This makes it easier to locate the exhaust ducts next to each other and far away from the fresh-air intake ducts.

Hiding ERVs in Apartment Ceilings

An ERV takes up more space than a simple exhaust fan, and it requires both supply ducts and exhaust ducts, which occupy more space than exhaust-only ducts. This makes hiding an ERV system in an apartment tricky. But it is worth doing because a space ventilated with an ERV system does not need as much heating and cooling energy as a space ventilated with an exhaust-only system and because an ERV system offers a choice of locations from which fresh outdoor air comes and to which it is delivered.

The photo at right shows an **ERV** tucked into an apartment ceiling and a **soffit** (box), which hides one of the ducts connected to the ERV. Acoustic ceiling tiles will be placed into the ceiling grid, hiding the ERV.

In the photo at left, an ERV is hidden above some acoustic ceiling tiles, which can easily be removed to service the ERV.

Hallway ERV Systems

The drawings on this page show an ERV system ventilating an apartment building hallway. This saves the expense of buying and operating other equipment to heat or cool ventilation air.

The system at right pulls some exhaust air from the garbage closet, which helps reduce the spread of odors. The system below pulls all the exhaust air from the hallway through an undercut (gap) under the closet door, then through the closet.

With a hallway ventilated by an ERV system, there is no need to provide heat in the hallway unless it has a lot of surface exposed to outdoors. During the winter, the ERV will supply ventilation air that is slightly cooler than the indoor air being exhausted. As soon as the hallway gets a little cooler than the apartments, heat will pass from the apartments to the hallway through the uninsulated walls, keeping it from getting much cooler than the apartments.

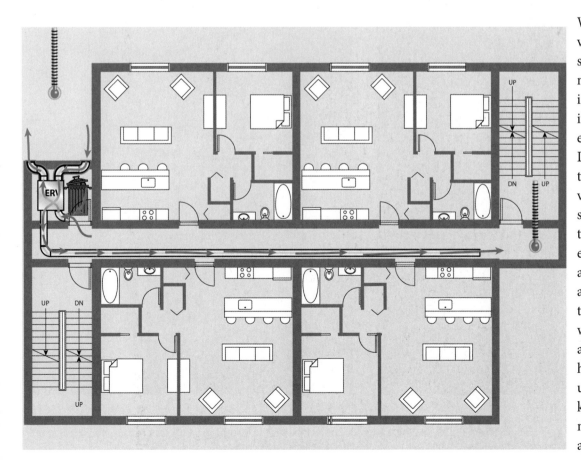

HEATING AND COOLING AN APARTMENT BUILDING

Individually metering electricity, water, and the energy required to heat and cool an apartment and heat its faucet water creates an important built-in incentive to save energy and water. Doing so has become easier because many manufacturers now produce gas-fired sealed combustion boilers that are small enough to fit in an apartment and still perform two important jobs: heating water for space heating and heating water for faucets. This makes it practical to install a boiler in each apartment and have the occupants pay for their own gas.

In a reasonably energy-efficient building, the cost of buying fresh water often exceeds the cost of buying all the energy the building needs. With individual boilers that heat both the space and the faucet water, it is practical to also install a meter that will measure all the water going to an apartment. Some building owners install water meters for each apartment but don't bother billing for the water unless usage exceeds an amount agreed on in advance.

However, sometimes the small amount of energy an energy-efficient building requires might be too little to meter. If it were possible to find a magic boiler that costs nothing to buy and never needs any energy to operate, yet costs the same to maintain as a normal boiler, it might not be worth installing. This is because the cost of maintaining a boiler that provides heat and hot water to one apartment can easily exceed the cost of the energy it requires. In urban areas where land is especially expensive, the value of the space that individual boilers occupy can also make them uneconomic—in such instances, it is better to use one central boiler for space heating and for heating faucet water. Heat meters can measure the volume and temperature difference of water going to and from an apartment's heating system, and hot water meters can measure hot faucet water going to each apartment. All possibilities should be considered when deciding how to provide heating, cooling, cold water, and hot faucet water for apartments.

This boiler heats water for one apartment's faucets and also heats water that gets pumped to heaters to heat the apartment. The boiler needs a closet with a floor drain. It also occupies valuable space close to outdoors (necessary to keep the exhaust vent pipe short).

Individual gas meters for each apartment enable apartment occupants to buy as much gas as they want for heating their apartments and faucet water. But the meters take up a lot of space, and the cost of all the gas pipes is not trivial.

Ductless Splits

The apartment at right will have a ductless split system. This system provides both heating and cooling, each of which can be metered apartment by apartment. The **ceiling-concealed unit** is hidden inside a soffit. **Air supply outlets** will supply heating or cooling air to each room. Ceiling cassettes, as shown on Pages 491 and 492, can also be used in apartments but have the disadvantage of being more visible than ceiling-concealed units.

Ductless split outdoor units are located on the balcony of each apartment in the photo at left. Locating them on balconies avoids problems with manufacturer-specified maximum distances between the indoor and outdoor units. The building also has **sidewall ventilation grills**.

Another good option for heating and cooling apartments is water-source heat pumps, as described on Page 512.

Solar Hot Water

Apartment buildings are a good place to use solar thermal systems for heating faucet water because their roofs are usually unshaded and the demand for hot water is steadier in apartment buildings than in office buildings, schools, or single-family houses. Office buildings usually don't have much of a hot water load. The load in schools is usually very low during weekends and summers. The load in houses is medium steady, but many houses are shaded by trees which makes solar systems impractical.

Because the hot water load in an apartment building is so high, a reasonably sized solar thermal system will always have work to do. Because of this, solar thermal panels on apartment buildings will be able to capture and deliver more heat than panels installed on other types of buildings where the hot water load is lower.

Which is a more valuable resource: energy or water? A better question to ask is what can be done to save a lot of both? These water meters are in the basement of an apartment building where each occupant pays for his own water use.

Cogen System

Another good way to heat faucet water for an apartment building is with a cogen system. Cogen is short for "cogeneration." A cogen system is a generator that burns oil or gas to produce electricity and also captures the "waste" heat produced by the generator.

A cogen system installed in an apartment building can turn approximately 35 percent of the energy in the fuel into electricity and approximately another 45 percent of the energy into useful heat for faucet water, allowing only about 20 percent to leave as low-temperature "waste" heat. This compares favorably with a typical fossil-fuel-burning electricity plant, which converts approximately 32 percent of the energy in the fuel into electricity at the customer's meter, with most of the rest of the energy turning into "waste" heat at the power plant and some "lost" (turned into heat) by the transformers and wires that bring it to the customer. (See the Appendix on Page 564.)

A cogen system should be sized to meet most of the faucet hot water load and no larger. A system sized large enough to heat all of the faucet hot water, or sized to also provide heat during the winter, will end up wasting heat and equipment. (During part of the winter and all summer, there will be unused equipment capacity, and the system will have to either turn off or dump "waste" heat.)

SUMMARY

The least expensive and most reliable way to heat and cool an apartment building and control humidity is with an air barrier. In this case, it should surround each apartment.

Each apartment should also have its own individual ventilation system.

Individual boilers in apartments give occupants an incentive to save energy. But each boiler also occupies valuable space and requires maintenance, which might cost more than the energy. An alternative worth considering is one central heat and hot water boiler that is metered to each apartment. Ductless splits for heating and cooling are also worth considering, with faucet hot water provided by a central boiler, a solar thermal system, or a cogen system.

Chapter 22 **OFFICE BUILDINGS**

VENTILATING, HEATING, AND COOLING AN OFFICE BUILDING

The challenge of keeping an office building comfortable is dominated by cooling, as well as the complication of needing to cool some rooms while heating other rooms.

Office buildings are the only type of building that typically has internal rooms with no windows. This is not the case with houses, schools, or apartment buildings, which codes usually require to have a window in most rooms. During the winter, internal rooms with no windows do not need heat because none of their walls are exposed to outdoor air. Yet internal rooms still require cooling to remove heat generated by people, lights, and equipment. During the summer, all rooms in an office building require cooling, but during the winter, rooms with walls exposed to outdoors require heating at the same time that internal rooms and computer rooms require cooling. Providing some rooms with cooling all year, while providing other rooms with heating during the winter and cooling during the summer, can be complicated.

HVAC systems are capable of providing "free" cooling to internal rooms by blowing outdoor air into those areas during a time when outdoor air is cold. But free can be costly because the same ducts may provide cold air to other areas of the building that need heat or need neither heating nor cooling. Also, HVAC ducts take up a lot of space, and their fans use a lot of energy, maybe more than another type of cooling system would use.

An office building should have an air barrier around each floor to ensure that the ventilation system delivers air where it is supposed to go and removes air from where it is supposed to be removed. Ventilation for an office building is best done with ERVs and dedicated ventilation-only ducts. The ERVs can be controlled with motion sensors or sensors that measure CO_2, either of which signal that people are present.

Internal rooms that require cooling all year can get some "free" cooling during the winter with a type of ERV that can stop exchanging heat when desired. When "free" cooling is desired during the winter, the fans continue ventilating while the ERV stops heat recovery. Because an ERV ventilation system's fans and ducts are much smaller than an HVAC system's fans and ducts, it cannot provide as much "free" cooling air as an HVAC system can. But when outdoor air is cold, almost any type of cooling system is very efficient, sometimes using less energy than a large fan providing "free" cooling with an HVAC system.

As shown in the drawings on the next two pages, an ERV with a rotating wheel can serve rooms in the core that never need heating, while normal ERVs connected to other ducts can serve perimeter rooms. Manufacturers sell ERVs with built-in "enthalpy calculators," which determine if outdoor air is cool enough or dry enough to provide useful cooling—by reducing either indoor temperature or indoor humidity, or both. If the outdoor air is so cold that not warming the incoming fresh air would overcool the space, the wheel automatically rotates at a reduced speed.

Some large cooling systems use wet cooling towers like these to reject heat to outdoor air. They are basically waterfalls with fans, which use both conduction and latent cooling to reject heat. These cooling towers are cooling an office building during the winter.

"Free" Wintertime Cooling for an Office Building Core
The drawing below shows three ERVs ventilating one floor of an office building during the winter. The **ERV ventilating the core of the office building** is delivering cold outdoor air to the core. The **ERVs serving the perimeter** are heating the incoming air.

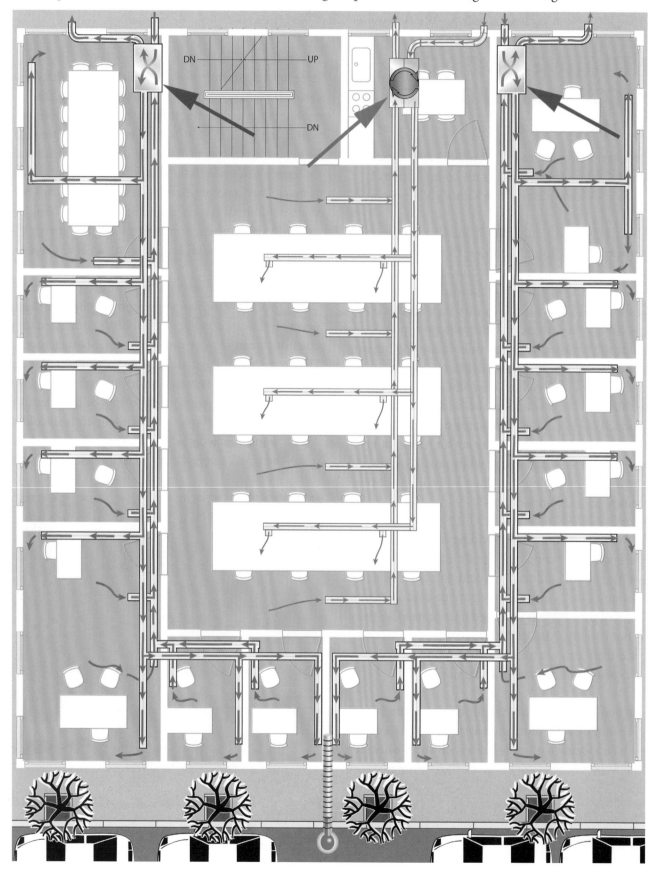

Reducing an Office Building's Summer Cooling Load
During the summer, all the ERVs are recovering heat, moving it from the incoming fresh ventilation air to the outgoing stale exhaust air to reduce the load on the cooling system. The drawings on the next page illustrate how this works.

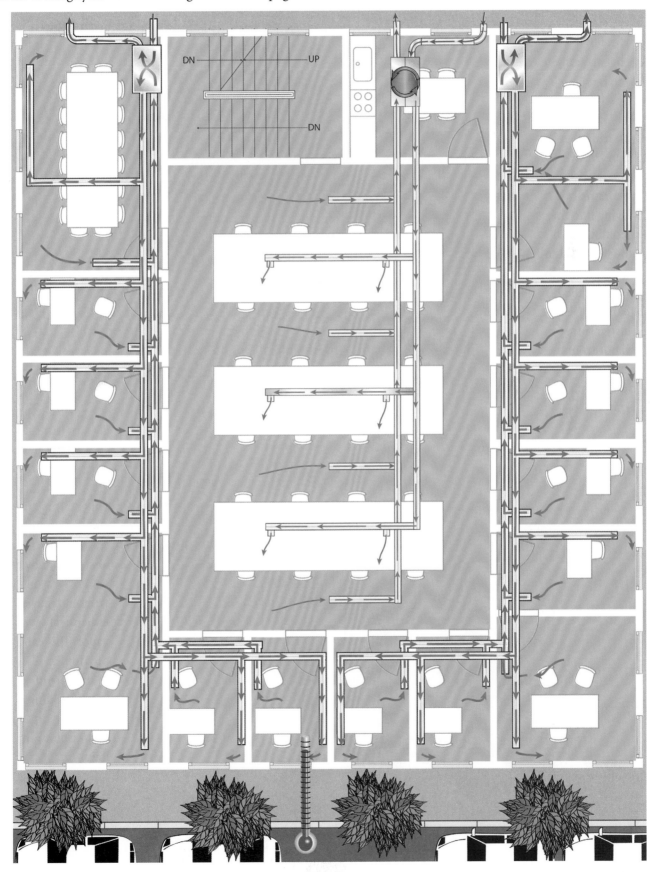

Rotating-Wheel ERV

The ERV in the drawing at right has a wheel that rotates between the incoming **fresh air** and the outgoing **stale exhaust air**. Shown during the winter, it is recovering heat from the warm exhaust airstream and moving it to the cold incoming fresh air. If the wheel is the type that also absorbs water vapor (called an enthalpy wheel), it will also transfer water vapor from the wetter airstream to the drier airstream.

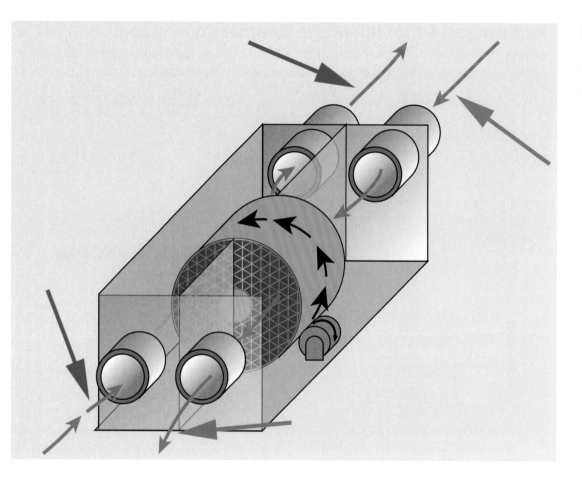

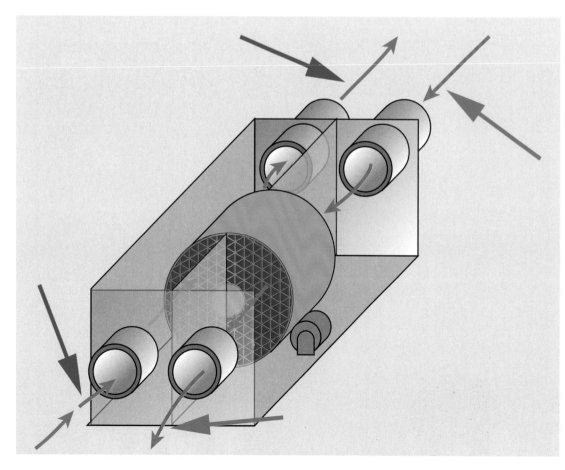

The drawing at left shows the same ERV with the wheel not rotating during the winter. The fans (not shown) simply bring fresh, cold **outdoor air** in and move **exhaust air** outdoors, without recovering either heat or water vapor. This can provide "free" cooling to the core of an office building when outdoor temperature and/or humidity is low.

This is one of several methods of varying the recovery capacity of an ERV.

Precious Space Occupied by HVAC Systems

The photo at right shows the space above the ceiling in a building with an HVAC system.

The space between a **structural steel beam** supporting the **floor above** and the **ceiling** is occupied by a fire sprinkler pipe and an **HVAC duct**.

The large steel beam at left is part of the support structure for a floor/ceiling assembly in a 48-story office building. A hole large enough for a duct has been cut through the beam, and the steel around the hole has been reinforced.

Ventilation-only ducts can fit through relatively small holes, allowing an entire ventilation system to fit within the structural part of a floor/ceiling assembly, which saves all the height HVAC ducts would normally occupy.

Saving Space with ERVs

Most office buildings sacrifice a significant amount of valuable space for HVAC equipment and for ventilation ducts running vertically. But it doesn't have to be that way.

The photo at right shows an **ERV** on the office and meeting room floor of a seven-floor hotel that is under construction. It is mounted in the space above where a hallway ceiling will be built. It ventilates the portion of the building in the top left corner of the drawing on the next page.

The photo below left is a different view of the same **ERV** and **ducts** before the ducts are airtightened.

The photo below right shows the same view with the ceiling installed. The ERV is above an access panel. Zero floor space is occupied by ventilation equipment or by ducts, which is very unusual. Because the ERVs are the type that never circulates used air for defrosting, the ventilation system does not have to be connected to smoke alarms or fire alarms.

This drawing shows four **ERVs**, each hidden above a ceiling, that serve the hotel's offices and storage rooms. The **red lines** show fire boundaries formed by fireproof demising partitions. No duct crosses a demising partition, therefore no fire or smoke can cross a fire boundary through a duct, therefore no fire dampers are necessary.

A mechanical room on the roof contains a boiler and a chiller, which provide hot and cold water, respectively, for heating and cooling with valences. Because the chiller is indoors, neither it nor the chilled water loop needs protection against freezing during the winter. The only equipment located outdoors is the part of the cooling system that rejects heat outdoors. An extra heat exchanger in the chiller heats faucet water with "waste" heat during the summer. The only scheduled maintenance on the heating, cooling, and ventilation systems is cleaning air filters in the ERVs. Except for the rooftop mechanical room, zero floor space in the whole building is occupied by ventilation, heating, or cooling equipment or ducts.

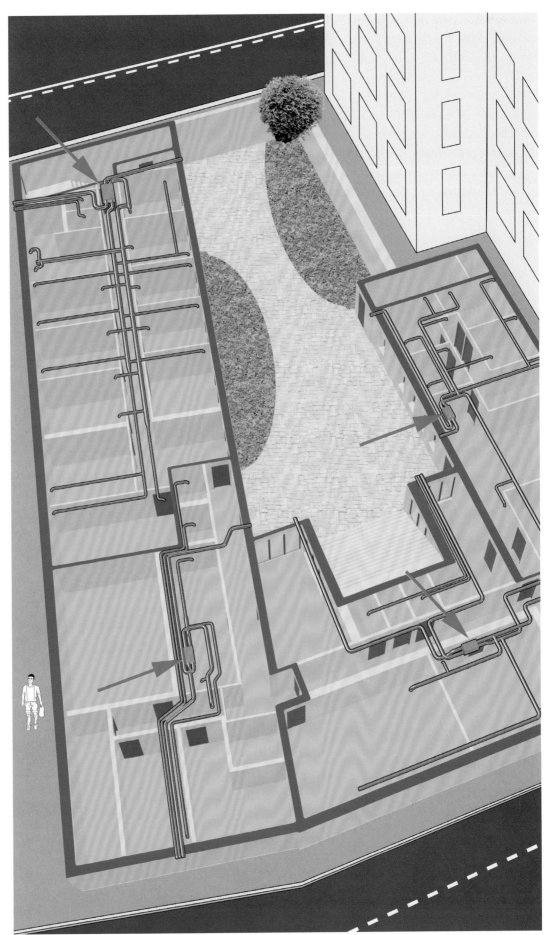

The three-story office building in the drawing below is ventilated by a system that takes fresh outdoor air from the roof and delivers it through vertical ducts to HVAC systems on each floor, which then mix it with the used air they are blowing around each floor. At the same time, the system exhausts stale air out the roof. This is probably how the building in the photos on Page 558 is ventilated. It is a challenge to get a system like this to deliver the correct amount of fresh air to each floor or even to determine how much fresh air each floor, or portion of a floor, is getting, if any.

Also, because ducts are penetrating floor/ceiling assemblies, fire dampers are necessary. Because ducts circulate used air, the system must be connected to smoke sensors in ducts and, depending on local codes, also to the building's fire alarm system. These life safety systems are expensive and complicated—and do not provide 100 percent dependable protection against smoke and fire spreading through ducts.

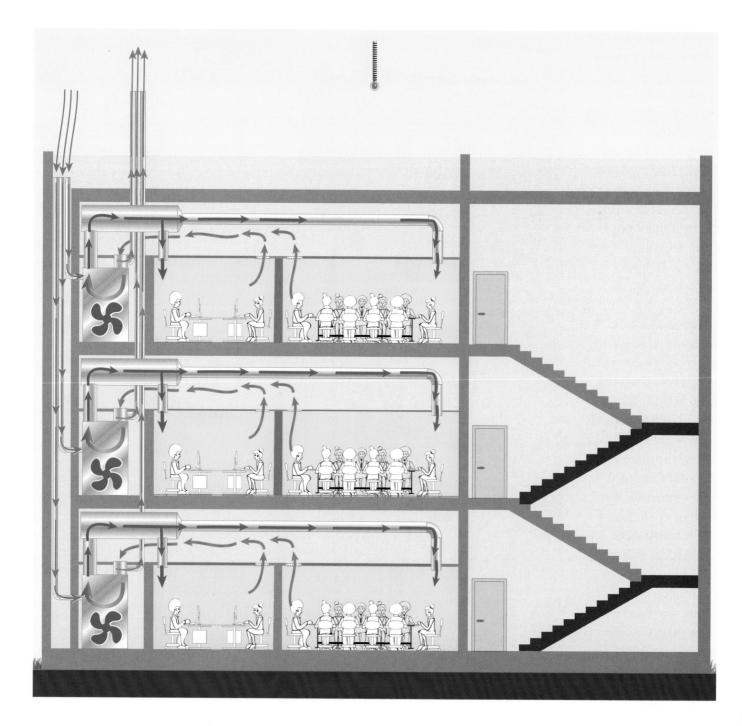

Each floor of the office building below has its own ERV ventilation system, which delivers the correct amount of fresh air. The ventilation-only ducts are so much smaller than HVAC ducts that the building can fit more floors (with the same floor/ceiling heights) in the same building height. Making each floor shorter allows the vertical structural supports to be smaller, which saves money and floor space. Because the stairs are shorter vertically, they are also shorter horizontally, which saves additional floor space. Eliminating HVAC air handlers and vertical ducts also saves additional floor space.

Because no ducts penetrate demising partitions, no fire dampers are necessary. If no ducts circulate used air (depends on how the ERVs handle defrost), the ventilation systems do not need smoke alarms in the ducts, and, depending on local codes, they probably do not need any connection to the building's fire alarm system.

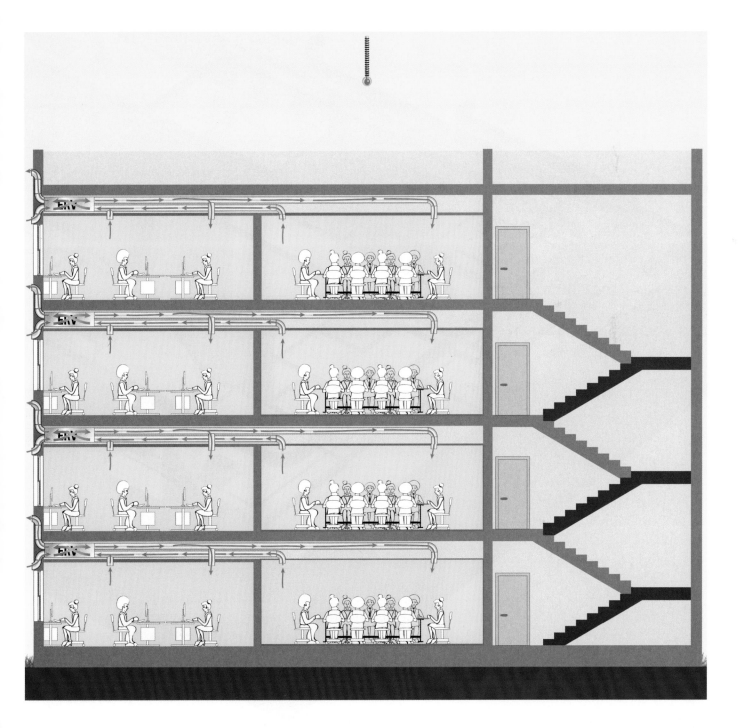

A Floor of Offices with Separate Ventilation, Heating, and Cooling Systems

The drawing on these two pages was part of the blueprint set for a floor of offices. The office is ventilated with one ERV hidden inside kitchen cabinets near the ceiling in a storage room. A sealed combustion boiler heats faucet water as well as water for heating the offices. Heating water is supplied to **wall-mounted heaters** through the red pipes and returns to the boiler through the blue pipes. Each heater is about the same hydraulic distance from the boiler, therefore the amount of heating water flowing to each heater will automatically be balanced. Ductless split ceiling cassettes provide cooling.

The ventilation supply and return ducts serving the conference room are equipped with **motorized dampers**. When someone enters the room, a standard motion sensor (the type normally used to control lights) opens the dampers. When the room is unoccupied for some time, the dampers close almost all the way, minimizing ventilation airflow to save energy.

Drawing by Henry Gifford.

How Much Space Do Ventilation-Only Ducts Save?

Ducts sized for an HVAC system for cooling an office space (the peak cooling load is relatively similar in different climates) are approximately five to ten times the size necessary for a ventilation-only system. Fire sprinkler system pipes are usually located below HVAC ducts, which adds additional height to the building.

Ventilation-only ducts (and ERVs) are so small that many of them can be located between the steel beams supporting the floor/ceiling structure. If the floor/ceiling structure is made of trusses, all the fire sprinkler pipes can also fit within the trusses, allowing the ceiling to be mounted on the bottom of the floor/ceiling structure, freeing up even more height.

HEATING AND COOLING AN OFFICE BUILDING

Heat should be moved to and from offices with water or refrigerant. Each area of an office building should, of course, have its own thermostat, which is easy to do with water- or refrigerant-based heating and cooling systems. Refrigerant can go to ductless splits, including ceiling-concealed indoor units or ceiling cassettes (see Pages 491-498). Water for heating can go to any type of water-based heater, such as a valence, fan coil (see next page), or radiator. Heating water can also go to an air handler, but that basically makes the system an HVAC system with all its disadvantages. Water for cooling can go to valences, fan coils, or radiant cooled ceilings.

The main disadvantage of radiant cooled ceilings, as discussed on Pages 505-506, is that water will condense on them and drip off if they are cooler than the dewpoint temperature of the indoor air. The combination of radiant cooled ceilings and operable windows is a potentially problematic combination because the large amount of water vapor in outdoor air can be overwhelming, even if the system is set up to automatically switch off if a window is opened. But operable windows are problematic in tall buildings anyway because wind speeds far from the ground are too high and would blow papers around and slam doors. Therefore, radiant cooled ceilings are a good choice for an office if the enclosure does not leak a lot of air, the windows are not operable, and the space has a separate dehumidification system.

An office building that is not very tall can have operable windows as long as it does not have an HVAC system. HVAC systems require predictable air pathways for circulating large volumes of air around the building for heating and cooling, therefore they will not work well if windows are open. It is less problematic to open windows in a building with ventilation-only ventilation systems, especially if each floor has its own separate ventilation system.

A computer room can be cooled with a dedicated ductless split system. The system that cools the rest of the building can serve as an emergency back-up system (people in the building will gladly sound the alarm if it doesn't work). The thermostat on the back-up system can be set to a slightly higher temperature than the dedicated system, so it will turn on automatically if the dedicated system fails.

This office is in the building shown on Pages 554 and 555. One of the ventilation grills is visible on the ceiling in the background. A ductless split ceiling cassette is visible on the ceiling in the foreground. A flat-panel wall-mounted radiator is mounted on the wall to the left of the window. The office is comfortable, healthy, and quiet all year round, while using very little energy.

The most comfortable and inexpensive heating and cooling system for an office building is a well-insulated opaque wall. The second most comfortable and inexpensive cooling system is outdoor window shades. The outdoor window shades mounted on all the windows on this building can be operated from indoors. Neither opaque walls nor exterior shades occupy any space within the building.

Heating and Cooling an Office with Fan Coils

The photo at right shows fan coils that heat and cool an office. A fan coil is a box containing a heat exchanger (a coil of tubing), which hot or cold water flows through, and a fan to move room air through the box and across the heat exchanger.

Fan coils make some noise and take up some floor space, but they do not require any ducts, and they are simple. In addition, each one can be controlled by its own thermostat.

RETROFITTING AN EXISTING OFFICE BUILDING

Many existing office buildings could be retrofitted with separate ventilation-only systems one floor at a time as tenants move out and in. The office buildings shown on Pages 480 and 481 are both candidates. They both already have water-based heating and cooling systems, which could continue to provide heating and cooling during and after the ventilation system upgrade. Eventually, after separate ventilation-only systems are installed on each floor, the large central HVAC fans could be removed, and the floors they occupy could be converted to offices. The vertical ducts that connected the central fans to all the floors in the building could also be removed, and that space could also be put to use.

Office buildings that have mechanical spaces full of large HVAC fans every ten or fifteen floors, such as the building on the right side of Page 63, can replace the fans and vertical ducts with small vertical pipes carrying steam to heat water and refrigerant to cool water, freeing up those floors for offices.

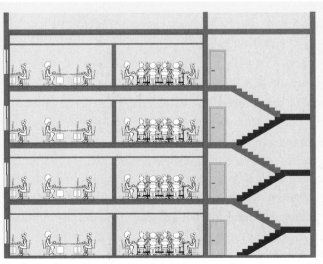

Each floor of an office building should have an air barrier around it. Fireproof demising walls between parts of an office building should also be barriers to air (and of course to fire and smoke).

This office building has no ventilation vents or operable windows on this side.

Here is the other side of the same building. Again, no vents or operable windows. Typical of many office buildings today, the ventilation air is probably being delivered all the way from the top or bottom of the building. It is unlikely that each floor is getting its correct share of fresh ventilation air.

SUMMARY

Office buildings can be challenging to keep comfortable because they typically have internal rooms that require cooling all year, even at times when the perimeter of the building requires heating.

The quietest, most reliable, and least expensive type of cooling system for an office building is a well-insulated, opaque wall.

An office building should have an air barrier around each floor to ensure that the ventilation system can deliver air to where it is supposed to go and remove it from where it is supposed to be removed, and that smoke is prevented from spreading in a fire. Dedicated ventilation systems for each floor, or part of a floor, have a good chance of working well, while preventing the spread of smoke and fire from one floor to another through ventilation ducts.

Office buildings with ERV ventilation on each floor and water- or refrigerant-based heating and cooling systems save enough height to fit more floors in the same building height that would fit significantly fewer floors with an HVAC system. An office building like this also is more comfortable, is quieter, has better indoor air quality, makes the building safer against the spread of smoke and fire through ducts, saves on the cost of the structure, saves cost by having greatly simplified mechanical systems, saves space required by taller (and therefore longer) stairways, saves space that would be required for HVAC ducts and air handlers, and saves energy. The disadvantage is that ventilation openings would be visible on the side of the building.

AFTERWORD

This stuff is real. The photos in this book show that many architects, engineers, contractors, and homeowners are moving in the right direction. These photos were taken in many parts of the world: in South America, North America, Asia, Africa, Eastern Europe, and Western Europe. The buildings are all real, as are all the mechanical systems. All of these photos show buildings in various stages of construction, repair, or deterioration—buildings under real-world financial pressures.

The only way to design and build better buildings is to make design and construction decisions based on sound building science. More scientific research and new technology won't improve buildings that are still being designed and built in ignorance of most building science principles.

However, change is stubbornly resisted in the building industry, due to increased cost—or what is perceived as increased cost. An architect working in 2015 said that in one area of his country the industry strongly resists building with masonry because of the higher cost and builds with wood instead. In another part of his country the industry resists building with wood because of the higher cost and builds with masonry. Situations like this can probably be found in every country, but the irony is that that architect is from Belgium, which is so small—the total population is only 11,000,000. Yet, despite its small size, conventional wisdom differs from one part of the country to the next. Probably there is truth to both claims: the industry in one part of the country knows how to build with wood, whereas in the rest of the country they know how to build with masonry. One lesson here is that conventional wisdom should be looked at with skepticism and an openness to change. Because everything changes, including codes, materials, and costs of materials and labor, the choice is not between changing and not changing but between moving in one new direction versus another new direction. Another lesson here is that whichever building material is chosen, the building should still be designed and built, or renovated, based on sound building science.

One challenge in the industry is that architects and engineers come out of school without much, if any, hands-on experience with buildings. Universities could help solve this problem by requiring architecture students to do paid work on construction sites during the summer. It has to be paid work—no volunteering allowed—so the students will be under pressure to perform well, or else get fired and risk not fulfilling a degree requirement. Education for engineers should not be neglected, either; students should be required to install ducts for a ventilation system, as well as pipes and wires for a boiler installation, and then be there to hear what the building inspector has to say about their work. The students may be horrified at how many design decisions are made by someone holding a hammer, a pipe wrench, or a phone connected to a material supplier, and anxiously rush back to school to add many more useful details to their plans, while perhaps deleting some details they would then consider superfluous.

Another challenge in our industry is lack of collaboration between architects and engineers. An engineer who was elected president of a prominent engineer's association acknowledged this problem in his acceptance speech when he said, "I am not like the rest of you, working in firms that design mechanical systems based on plans the architects send you from across town, without ever working on a design together. I spent my career working in an integrated firm. Our firm does both architecture and engineering. That means that the architects finish their design without ever talking to us and then they toss the plans across the transom to us engineers, who do our designs without ever talking to the architects on the other side of the office." He was acknowledging that even in his office, cooperation was sorely lacking. One way to increase the number of architects and engineers who understand what it takes to work together to create a successful design is for universities to require that architecture and engineering students collaborate with each other on school design projects. That way, when the students graduate, they might be inclined to actually collaborate in a way that is sorely lacking in the industry now. The class projects could more realistically resemble the real world if the architecture students were told they had to choose engineering students to collaborate with, and the engineering students had to market their services to the architecture students, which is how design teams are formed in the real world.

QUIZ ANSWERS

Wall Quiz #1 Answer

The darker areas of the wall on the top of Page 42 are colder. Some of the mechanisms that make colder walls darker are explained on Page 22. Apparently, the residents primarily heat the first floor and leave the upper part of the house unheated most of the time.

The light-colored area between the windowsills on the second floor is about the size and shape of a radiator. Probably a radiator is mounted on the wall there, which would explain why the wall in that area is not dark. The radiator must not be used frequently enough to keep the room warm enough to prevent darkening of the rest of the second-floor wall.

Mirror Quiz Answer

This mirror shown on Page 146 is not fogging in the middle because an electric heater behind it keeps the mirror's middle warm 24 hours a day to prevent fogging when hotel guests shower. Wiping a foggy mirror with a towel takes only a second and uses a lot less energy.

Snowy Roofs Quiz #1 Answer

The pattern in the photo on the top of Page 39 could have been caused by different levels of insulation in the roofs above the three stores, but on the day the photo was taken, the temperature in the store on the left was 20.5 °C (69 °F), the temperature in the store in the middle was 17 °C (63 °F), and the temperature in the store on the right was 21 °C (70 °F). The pattern was apparently caused by different temperatures in different stores. The snow hardly melted on the roof of the coldest store.

Water Quiz #1 Answer

Water condensed out of the air onto the roof and back window of the car in the photo on Page 151 because these surfaces are colder than the dewpoint temperature of the air.

The front and side windows are dry because they did not get colder than the dewpoint temperature of the air. The building in front of the car radiated heat toward the front of the car all night, which kept it warm. The side windows received a little infrared radiation from the building, some infrared radiation from the pavement, and some from nearby cars.

Water condensed onto the rear window and the trunk lid because they received little infrared radiation from the building (except what little was transmitted through the front window), and because the car underneath them shaded them from infrared radiation from nearby cars and the pavement. Perhaps more importantly, the car trunk and the rear window both face the sky, which on a clear night has no clouds to absorb and re-emit infrared radiation back to the earth's surface. This effect is sometimes called "night sky cooling." During a cloudless night, building roofs can become cooler than the surrounding air, too, which causes water vapor to condense out of the air onto the roof. This is not a problem, but, if an attic is vented to outdoors, water vapor can condense onto the attic side of the wood under the shingles (called the roof deck), and mold can grow as shown in the photo on the bottom of Page 414.

The ice on the car's roof shows that it is the coldest surface of all. Like the rear window and the trunk, it faces the sky, but it is colder because all the glass allowed the passenger compartment to cool to a lower temperature than the trunk.

Thermostat Quiz #1 Answer

The thermostat in the first photo on Page 473 is mounted on the wall above where a beam of sunlight hits the wall every day. The sunlight is heating the wall, making it much warmer than the air in the rest of the room. Even though sunlight does not hit the thermostat, the warm air rising up from the heated part of the wall will trick the thermostat into sensing that the room is much warmer than it really is. This will make the heat turn off when it should not, which will make the room cold.

Thermostat Quiz #2 Answer

The thermostat in the second photo on Page 473 is the type with a **temperature adjustment knob** and **room temperature sensor** that can both be mounted some distance away from the thermostatic valve (the valve is not visible—it is inside the radiator enclosure). The knob and sensor are connected to the valve with a **small-diameter tube** that the heat-sensitive fluid flows through.

The adjustment knob is conveniently mounted on the wall where nobody will have to bend down to adjust it. But the room temperature sensor is mounted next to the adjustment knob, where hot air rising up from the heater will fool it into sensing a very high temperature, which will turn the heat off long before the heater heats the entire room. Because of heat movement through the window, its location near the window doesn't help either. The solution is to mount the sensor near the floor where it will sense the temperature of the air being pulled across the floor as the radiator heats air that rises up and away from the heater by convection. The sensor can be mounted either **on the wall next to the heater just above the floor** or inside the heater enclosure, under the heater.

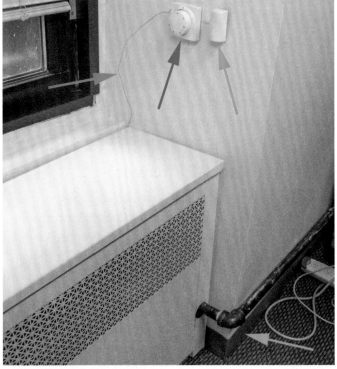

Wall Quiz #2 Answer

Condensation formed on only some parts of the wall on the bottom of Page 42 because heat conducted through studs and rim joists kept the other parts of the wall too warm for condensation to form.

Water Quiz #2 Answer

In the photo on Page 151, capillary suction moved tea up against gravity, wetting the paper tea bag, including the part hanging over the side of the cup. When tea moved into this part of the tea bag, gravity moved it down into the saucer. The photo below shows what happened next: tea kept moving via the tea bag into the saucer—and there is now more tea in the saucer than before.

Stove Quiz Answer

In the photo on Page 338, the toaster oven and its electric cord will be sitting over an open flame when the burners are turned on. This could start a fire. Both the toaster oven and the wood shelf it rests on should be removed.

Wall Quiz #3 Answer

In the photo at the top of Page 229, green moss is growing on the wall in a curved pattern because the sprinkler system that irrigates the lawn has also been "watering" the wall, likely damaging the building in the process. There is more wetting in that area; there is no difference in storage capacity or drying. The sprinkler system should be modified to spray water only where necessary.

Windows Heat Movement Quiz Answer

Yes, heat can move through a window in two directions simultaneously. Infrared radiation is almost always passing through windows in both directions. And heat can be conducted through a window in one direction while it is radiated through the window mostly in the other direction. For example, on a sunny winter day, heat from the heating system is conducted through windows from indoors to outdoors, while sunlight radiates more heat from outdoors to indoors than is radiated from indoors to outdoors.

Elevator Quiz Answer

If someone has to answer a quiz correctly to get an elevator to take her where she wants to go, the design is flawed. At this particular hotel (see Page 370), the key is:

BR - Ballroom
HL - Hotel Lobby
LL - Lower Lobby
P2 - Parking 2
P1 - Parking 1

This elevator presumably makes many extra stops, as riders who are not good at quizzes go to the wrong floor.

Mold Quiz Answer

The moldy walls on Page 230 are colder and therefore experience more wetting and less drying than the other surfaces. Steam leaking from the **steam heater**, shown below in a different photo of the same room, made the air in the room very humid. Water condensed out of the air onto the coldest surfaces, the two exterior walls, but not onto the ceiling or the wall on the right side of the photo (on Page 230), because there are heated rooms behind those surfaces. Water did not condense on the wall on the left side of the photo below for the same reason. The part of the wall to the right of the window and close to the ceiling stayed dry because hot air rising up from the heater by convection keeps that part of the wall warm and therefore mold free. Each surface has the same storage capacity, but the higher temperature of the warmer walls reduced wetting and increased drying. It is appropriate to say, "to find the cold, look for the mold." It is also appropriate to say, "to find the mold, look for the cold," but, in this case, finding the mold is very easy.

Fire Door Quiz #1 Answer

In the photo on the top left of Page 346, the sign says "Boiler Room." Because a boiler room is required to be resistant to the spread of smoke and fire, its door should also resist the spread of smoke and fire. However, the door in the photo has an air louver (a series of slits), probably to supply combustion and ventilation air to the boiler. This makes the door useless for preventing the spread of smoke and fire. The louver should not be there. An opening to supply air should connect the boiler room to outdoors, located a safe distance from doors and windows.

Heating and Cooling Quiz Answer

The outdoor air conditioning units on the ends of each of the row houses on Page 524 are larger than the others. They should be because each end apartment has an additional exposed wall, which increases the cooling load. In many row houses, all the cooling units are the same size, which means either that the ones serving the end apartments are undersized (unlikely—most heating and cooling equipment is oversized) or that the units serving the middle apartments are too large, which causes discomfort while wasting money and energy.

Water Quiz #3 Answer

In the photo on Page 151, the floor tiles are glazed, which greatly reduces water absorption into the tiles by acting as a capillary break. The grout between the tiles, however, is not glazed, thus it absorbs more water. The grout even absorbs water from the edges of the tiles, leaving the tiles drier at the edges and wetter in the middle.

Fire Door Quiz #2 Answer

The photo on the top right of Page 346 shows a fire door in a loft building, which separates a stairway from a hallway. Of course, it is useless when it is propped open, in this case by a fire hose. If a fire did start, the hose would also be useless because its nozzle is missing.

Wall Quiz #4 Answer

The green part of the wall on Page 229 gets more wetting than parts of the wall that are protected by the roof. Storage capacity is equal for all parts of the wall. Moss is growing on one area of the wall because there is no warm house behind it; therefore, it gets much less drying than other parts of the wall. The fence gets as much wetting as the wall—and no more drying—but is plastic, which stores no water. Thus it dries too fast to grow moss.

Snowy Roofs Quiz #2 Answer

The right side of the shed on the bottom of Page 39 faces toward the noon sun. The sun heated the right side of the shed, and the warm air near the wall rose by convection and warmed the eaves on the sunny side of the shed, melting the snow.

Thermostat Quiz #3 Answer

Each of the four **thermostats** in the third photo on Page 473 is attempting to control the temperature in a different part of a restaurant. But at least three of them are not sensing temperature in the space they are supposed to be controlling. Some types of thermostats can be connected to a remote sensor that allows a thermostat to be located in one place while sensing temperature in another place, but these particular thermostats do not have that capability. Presumably much time is spent fiddling with the thermostats in a futile effort to maintain comfort. The situation is not helped by the heat given off by the six **lighting dimmer switches** directly below the thermostats or by the large **electric bug zapper** next to them. The "Do Not Touch" notes (see close-up, Page 473) are a sign that the situation is desperate.

Thermostat Quiz #4 Answer

There is a large hole in the wall behind the thermostat in the fourth photo on Page 473. Air will leak through the wall from elsewhere in the building, or from outdoors, and exit this hole, causing the thermostat to sense that the room is a different temperature than it really is. This is a common problem because most thermostats are connected to a wire that comes through a hole in the wall. The solution is simple: airtighten the hole with caulk.

Roof Overhang Quiz Answer

Rain separates out from the air as it turns to pass under the porch roof on Page 175, splattering the wall directly under the roof overhang.

Water Quiz #4 Answer

The window in the photo on Page 151 has two panes of glass. Multi-pane windows are built with an airtight space between the panes. In the middle window, the air barrier has failed. It is allowing water vapor to get into the space between the panes. The condensation is occurring only in the middle of the pane because the frame of the window conducts much more heat (from indoors) than the glass, and the heat is heating the edges of the glass above the dewpoint temperature, while the middle remains colder than the dewpoint temperature. (The photo was taken during the winter.) The water must be condensing on one of the surfaces between the panes because otherwise the water would evaporate into the indoor or outdoor air. This leaves only the question of which pane the water is condensing onto: the pane on the outdoor side because that pane is colder during the winter.

Wall Quiz #5 Answer

The green part of the brick work on Page 229 is not vertical, thus it gets more wetting from falling rain. It has storage capacity and drying capacity equal to the rest of the brick work.

Science History Quiz Answer

In the early 1800s, scientists measured infrared radiation by aiming the rainbow of colors from a prism onto a piece of black cardboard wet with rubbing alcohol and watching which parts of the cardboard the alcohol evaporated from the fastest: the cardboard heated by the infrared radiation just past the visible red light.

Wall Damage Quiz Answer

Capillary suction pulls water up between the cellar windows in the photo on Page 208. The water evaporates at the surface of the wall between the windows and above the dark stone. The masonry is damaged by the process of subflorescence as the water leaves behind dissolved salts. The strange damage pattern is caused by the small basement window openings acting as capillary breaks, stopping capillary suction from moving water up to the wall above them. Also, the dark-colored stone on the surface of the wall below the damage has pores too small for capillary suction, which prevents water from moving through it and evaporating at its surface. The lighter-colored stone on the surface of the wall at left in the photo below is not a capillary break, as shown by minor damage at its surface and little or no damage on the wall above it. Water apparently moves through its pores and evaporates at its surface instead of being pulled higher up in the wall. The light-colored stone is probably relatively new, as it is not badly damaged (yet).

APPENDIX: COMPARING SITE ENERGY TO SOURCE ENERGY

Calculating the overall amount of energy required for different types of heating or cooling systems, or any other use, involves understanding the difference between "site energy" and "source energy." Site energy is the amount of energy delivered to a building, such as oil or gas that enters a building through a pipe or electricity that enters a building through a wire. Source energy is site energy plus the energy required both to transform the energy into a form the building can use and to deliver it to the building.

Fossil fuel source-energy calculations generally include the energy required to extract the fuel from the earth and transport it to either a fossil-fuel-burning power plant or a building. Even electricity produced with wind turbines, solar panels, or a hydroelectric dam requires some energy to produce and deliver the electricity.

The difference between site and source energy is largest for electricity. The majority of the world's electricity is still produced by burning fossil fuel, and the dominant type of fossil-fuel-burning power plant used today burns about three watts of fuel to provide one watt of electricity at the customer's meter (after transmission losses).

Some people assume that electricity delivered near a renewable source has less environmental impact than electricity delivered near a fossil-fuel-burning plant. But grid electricity is fungible (each unit is indistinguishable from and interchangeable with any other unit). Because the grid is fed mostly by energy from fossil fuel, and renewable sources generally operate at capacity, turning off a light in any building connected to the grid, even a building with a solar electric panel, will save fossil fuel somewhere (although the exact place cannot be known).

Because the energy required to extract and deliver fossil fuel to either an electricity-producing plant or a building is similar, calculations can be simplified by ignoring differences between site and source energy for fossil fuels and instead considering one watt of site electricity as equivalent to three watts of fossil fuel site energy. Until a much larger percentage of the world's electricity is produced without fossil fuel, ironically, sometimes the best way to reduce the amount of fossil fuel burned is to switch away from electricity and burn fossil fuel directly.

Glindex (Glossary + Index)

A

Absolute humidity: the amount of water vapor contained in a volume of air, which is confusing because air volume changes with temperature and pressure. The term is not used in this book. See Specific humidity.

Absorb: take in or soak up. 2, 129, 133

Accent light: light that highlights architectural details or artwork. 256, 261

Air barrier: building materials arranged and connected in a way that prevents the movement of air. Depending on the material and the connections, an air barrier might or might not also be a barrier to heat or water vapor or liquid water. **70**, 103–128, 376

Air filter: a device that removes particles from air when air moves through it. 71, 429, 444, 445, 449, 453, 551

Air gap behind cladding: a gap intentionally created behind cladding to reduce water penetration, to drain water, and to circulate air for drying. 393

Air handler: a box that contains a fan and uses an external source of heating or cooling to heat or cool (or dehumidify or humidify) the air it moves. 433, 438

Asbestos: a naturally occurring mineral that was once commonly used for insulation and fireproofing. It causes lung cancer in people who inhale the fibers. 427–428

Assembly: the series of building materials that make up a wall, floor slab, ceiling/floor, or ceiling/roof. 26

Asthma: a chronic lung disease that inflames and narrows the airways. Symptoms include wheezing and shortness of breath. It can be deadly. The name comes from the Greek "asthma" (panting). 222, 347, 429

Attic: the part of a building between the ceiling and the roof, which is typically partly indoors and partly outdoors. 412–423, 529

Automatic sprinkler system: a system of pipes and spray heads within a building that automatically sprays water on a fire. 308–315, 319

B

Band joist: another name for a rim joist. See Rim joist. 24

Batt: the form that some insulation is sold in: pieces that fit between studs or joists. 20, 26, 28, 289

Bedbug: 347–349, 356

Boiler: a device that heats water, usually for heating a building, sometimes boiling the water to produce steam, sometimes keeping the water as a liquid that is pumped to heaters throughout the building. Many boilers also heat water for faucets. 5, 514–518, 522–524, 530

Boom box test: a test for checking sound isolation by playing a loud radio on one side of a wall and listening on the other side of the wall. Though not very scientific, it avoids the difficulty of isolating low-level test sound from background noise. 288

Boric acid: a chemical that kills insects but is relatively harmless to people. 33, 360–361

Breathe: in the building industry, a non-specific term that means a building is leaking something, perhaps water vapor or perhaps air. 103, 379

Building enclosure: the combination of a building's walls, windows, doors, roof, and floor slab or basement that separates indoors from outdoors. See Chapter 16: Building Enclosures. 375

Building envelope: another name for a building's enclosure. See Building enclosure.

C

Capillary break: a construction detail that stops water from moving through a building by capillary suction. 204–205, 214–215, 398, 562, 564

Capillary suction: a mechanism that spreads liquid water out within porous materials and can move liquid water uphill against gravity. Capillary suction moving liquid water from soil into a building is a major wetting mechanism. 129, 132–134, 181, 202, 203–215, 223, 227, 393, 394–395

Chiller: a machine that cools water for use in cooling a building. 470, 480, 501, 551

Chipboard: a sheet material made of chips of wood glued together and often used for wall sheathing, roof decking, or subflooring. Similar to particleboard but made of larger pieces of wood. 382

Cladding: the outermost layer of a wall assembly. Examples include shingles, brick, stone, and stucco. 184–189, 380

Cockroach: There is never just one. See Cockroaches.

Cockroaches: 347–348, 356

Cogeneration: the process by which a generator burns fuel to produce electricity and then captures the "waste" heat. Also called "cogen" or a "cogen system." 10, 544

Cold: a lack of heat. There is no unit of measurement for cold, just as there is no unit for measurement for darkness.

Cold side: the side of an assembly that is cold, which is usually a meaningless concept because temperatures change with season. 200–202, 218, 376–377, 380–386

Color: 231

Color rendering: the effect the color of a light source has on the appearance of objects lit by that light. 232–234

Color temperature: a way of describing the mix of colors in a white light source. 234

Concrete: a building material made from a mixture of Portland Cement, gravel, sand, and water. It is used for making sidewalks, floor slabs, and often basement walls. From the Latin "concretus" (compact, or condensed). 32, 214–215, 230, 266, 334–339, 343, 394

Condensate: liquid water condensed from water vapor. 354, 444–445, 492, 501, 524

Condensation: the process of water vapor (water in its gas state) becoming liquid. 6, 200

Condenser: the hot, or outdoor, heat exchanger part of a cooling system, so named because the refrigerant condenses in that part of the system. The term is not used in this book because many modern systems can also provide heat during the winter, turning the outdoor part of the system into an evaporator. To avoid confusion, "indoor unit" and "outdoor unit" are used in this book. 499, 511

Conduction: the mechanism by which heat moves between things that touch each other. Can also refer to sound transmission from one place or object to another. 2

Contrast: a noticeable difference between things, especially things located close enough to each other to be viewed at the same time. 234, 236, 243–247, 254, 256

Convection: a gravity-driven movement of fluids of different densities (weights). 2, 5, 72–73, 76–77, 80–82, 502, 515, 522

Cooling dehumidifier: a mechanical device that removes water vapor from air while also removing heat. Unlike a normal dehumidifier, which rejects heat indoors, a cooling dehumidifier is connected to outdoor equipment that rejects heat outdoors. 466–467

Cooling load: the amount of heat and water vapor that equipment cooling a building needs to remove. The peak load is equal to the largest sum of all the heat and water vapor entering or being generated within a space at a given point in time, which might or might not occur at the hottest time of year. Heat removal and dehumidifying loads can be added together by converting dehumidifying load to heat units: the latent heat of condensation of the water vapor being removed from the air. 43–68, 248, 266

Cooling system: a mechanical system that cools, and usually also dehumidifies, a building. Also known as an "air conditioner," a term that sometimes describes a system that also performs other functions. See Chapter 18: Heating and Cooling. 469

Coping: the material that forms the top surface of a wall that has both sides exposed, such as a parapet wall that extends above surrounding parts of a building. 171, 177

Cornice: an ornamental molding at the top of an exterior wall that protrudes from the wall and helps protect it from wetting by rain. 165

Crawl space: as used in this book, the space between the lowest floor and the ground, which is typically partly indoors and partly outdoors. Can also mean a low-ceilinged part of an attic. 406–411

D

Damper: mechanism that closes off the flow of air in a duct or chimney when desired. One example is the damper in the flue of a fireplace, which can be closed when the fire is not burning to prevent warm indoor air from escaping up the chimney. See also fire damper. 431, 436, 440, 454

Dehumidifier: a mechanical device that removes water vapor from air. See also Cooling dehumidifier. 139, 143, 225–228, 398, 464–468

Dehumidify: the process of removing water vapor from air. 16–17, 140, 463–468

Dehumidistat: a control used to turn a dehumidifier on when the sensed humidity is above the setpoint and off when the humidity is lower. 466, 468

Demising assembly: an assembly specifically designed and built to resist the spread of smoke and fire. 320

Desorb: the opposite of absorb: to give up. 360

Dewpoint temperature: the temperature to which air needs to be cooled to start condensing water out of the air. 143, 148–150, 154, 200, 353, 376–377, 396–398, 407, 413, 444

Diatomaceous earth: a fine powder made from ground-up sedimentary rock formed many years ago from shells of marine animals. It kills insects that crawl on it. 360

Direct ambient light: light that comes directly from light fixtures into the area being lit. 256

Dissipate: the process of something scattering or dispersing. For example: "the water will dissipate." The word can be confusing, because it implies that something will simply disappear, which is impossible.

Drainage plane: the system of materials that liquid water drains down on its way to the bottom of a building's enclosure.

Drip edge: the edge created by cutting a groove in a downward-facing part of an exterior wall. Because water running down along the wall can't cross the groove, it drips off the wall instead. 170–173, 177, 179

Drying a flooded building: 222–227

Drying of building materials: 218–221, 393

Dry rot: a mechanism that destroys wood. First, the wood gets wet, then fungi or mold eats the wet wood, and then the wood dries out. Though it appears to have rotted while dry, it actually rotted while wet.

Duct: a tube, the purpose of which is to move air from one place to another. 98, 102, 138, 143, 319, 325, 433

Duct cover: See Attic. 412

Ductless split: a system that cools (and usually can also heat) a space without ducts, using refrigerant tubes to connect the outdoor unit with one or more indoor units, each of which conditions a portion of a building. 489–500

Duct mastic: a material that is sticky when it comes out of the container but hardens into a durable and slightly flexible coating. It is commonly used for airtightening connections in ducts made of sheet metal. 120, 458–459

E

Eaves: the part of a roof assembly that extends out past the wall below it. From the old English "efes" (edge). 35, 161–164

Efflorescence: salt deposits left on a surface such as an exterior wall when water evaporates. See also Subflorescence. 152–153, 176–177, 194, 206–213

Emit: to give off something, usually sound, heat, or light. 4

Enclosure: the combination of a building's walls, windows, doors, roof, and floor slab or basement that separates indoors from outdoors. See Chapter 16: Building Enclosures. 375

Energy recovery ventilator, or ERV: a device that recovers heating or cooling energy and humidification or dehumidification from exhaust air and transfers it to incoming fresh ventilation air. 444–455, 525, 533–534, 539–541, 545, 550–553

Enthalpy: a measure of the total energy present in a system, compared with absolute zero or another convenient reference point. 13

Entropy: a measure of disorder, or randomness, in a system. 10, 131

Envelope: sometimes used to refer to a building's enclosure. See Building enclosure.

ERV: acronym for energy recovery ventilator, also called an enthalpy recovery ventilator because recovering both heat and water vapor involves transferring both types of energy to/from exhaust air. 444–453

Evaporator: the cold, or indoor, heat exchanger part of a cooling system, so named because the refrigerant evaporates in that part of the system. The term is not used in this book because many modern systems can also provide heat during the winter, turning the indoor part of the system into a condenser. To avoid confusion, "indoor unit" and "outdoor unit" are used in this book. 499, 511

F

Fan coil: a device that cools or heats a room by using a fan to blow air over a coil containing cold or hot water. 510, 556, 557

Fire damper: a metal door that closes to stop the spread of smoke and fire through ducts. 319, 325

Fire sprinkler system: See Sprinkler system.

First law of thermodynamics: the law that says that energy cannot be created or destroyed. 8, 11–13, 276, 301, 466

Flashing: thin pieces of liquid water barrier material positioned to prevent liquid water from entering a building or to direct liquid water that has leaked through cladding back out of a building. Flashing often protects connections between other materials. 182–193

Flat roof: a roof that might actually be completely flat. Most "flat" roofs have some pitch (slope). 157–160

Floor slab: a floor of a building with no basement or cellar, which rests on soil. Also called a slab-on-grade. 19, 215, 394, 399, 406, 411

Flu: short for influenza, an infectious disease caused by the influenza virus. 147

Fluid: a substance that takes the shape of its container—for example, water or air. 2

Fully adhered membrane: a building material that is a barrier to air and to liquid water. Depending on the type, it might also be a barrier to water vapor. It is sold in sheets and has a strong adhesive backing that is used to attach it to the building. 105–107, 184–185, 188, 190, 392, 400–401

Furnace: a device used for heating a building that blows hot air around the building with a fan. The heat can come from an electric heater or from gas or oil burned inside the furnace. An air handler is similar but uses heat from elsewhere (boiler, etc.). 80, 479, 485–488

G

Glare: an uncomfortably bright or distracting light. 56, 237–238, 240, 260

Gypsum board: a building material used as surfaces of walls and ceilings. Also called plasterboard or drywall. The core is made of gypsum, a mineral dug out of the ground. The surface of the board is either paper or another material such as fiberglass. 44, 114–119, 124, 203–204, 286, 290, 330–333, 337, 378, 506

H

Heating load: the amount of heat required to keep a building warm. The peak heating load is the sum of all the heat leaving a space at a given point in time, assumed to be the coldest night normally encountered in that climate, with a moderately strong wind. 20, 470–471

Heat pump: in most branches of science, a mechanism that moves heat from something cold to something hot. Examples include an air conditioner and a kitchen refrigerator. In the building industry, the term refers to an air conditioner running "backwards" to heat a building during the winter. 510–512, 530, 543

Mineral wool: a fiber-type insulation, sometimes made from slag left over from making steel and other times made from glass or other materials. Also called mineral fiber. Different types (depending on raw material) include stone wool, slag wool, glass wool, and rock wool. 30, 70, 90, 288, 392

Moisture: another word for water vapor.

Mold: a fungus that eats organic materials, including building materials. 3, 22, 71, 146, 150, 155, 222, 353, 431, 434

Mortar: the type of cement used between bricks or stones or concrete blocks. Modern mortar is a mixture of Portland Cement, lime, sand, and water. Unlike concrete, it contains no gravel. From the Latin "mortarium" (crushed). 30, 103, 109, 152, 195, 206–213

Mosquito: There is never just one. See Mosquitoes.

Mosquitoes: 354

Mouse: There is never just one. See Mice.

N

Night sky cooling: the mechanism that cools an object or surface through infrared radiation emitted to a clear sky at night, which returns far less infrared radiation than a cloudy sky would. 415, 560

O

Opaque: not transparent to light. 15, 248, 254, 556

P

Pane: a sheet of glass in a window. 46–48, 69, 151, 297

Parapet: the wall around the edge of a balcony or a roof, typically a flat roof. 97, 167, 177, 403, 404–405

Peak cooling load: the largest amount of heat and water vapor a cooling system must remove to keep a space comfortable, which is the sum of all the heat and water vapor entering or being generated within a space at a particular point in time. The peak might or might not occur at the hottest time of year, or hottest time of day. Load calculation methods are not covered in this book. 45, 470–471

Peak heating load: the largest amount of heat a heating system must add at any one point in time to keep a space comfortable. The peak occurs during the coldest night of the year. Calculations assume a moderately strong wind on that night. Load calculation methods are not covered in this book. 20, 470–471

Perfect sequence: the optimum sequence for arranging the layers of an assembly to maximize people's comfort and health while making a building more durable and energy efficient. 380–387

Pigeon: There is never just one. See Pigeons.

Pigeons: 362

Pitch: in building science, the slope of a roof. 157

Plumbing vent: a pipe that extends through the roof to relieve air pressure differences in drain pipes. Without a vent, sewer gas can escape into indoor air, bringing disease and foul smells with it. 424–425

Portland Cement: the chemically active ingredient in concrete and mortar. Mixing it with water starts a reaction that hardens the concrete or mortar. It is made by grinding limestone into a powder, baking the powder to drive off oxygen, and adding clay. 31, 213, 335

Psychrometrics: the science of how much water vapor air can hold under different conditions. From the Greek words "psuchron" (cold) and "metron" (means of measurement). 140–143

PTAC: acronym for package terminal air conditioner. Refers to a piece of equipment that provides heating and cooling to a room, typically using a heat pump connected to a piping network that circulates water around the building. 510

Pyrolysis: the process of converting solids and liquids into gases by applying heat. 84, 301, 430

R

Radiant ceiling: 505–507

Radiant floor: 504

Radiate: emit in the form of rays or waves. 2

Rat: There is never just one. See Rats.

Rats: 352, 356–357

Refrigerant: a substance used in a refrigeration system or a heat pump. In most equipment, the refrigerant changes phase during the refrigeration cycle to increase the capacity and efficiency of the system. 226, 490, 511

Relative humidity: a measure of how much water vapor air contains relative to (compared to) how much water vapor it could hold under the prevailing conditions. Its unit of measure is a percentage, which can vary from 0 to 100 percent. 140

Resilient channel: a flexible metal strip that reduces sound transmission through an assembly by making a flexible connection between materials. 290–293

Rim joist: the final joist on the end of a row of joists, or the joist that runs along the ends of a row of joists. It is part of the exterior wall where a floor/ceiling assembly meets an exterior wall. 24–25, 27

Roach: See Cockroach.

Roof deck: the layer of a roof assembly on the outdoor side of the roof joists (structural members). Typically, other materials such as insulation, a liquid water barrier, and shingles are mounted onto the roof deck. 413–415

Roof overhang: the part of a roof that extends past the wall below. Also called an eave or eaves. 161

R-value: a property of a material that describes resistance to heat flow. An R-value can be assigned to a whole assembly of materials, to a layer of material, or to a specified thickness of a material. Instead of being described in units of its own, R-value is described as the mathematical inverse of U-value: $R = 1/U$. The great advantage of using R-value instead of U-value is that the resistances (R-values) of the layers of material in an assembly can simply be added together to determine the R-value of the whole assembly, which is mathematically much simpler than calculating the U-value of an assembly based on the U-values of its component parts.

S

Seal: a non-specific word that can mean closing off air leaks, water leaks, heat transmission, sound transmission, transportation routes for pests, etc.

Sealed combustion: as used in this book, a combustion appliance that has one pipe to supply outdoor combustion air to the appliance and a second pipe to eject combustion exhaust outdoors, with no connection to indoor air. 430, 485, 516–521, 524, 530, 542, 554

Second law of thermodynamics: the law that says that heat moves from hot things to things that are less hot. 9–13, 130–136, 455

Sheathing: the material on the outdoor side of wall studs (or roof joists) that adds strength and serves as a layer to mount other materials onto. 108, 377

Sheetrock®: a tradename for gypsum board manufactured by United States Gypsum Corporation. See Gypsum board.

Slab-on-grade: a floor slab resting on soil at grade level (in a building without a basement or cellar). See Floor slab.

Solar gain: energy from sunlight—in the forms of visible light and infrared radiation—that adds heat to a building. Solar heat gain is usually dominated by sunlight entering windows, but sunlight on walls and roofs also heats buildings. 43–68

Solar panel: a panel that transforms some of the energy in sunlight into electricity or heat. There are two types of solar panels: photovoltaic, also called PV, which makes electricity, and solar thermal, which heats water. 514

Sound: energy in the form of vibrations or waves traveling through air or other material. 271

Specific humidity: a measure of how much water vapor air holds. The unit of measure is the ratio of water vapor to mixture by mass (weight). 135, 140–144, 149, 220, 446

Split system, or split equipment: a type of heat pump (or cooling system) that has one part located indoors and the other part located outdoors. A ductless split system is one example. Another example is a cooling system with ducts and an air handler located indoors and a compressor and a condenser located outdoors, which is commonly used in single-family homes in North America. 489

Spray foam insulation: a type of insulation that starts as a fluid but hardens into rigid foam that can be simultaneously a barrier to heat and a barrier to air. 25, 26, 27, 422

Sprinkler system: a system of pipes and spray heads within a building that automatically sprays water on a fire. 308–315, 319

Stack effect: the mechanism that moves air through a building by convection. 80–82, 146, 223, 228, 324, 363, 376, 413, 420–421, 432, 436, 469

Stage One building: a building with an enclosure that does not include barriers to either heat or air. 376

Stage One fire: a fire in a building with a burn rate limited by availability of heat. 302

Stage Three building: a building with an enclosure that includes barriers to both heat and air. This type of building is the most comfortable, healthy, durable, and energy efficient. 376

Stage Three fire: a fire in a building with a burn rate limited by availability of fuel. 304

Stage Two building: a building with an enclosure that includes a barrier to heat but no barrier to air. 376

Stage Two fire: a fire in a building with a burn rate limited by availability of oxygen. 302–303

Staggered stud wall: wall built with studs narrower than the tracks or floor and ceiling plates, and located on alternating sides of the wall, which helps reduce sound transmission through the wall. 288–289

Standpipe: a piping system that supplies water to a handheld firefighting hose. 316–317

Steam heat: a system for heating a building using a boiler to heat water until it turns into a gas (steam), pipes to bring steam to radiators that transfer heat from the steam to the rooms, and pipes to return the condensate to the boiler. 6, 43, 84, 230, 430, 522, 524

Step flashing: flashing positioned to alternately overlap and underlap shingles at the end of a row of shingles to prevent water from escaping off the edge of the shingles, then leaking under the shingles, and eventually leaking into the building. 189–192

Storage of water within building materials: 216–217

Structural insulated panels: panels made from foam sandwiched between boards. Because they provide structural strength, no studs or joists are needed. 109

Stud: a vertical support within a wall. Studs are sometimes made of wood, sometimes metal. Sometimes studs are only strong enough to support the wall, sometimes they are strong enough to make the wall strong enough to support the floor(s) above. 19–25, 117–119, 216, 288–291, 497

Subflorescence: efflorescence that forms beneath the surface of a material. It can damage masonry. 206–213

T

Task light: a light fixture that directs light toward a specific area to increase the light level there above that of the ambient light. A typical example is a lamp on a desk. 256

Temperature: a measurement of the concentration of heat in something. 1

Termite: There is never just one. See Termites.

Termites: 350, 354

Thermal barrier: insulation or other material that slows the movement of heat. 19–41, **70**

Thermal bridge: a place where insulation is interrupted, allowing increased heat flow through an assembly. A typical example is the studs in a wall that is only insulated between the studs, which act as heat bullet trains. 20, 24, 26, 40

Thermal mass: a material's ability to store heat. Described another way, the amount of heat that needs to be added to a substance to increase its temperature. Called heat capacity in some branches of science. 13, 344–345, 380, 387, 504, 506

Thermodynamics: the science of heat and mechanical energy (or work), and the conversion of one into the other. From the Greek "therme" (heat) and "dynamis" (power). 8

Thermostat: a device that automatically regulates temperature by turning a heating or cooling system on or off when the temperature the thermostat senses (room temperature) reaches a setpoint temperature. 14, 17, 122, 147, 427, 472

Third law of thermodynamics: the law that says that nothing can ever be cooled to absolute zero. 8

Trickle vent: a hole in a building intended to act as a deliberately sized and located air opening for ventilation purposes. 441–442, 448, 525, 536

U

Unitary system, or unitary equipment: a type of heat pump (or cooling system) that has both the hot part and the cold part contained within one piece of equipment. A window air conditioner and a typical rooftop HVAC unit are two examples. 507

U-value: a property of a material that describes the rate at which heat will flow through the material when there is a temperature difference from one side of the material to the other. A U-value can be assigned to a whole assembly of materials, to a layer of material, or to a specified thickness of a material. The unit of U-value describes the rate of heat flow through a specified area of a material at a specified temperature difference. Sometimes called U-Factor when describing a window. The U-value of an assembly is used for calculating the heating load and the cooling load for a room. This book does not cover how to perform those calculations.

V

Valence: a device that cools or heats a room by using convection to move air over a coil containing cold or hot water. 501–504, 534, 551, 556

Vapor barrier: any material, such as a sheet of plastic or foil, that is a barrier to the movement of water vapor by diffusion from an area of high concentration to an area of low concentration. **70**, 135–136, 139, 157, 200, 215, 218, 377–378, 383, 387, 398, 402, 456

Ventilation: the process of removing stale indoor air and replacing it with fresh outdoor air. In this book, moving stale air around a building is not considered ventilation. 71–72, 79, 103, 128, 146, 150, 353, 356, 369, 398, 407, 410–411, 412, 434–455, 470, 478, 525–526, 531–533, 535–541

VOC: acronym for volatile organic compound. See Volatile organic compound.

Volatile organic compound, or VOC: a chemical that is volatile, meaning it has a tendency to mix itself with air, and organic, meaning it is made of carbon-based molecules. 429

W

Warm side: the side of an assembly that is warm, as in "put the vapor barrier on the warm side of the assembly," which is usually a meaningless concept because temperatures change with season. 200–202, 381–386

Water barrier (barrier to liquid water): a series of materials through which liquid water cannot pass, joined to each other with connections through which liquid water cannot pass. **70**

Water heater: a device that heats water for use in faucets or showers. 514, 530

Water storage within building materials: 216–217

Water vapor: water in its gas state. The words "gas" and "vapor" have slightly different meanings but are used interchangeably in this book and in most areas of science and industry.

Water vapor barrier: See Vapor barrier.

Weep hole: a deliberate hole in cladding or in a window for the purpose of allowing liquid water to drain out of the building. 30, 194–196